ELECTRIC UTILITY

PLANNING AND REGULATION

American Council for an Energy-Efficient Economy
Series on Energy Conservation and Energy Policy

Series Editor, Carl Blumstein

Energy Efficiency in Buildings: Progress and Promise
Financing Energy Conservation
Energy Efficiency: Perspectives on Individual Behavior
Electric Utility Planning and Regulation

ELECTRIC UTILITY
PLANNING AND REGULATION

EDWARD KAHN

Applied Science Division
Lawrence Berkeley Laboratory
University of California, Berkeley

American Council for an Energy-Efficient Economy
Washington, D.C. and Berkeley, California

in cooperation with:
Universitywide Energy Research Group
University of California

1 9 8 8

Electric Utility Planning and Regulation

Copyright © 1988 by Edward Kahn.
ISBN 0-918249-07-4

Published by the American Council for an Energy-Efficient Economy
1001 Connecticut Ave., NW, Suite 535, Washington, DC 20036.

Cover art copyright © 1988 M.C. Escher Heirs/Cordon Art -
Baarn - Holland.
Cover design by Wilsted and Taylor.
Book design and layout by Paula Morrison.
Printed in the United States of America by Inter-Collegiate Press.

Library of Congress Cataloging-in-Publication Data

Kahn, Edward, 1944–
    Electric utility planning and regulation.

    (series on energy conservation and energy policy)
    Bibliography: p.
    Includes index.
    1. Electric utilities—United States—Planning.
2. Electric utilities—Law and Legislation—United
States. I. Title. II. Series.
HD9685.U5K34 1988   363.6'2'0973   88-24124
ISBN 0-918249-07-4

*To the memory of
my father, who first taught me
about electrical and political power.*

Acknowledgements

Anyone who is foolish enough to write a book has no one to blame but himself. Along with the ultimate responsibility, however, also come a lot of debts. I would like to acknowledge these here without pretending to repay them.

Carl Blumstein probably did more to encourage me in this project over many years than anyone. He did this in a number of ways, from severe criticism to substantial help obtaining financial and logistical support. The most significant step along the way was six months spent at the Universitywide Energy Research Group on the Berkeley campus. Without the hospitality of this institute and its director, Richard Gilbert, I would never have finished the manuscript.

The original version of this book arose from my lecture notes in a class I have taught on electric utilities in the Energy and Resources Program at the University of California, Berkeley. The support of John Holdren, Mark Christiansen and Bart McGuire made this opportunity possible. My students have been a real challenge. Those whom I managed to turn into collaborators have helped me in many large and small ways. I would like to thank Joe Eto, Chuck Goldman, Chris Pignone, and David Yardas.

Many people read different versions of particular chapters and offered advice that I would usually accept the second or third time I heard it. Michael Crew read the entire manuscript. Bob Weisenmiller had lots of useful suggestions on both big and little issues. Mark Levine was a major source of support over the years. Other readers included Bob Budnitz, Dan Kirshner, Kermit Kubitz, Rich Gilbert, Cynthia Praul, Chuck Goldman, Jerry Delson, Carl Blumstein, and Menasha Tausner.

The logistics of producing a book are formidable. Seth Zuckerman was a superb editor, helping to tame my prose and my logic. Copy editing was performing during the initial stage by Beryl Magilavy and then, during final production, by John Schacht. Peter du Pont organized the production in a totally relaxed and competent fashion. Through many versions of the manuscript I received word-processing help from Dorothy Turner, Beverly Strisower, Charlotte Standish, John

Randolph, and Carol Koslowski. Thanks also to Jean Wolslegel for her expert typesetting.

Finally, I would like to thank the Kahn girls, Alice, Emma and Hannah for comic relief.

Preface

This book is about the process of planning electric power systems. The large capital requirements for building power stations have always meant that careful thought must go into the decision to build them. Because electricity is a public service, government has played a substantial role in defining the terms of the business. This interaction between private decision-making and public policy makes for a complex economic environment.

Conditions in the electric utility industry have become increasingly unstable in recent years. The planning problem has changed as new forces have emerged. Traditional rules of thumb are no longer adequate, but a new paradigm has yet to be formulated. There are no longer any firm guidelines that even delineate the division of responsibility between government policy and private prerogative.

This book investigates the planning problem for electric power from an inter-disciplinary perspective. It characterizes engineering constraints and possibilities but does not focus on them solely. Economic decision rules are described in connection with the particular circumstances under which they arose. Changes in the economic, financial and political arenas are placed in an historical perspective. As much as possible, I use concrete examples to illustrate particular issues.

Readers who are looking for a working knowledge of contemporary conditions in the U.S. electric utility industry are apt to benefit most from this discussion. Such a search will most likely arise out of confusion about the turmoil and instability that seem to characterize this industry today. Thus, I hope this book may serve as a modest guide for the perplexed.

Table of Contents

Chapter 1

Electric Utilities at the Crossroads

1.1 Introduction

Electricity is a fundamental commodity of modern civilization. It is responsible, directly or indirectly, for the technological shape of society and the character of its economic base. Electricity utilities are a fundamental institution in each developed nation, although the history of their development differs widely from country to country (Hughes, 1983). This book traces the development of electric utilities and their associated institutions in the United States, with the aim of preparing the reader to understand the turmoil pervading the industry in the 1980s. The approach taken is a historical one, focusing on changes in the electricity business during this century.

The history of the utility industry has been characterized by profound changes in industry cost structure and regulation. Its early years were marked by a long period of falling prices, rising demand, and growing profit and productivity.

Regulation provided stability by limiting competition, while controlling the worst monopoly abuses. Investors, managers and customers all benefited from the relatively light hand of government control. This happy state of affairs persisted until the 1970s when the direct and indirect effects of the oil price revolution destabilized the entire structure. The cost of everything the utilities needed began to rise rapidly. The cost of building power plants and providing them with fuel grew far beyond the expectations of conventional wisdom. The enormous amounts of capital electric utilities required to expand became more expensive to finance as the cost of money skyrocketed.

The transition from declining to increasing cost was painful for those in the electric utility business and for their customers. The marginal cost of electricity now exceeded the average prices that regulators allowed utilities to charge, making the classical business strategy of expansion and growth untenable. Investors suffered as returns on investment lagged. Utility regulators became unpopular because they were continually required to increase rates. In this volatile environment, electricity became a highly politicized industry, and utility executives no longer lived tranquil lives. Traditional wisdom seemed increasingly inappropriate for dealing with the problems of the industry, leading to a period of debate over the re-definition of regulatory goals and objectives. New strategies emerged from these political conflicts and economic upheavals.

The price shocks of the 1970s were followed by further instabilities in the 1980s. In many regions, electric utilities developed substantial excess capacity. New plants that were built to meet the previous decade's expectations of load growth came on line at high cost. Fuel prices reversed course and began to decline. This development defied the "permanent scarcity" orthodoxy that had formed at the end of the 1970s, when the price shocks of that decade had created the impression that oil and gas prices would increase forever. High prices in the 1970s had raised marginal prices above average cost, but declining fuel prices in the 1980s again created an environment in which short-run marginal costs were lower than average costs, the norm in the early era of growth in demand and productivity. The cost explosion of the 1970s had been an anomaly characterized by a topsy-turvy world of higher marginal than average costs. Now the classic pattern re-emerged, but in an era in which stagnation and competition replaced earlier expansion and monopoly.

In this chapter, we sketch these changes briefly, illustrating the declining cost era through the career of Samuel Insull (Section 1.2). We then describe the transition from declining to increasing cost conditions, and the emergence of the instabilities of the 1980s. We discuss the regulatory changes that accompanied these shifts in the economic environment, and new strategies and challenges to traditional institutions that resulted from questioning the nature and structure of the traditional utility firm (Section 1.3). Finally, we outline the rationale for the vertically integrated electric utility and discuss the challenges to this structure (Section 1.4).

This chapter goes quickly over difficult and controversial territory. The drama will be described more fully in subsequent chapters.

1.2 Scale Economies: The Historical Background of a Former Growth Industry

Electricity use and electric utility companies grew enormously in the first 70 years of this century, thanks to scale economies in both supply and demand. Larger markets meant larger, more efficient plants, which led to lower costs and more growth. We will illustrate this process with a concrete example: the personality and achievements of the industry's largely forgotten master builder, Samuel Insull. His career is both a symbol of the past and a foreshadowing of later developments.

Insull, born in England, came to America as a young man to become personal secretary to Thomas Edison. He participated in Edison's struggles with the financial community over the development of the power industry, which culminated in the formation of what was to become the General Electric Company in the 1890s. Learning the intricacies of high finance as well as high technology from this experience, Insull went out on his own at the turn of the twentieth century to direct the development of the Commonwealth Edison Company of Chicago. He built up this utility through a combination of technical, marketing, financial and political skills. At Commonwealth Edison, Insull not only unified the many small competing companies in Chicago, but also began the process of rural electrification. This would eventually enable electric utilities to become large regional entities, serving ever increasing demands from all segments of society.

Before World War I, however, rural electrification was a piecemeal process. Only small, isolated systems existed, typically serving a single town. In 1911, Insull began an experiment in Lake County, Illinois designed to link up a number of

Table 1-1

Lake County experiment, general statistics

	Separate Management (1910 conditions)	Unified Systems (1912 Conditions)
Population Served	15,395	22,188
Number of Towns Served	10	20
Number of Customers	1,422	3,457
Connected Load in Kilowatts	2,033	4,503
Kilowatt-Hours Sold	699,574	1,898,978
Kilowatt-Hours Sold per capita	45	86
Income	$67,371	$136,694
Income Per Kilowatt-Hour	8.9¢	7.26¢
Income Per Customer	$43.86	$39.54
Income Per Capita	$ 4.05	$ 6.16
Maximum Kilowatts	573	963
Annual Load Factor	14.6%	28.9%

these small systems with a high voltage transmission network. The production economies achieved by this expansion were so substantial that the extra investment could be paid for easily, profit margins more than doubled, and customer prices declined at the same time.

Insull presented the results of the Lake County experiment in a famous address to the Franklin Institute in 1913. Tables 1-1 and 1-2 are the statistical summaries he offered at that time. Table 1-1 shows the changes on the demand side. In the two years from 1910 to 1912, the unified system doubled the number of towns served, and more than doubled customers, connected load and kilowatt-hour sales. Over the same period, the system reduced prices 18%, from almost 9 cents/kWh to about 7.25 cents/kWh. The aggregated markets were easier to serve, creating a more efficient load: the maximum demand on the system rose by only 68% (963 kW vs.

Table 1-2

Lake County experiment
comparison of cost of energy

	1910	1912
Investment Per Kilowatt		
of Maximum Demand		
Generating Station	$178	$122
Substation	...	70
Transmission	...	190
Total		
	$178	$382
Fixed Charge of Investment		
Per Kilowatt of Maximum	$20.85	$42.60
Maximum Kilowatts	573	963
Load Factor	14.6%	28.9%
Costs Per Kilowatt-Hour at		
Local Plant or Substation		
Fuel	2.04¢	.61¢
Other Operation, including Substation		
and Transmission	3.42¢	.56¢
Fixed Charges on Investment	1.62¢	1.68¢
Total Costs*	7.08¢	2.85¢

*Showing a savings in supplying the district from unified power supply and transmission system of 4.23 cents per kilowatt-hour.

573 kW) even though total kilowatt-hour sales went up 2.7 times. This meant a smoother load that could be served by more continuous operation of the most efficient generating units. Table 1-1 uses the load factor, the ratio of the average to peak loads, as a measure of this smoothness. The unified system shows a load factor twice as high as the separate systems.

The effect of the consolidation on cost is shown in Table 1-2. On the whole, investment requirements are proportionally (per peak kilowatt) greater for the larger system. This relationship will turn out to be an invariant feature of growing systems, since growth is capital intensive. The increased capital expenditures are offset by gains in efficiency and market increases. In this example there are two offsetting cost effects at work. First, scale economy at the individual plant level reduces the cost per kW of generating capacity by 30% ($178 vs. $122). Second, larger generating stations can be built to serve the aggregated loads, thereby reducing per-kilowatt operating costs for fuel and maintenance. Offsetting these savings is the extra need for transmission and substation facilities in the unified system. They overwhelm the scale economy in capital cost for generation, so overall capital intensity increases.

Fixed charges per peak kW demanded are twice as large in the unified system, compared to the isolated ones. But when these fixed costs are spread over units of energy production (measured in kilowatt hours), the two systems have comparable fixed costs, thanks to the load factor improvement resulting from a more aggregated demand. Although each unit of capacity costs twice as much as in the small systems, the large system uses capacity twice as intensively. The unit fixed cost is given by

$$\text{Unit Fixed Cost} =$$

$$\text{Annual Fixed Charge per KW}/(\text{Load Factor}*8760) \ . \ (1\text{-}1)$$

For the isolated systems this takes the value

$$0.85/(0.146*8760) = 1.62 \text{ cents/kWh} \ ,$$

and for the unified system the corresponding value is

$$0.60/(0.289*8760) = 1.68 \text{ cents/kWh} \ .$$

The real scale economy comes from the steep drop in operating costs. Fuel cost per kilowatt-hour falls 70%. This is due to improved combustion efficiency and perhaps lower fuel prices for larger quantities purchased. Operations and maintenance costs per kWh decrease almost 85%, probably due to decreased labor requirements.

The net result of network unification is an increased profit margin. Although Insull did not explicitly perform the subtraction, it is easy to see that per-unit profits go from 1.82 cents/kWh (8.9 − 7.08) to 4.41 cents/kWh (7.26 − 2.85). The driving force behind these figures is that growth in consumption has expanded rapidly, which has made possible a more efficient pattern of production. A small part of the efficiency gain goes to lower consumer prices, but producers retain the bulk of the productivity increase as profits.

Over time utility operators such as Insull plowed their profits back into expansion. Larger and larger systems were constructed, requiring tremendous capital investment. Among his many innovations, Insull introduced the retail sale of electric utility common stock to the public as a means of financing expansion. This was an astute political move as well as a good financial strategy. Insull wanted his utility customers to share in company profits through stock ownership. This would create a political constituency to support the expansion of his utility franchises through the purchase and consolidation of smaller companies.

During the 1920s this stock strategy was widely imitated throughout the industry. The principal corporate form fueling expansion became the utility holding company, a financial shell whose assets were shares of common stock in many different operating utilities. The speculative fever of the time soon transformed this growth process into abusive directions. Holding companies purchased one another, creating financial pyramids based on exorbitant estimates of underlying value. When the stock market crashed in 1929 and industrial activity began to contract, the holding company bubble burst, and the large group of investors who shared both real economic profits and speculative gains lost large amounts of money. In the political reaction which followed, Insull was painted as a principal villain.

Thurmond Arnold, founder of Arnold and Porter, a distinguished Washington law firm wrote about this period in his classic study *The Folklore of Capitalism*. He expressed the common opinion of the time in the following way.

> . . . Once an organization has become so respectable that it is a proper one for widows and orphans to trust, great pressures exist to use that respectability to get all the funds possible. Then, at the height of its powers when it is most

respected, it becomes the worst organization for widows
and orphans to trust . . . It is always the most respectable
organizations which levy the heaviest tribute. Frankly
speculative organizations collect money from a different
source and cause much less suffering. It was Insull, not
Capone, who wrecked the financial structure of Chicago.

The economy of scale and expansion strategy which Insull
epitomized suffered a brief setback in the 1930s, when consumption declined slightly because of the Depression. The
growth path resumed, however, as new uses were found for
electricity, and the old pattern re-emerged in the late 1930s.
One of the great marketing success stories of this period was
the widespread adoption of the domestic electric refrigerator.
This appliance only came into wide usage as utilities sought
to expand residential electricity use to compensate for reduced
industrial sales. Wainwright's *History of the Philadelphia Electric Company* recounts this story as a great strategic triumph.

The financial collapse of the holding company empires that
occurred at the beginning of the Depression resulted in a new
level of utility regulation. Local oversight by state commissions or through municipal control was supplemented by
regulatory intervention at the national level. The Securities
Exchange Commission was created to bring federal government authority into the investment arena to guarantee that
the financial abuses of the 1920s would not be repeated. The
political backlash against private electric utilities also supported government entry into electricity supply and distribution through agencies such as the Tennessee Valley Authority,
Bonneville Power Administration and Rural Electrification
Administration. Investor-owned utilities were anxious to forget Insull, even if they did not forget his basic business strategies.

Among the many forgotten lessons of the holding company
debate was the intensity of public controversy when electric
utility management fails in its public service functions. As a
highly visible and highly regulated industry, electric utilities
are particularly vulnerable to disappointed public expectations.
This vulnerability and disappointment would recur in the
1970s when the industry's era of declining costs came to an
end.

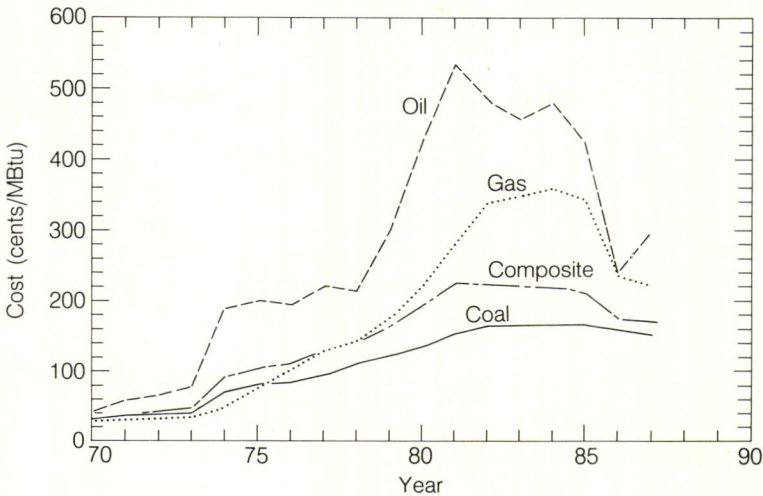

XBL 887-8491

Figure 1-1. Costs of fuels for electric utilities.

1.3 Transition from Declining to Increasing Cost and the Onset of Instability

Scale economies simply mean that bigger is cheaper. But, the technological conditions that create such happy outcomes cannot be expected to continue forever, and sooner or later, diminishing returns set in. In the case of electricity, a number of external factors came together in the 1970s to transform the cost structure. Fuel costs escalated due to OPEC cartel actions and their spillover into non-oil fuel markets. Figure 1-1 shows how these factors changed from 1950 to 1976. Oil prices escalated still further in the late 1970s, reaching a peak of $35 to $40 a barrel before subsiding in the mid 1980s. The cost of power plant construction increased in a steadier and more persistent manner. Figure 1-2 shows the Handy-Whitman Index of material and labor construction costs and the cost per kilowatt. Again these data only go through the mid-1970s: current prices are 2–3 times as great.

Figure 1-3 shows the change in both current-dollar and constant-dollar (adjusted for inflation) electricity prices along

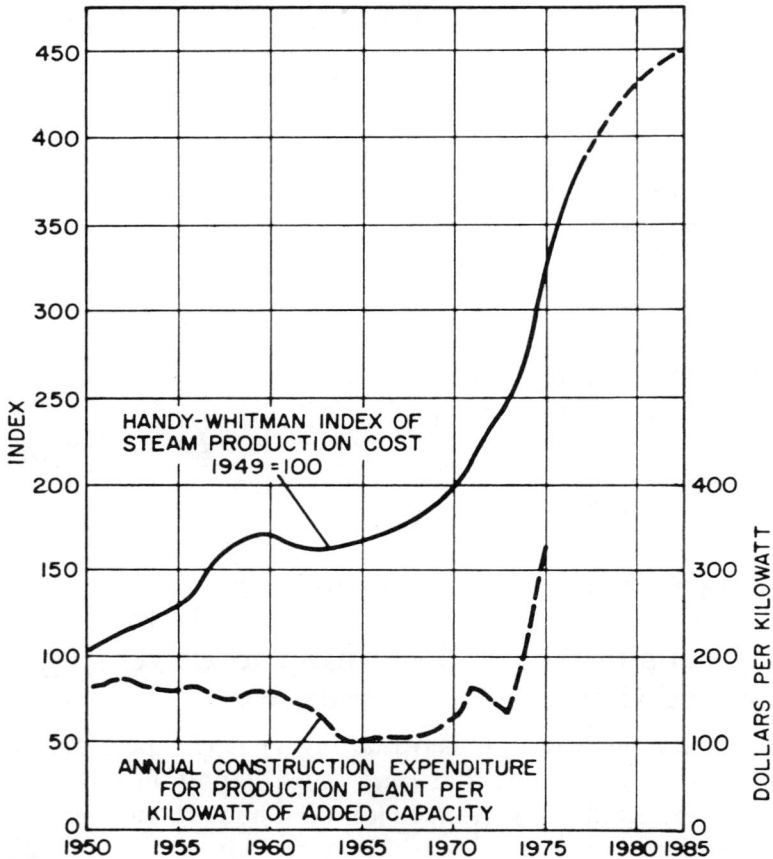

XBL 842-657

Figure 1-2. Handy-Whitman index and cost per kilowatt.

with a representation of the growth in production over a 90-
year period. We see that declining costs have been the norm
during most of the history of the electric utility business; still,
future conditions are very difficult to predict. Figure 1-4
shows a projection into the speculative future of marginal and
average costs and the relation between them. During the dec-

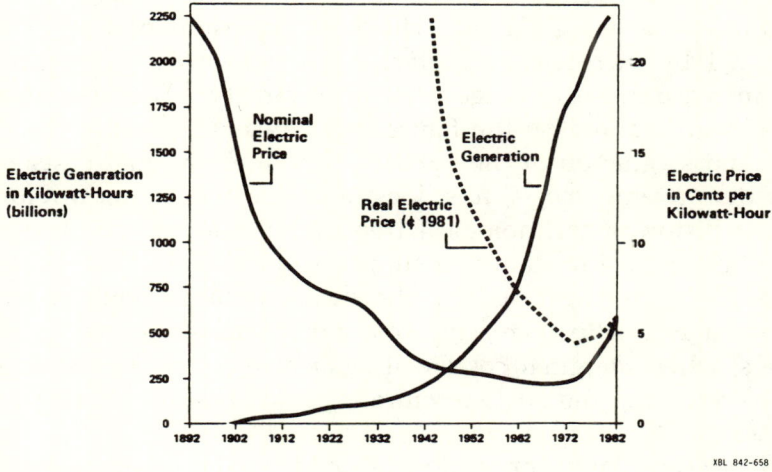

Figure 1-3. U.S. electrical generation and price.

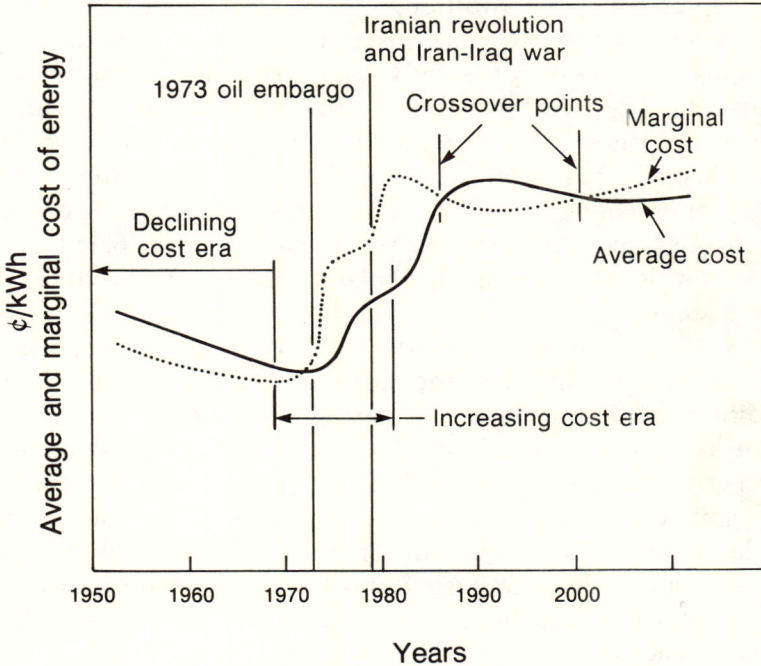

Figure 1-4. Marginal and average cost of energy (Sioshansi, 1984).

lining cost era (ending in the late 1960s) both marginal and average costs went down. The cost explosion of the 1970s was led by increasing marginal costs, which far outstripped the increase in the average price of electricity. The first cross-over point marked on the figure delineates the onset of the oil glut and stagnation of the 1980s. Although marginal costs are less than average costs, this does not appear to signal a return of the historical technological trend of increasing productivity so much as an imbalance in supply and demand. The imbalance theory is suggested by the next crossover point, which shows a return to increasing-cost conditions sometime in the 1990s, when marginal costs will again rise faster than average costs, returning the cost structure to conditions resembling the 1970s.

These speculative projections should not be taken as literal predictions, but rather as thought experiments. The long-term forecast of increasing costs grows out of a view of diminishing resources, particularly oil and natural gas, which are finite and depletable. The flip-flopping relation between marginal and average costs suggests instability in the adjustment to changing conditions of supply and demand. Planning and regulation, however, require assumptions about the future course of costs — which tend to imply a stable view of the world, usually based on an extrapolation of recent trends. As these trends change, the rules of thumb developed for one set of circumstances become inappropriate. A principal goal of this book is to explain the relation between the rules of thumb developed by planners and regulators and the larger economic environment. A brief survey of regulatory history will show how different the tasks and outcomes are under conditions of decreasing or increasing costs.

The regulatory procedures developed during the declining-cost period addressed the politically pleasant task of deciding how much to reduce prices. The issues which dominated regulatory attention during this period were the valuation of capital assets ("the rate base") and the determination of a fair rate of return to stockholders.

The basic process of regulating rates involves dividing estimated revenue requirements by estimated sales. It is typical to separate revenue requirements into a variable portion reflecting operating costs, and a fixed portion reflecting capital costs. Since operating costs are easily audited, there was seldom much conflict over these. Most regulatory attention in the declining-cost era was devoted to determining the value of capital invested (rate base) and fixing the level of reasonable earnings. Because of the underlying scale economies, new capital investment always lowered operating costs. If utility rates were based on old data about costs (i.e., before the cost-reducing investment), then revenues based on those rates would be too high, and profit margins would yield a higher return to stockholders than regulators deem reasonable. To correct this, the regulator lowered the price to consumers so that only required revenues were produced.

At the rates that prevail before the rate case, the utilities would earn too high a profit; after the rate case, they are still left with adequate profit, and ratepayers pay less for electricity — everyone fares well.

The basic procedure under increasing cost is somewhat similar, but yields a very different outcome. Under increasing cost conditions, rates always go up. In this instance, prevailing rates would yield too scant a profit (or none at all) to the utilities. So the utilities must ask for an increase in rates just to earn enough profit to continue to attract capital from potential shareholders. There can also be an inherent dynamic forcing up rates because of inadequate demand forecasts. Since rates are the ratio of revenue requirements to estimated sales, if the sales forecast is too high, then the rate will not yield revenue requirements. Broadly speaking, utilities did over-estimate sales growth in the 1970s. Figure 1-5 illustrates the mismatch between electric utility industry forecasts in 1973 and subsequent developments. This graph also shows the 1974 predictions of Chapman and associates. The Chapman estimates represent a line of thinking about the market for electricity in the 1970s that diverged from the conventional industry view. The industry's error led utilities to persistently fail to earn their required capital cost. Rates never gave high enough returns to stockholders. (This theme will be pursued in some detail in Chapter 3.)

Increasing costs and demand over-forecast had serious political repercussions. The result of the inaccurate projections

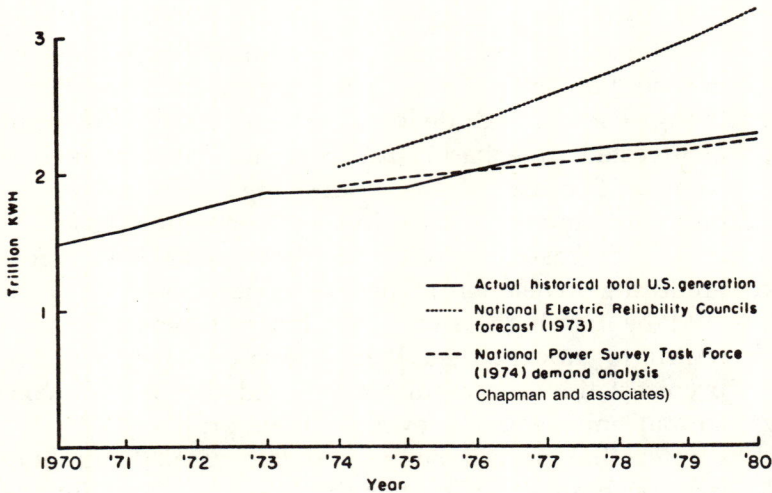

XBL 842-660

Figure 1-5.   Total U.S. electricity generation, actual and forecasts.

was the emergence of an anti-utility political constituency. As in the days of Insull the financial troubles of utilities were blamed upon mismanagement.   As the 1970s progressed, regulatory proceedings became both more frequent and more acrimonious.   Various public and private agencies intervened in utility rate hearings to argue against rate increases generally, or at least not for the group they represented. A common thread in many of these arguments is that utility management was inefficient.   Rate hearings became a forum for investigating utility management's planning processes. Fuel purchase arrangements came under attack. Construction programs were criticized for being extravagant, unnecessary and wasteful.

These political battles became constant struggles. More and more of the traditional assumptions, practices and industry rules of thumb were criticized.   Year in and year out, opponents of utilities found more ways to obstruct utility rate requests and expansion plans. Gradually, utility opponents began to coalesce around a new strategy for the electric utility industry based on the assumption that scale economies for central station plants were no longer significant.

The new paradigm advocated by many opponents of the utility industry's traditional strategy was based upon small-scale and independently owned supply alternatives and end-use conservation. This alternative strategy was advocated on environmental, political and economic grounds. Years of administrative hearings followed, based on abstruse engineering, financial and social cost theories. California was a principal arena for the battle over utility planning strategies. Often called "soft technology" after a phrase coined by Amory Lovins, this collection of smaller-scale technologies was argued to be more appropriate to all of society's needs than central/station coal or nuclear power plants. Its proponents were quick to claim credit when several major utilities began to shift emphasis toward this new direction. David Roe, an intervenor for the Environmental Defense Fund, summarized this experience:

> With years of hard analysis to help them overcome previous bias, these utilities found that the alternatives were not only at hand, but that their *economic* advantages were substantial. Besides being cheaper, they offer greater planning flexibility, reduce financing risks, and have a near miraculous effect on earnings.
>
> New York Times, Jan. 15, 1984.

Although argued in the language of economics, the strategic debates over utility planning and regulation were in fact also political conflicts. Roe himself has been compared to V.I. Lenin by executives of the very companies he currently finds himself praising. By the same token, the view of these conflicts Roe presents in his autobiographical account, *Dynamos and Virgins*, is far from flattering to these executives. Still, not all elements of the 1970s anti-utility coalition endorsed the soft technology alternative. But political opposition to business as usual eliminated traditional choices or made them very expensive. In an industry as highly regulated as electricity, social and political objectives get translated into financial costs by forcing the industry to bear its formerly hidden social costs of doing business — through internalization of externalities. In particular, health, safety and environmental risks of power production that are deemed socially unacceptable generate large mitigation costs.

Among the many consequences of the upheaval in the cost structure of electricity production was the re-emergence of a debate on the organizational structure of utilities. If scale economies were no longer achievable on a meaningful level, then perhaps the natural monopoly status of utilities had also ended. The same economic arguments that were used to buttress the claim that conservation and small-scale generation were efficient might be used to support the deregulation of electricity generation. As the marginal cost of electricity declined with falling oil and gas prices in the mid-1980s, large electricity customers began to bypass the utility altogether by producing their own power. This process shortcuts debate about the future structure of the utility industry by simply transforming it de facto. The question of industry structure is complicated, and will be assessed at greater length in Chapters 8 and 9. Nonetheless, we will introduce it briefly now.

1.4 Cost Structure and Vertical Integration

Why do firms choose to perform some economic functions in a particular business and not others? Industrial organization theory studies such behavior. Monopoly (one seller), or oligopoly (few sellers) firms are a particular focus of such studies. To get a simple view of electric utilities from the perspective of industrial organizations, it is useful to compare their traditional structure with the structure of similar industries. The rationale for regulation can become clearer in this context. We will consider natural gas, petroleum, and telecommunications. In each case we can define four roughly comparable economic functions that must be performed. We will see that the integration of these functions within individual firms varies across industries. To highlight the role played by cost structure with respect to vertical integration we sketch the regulatory revolution in telecommunications. The break-up of the Bell system into an unregulated AT&T plus seven regional companies may suggest ways to think about the cost revolution in electricity.

In each industry we will consider, we can distinguish the following four technological functions: (1) equipment vending, (2) generation/production, (3) transmission and (4) distribution. Let us start with distribution. If a physical connection must be made to each customer, it is easy to see that spatial economies will favor having a single firm in a given area. Petroleum distribution can be accomplished without such a connection. Consumers either drive to a gas station or the fuel truck comes to their house. There is no network of pipes or wires to ultimate consumers, so many firms can compete. Gas, electricity and telephone do require such a point-to-point network. Rather than incur the social waste of competing firms installing redundant networks, society grants a regulated franchise to one firm that exploits the natural monopoly in distribution.

Consider transmission. In telecommunications, satellites and optical fiber technology have revolutionized the economics of long distance telephone transmission. This new technology is so productive that it has made room for many firms where before the spatial economies of a point-to-point network dictated a regulated monopoly. Terrestrial transmission in other industries is usually integrated with production (petroleum and sometimes natural gas) or with distribution (natural gas) or with both (electricity).

The transmission function is regulated at the federal level, particularly where interstate commerce is concerned. This regulation involves not only price and rate of return, but also service conditions and dealings with other firms. Natural gas pipelines have common-carrier obligations and cannot deny transmission services. Electric utilities, on the other hand, are typically not under the same obligation. Broadly speaking, the reason for this difference is that firms in the natural gas industry are not fully integrated from production to distribution, whereas in electricity they are. Therefore, a multiplicity of suppliers (producers) can be available to a given gas distribution market. In the electric industry, the historical role of production scale economies has led firms to be vertically integrated. With a relatively competitive production market, gas distribution companies could be at a serious disadvantage if pipelines were unregulated.

As we saw in Section 1.1, transmission costs for electricity were historically more than offset by economies at the production level when large systems could be built. Insull and Westinghouse had to prove to their small-scale opponents in the industry, such as Edison, that this high-tech strategy was efficient. In fact, electric power generation became one of the major high technology industries of the period 1890–1930 (Hughes, 1983). There was a very close relation between equipment vendors and the utilities which purchased this equipment. Very often suppliers had to accept the securities of operating utilities as payment instead of cash. A well-known example of this close link was the Electric Bond and Share Corporation, which was a utility holding company owned by General Electric. Although financial interconnections between vendor and user firms can help develop new technology, there is also a potential for speculative abuse. A vendor who owns a large fraction of an operating utility's shares can obtain lucrative equipment contracts at prices above the competitive level. Such predatory practices helped bring about passage of the *Public Utility Holding Company Act (1935)*.

Telecommunications was perceived until recently as an area in which scale economies of innovation were so great that a natural monopoly on technology management existed. Bell Laboratories and Western Electric performed the research and development (R&D) and mass-produced standard equipment for all aspects of the telephone business. This is no longer the case. Since communication technology is merging with the computer industry in such a way that innovation can come from firms which are relatively small, the equipment vending side of American Telephone and Telegraph (AT&T) no longer deserves the special protection of a regulated monopoly status. Society's interest in innovation is better served by the competition which now exists.

The distribution function of telephone companies, i.e., the local and regional networks, still has natural monopoly characteristics. At some point, however, transmission over longer distances becomes competitive. With the break-up of AT&T, the integrated and regulated firm spanning all four functions splits into two new forms. The equipment vendor, production and transmission function remain integrated but are now unregulated. Distribution and some regional transmission are split off, remaining regulated.

It is important to remember that all these changes in the telephone industry are, in principle, related to an attempt to improve total social productivity. The new industry structures allow for more service to consumers, provided at lower total cost to society. This, at least, is the basic intention. The situation would appear to offer some analogies to the increasing competition and decline of scale economies in the electric utility industry. In both cases traditional sources of production economy have lost their privileged status. Small-scale technology becomes competitive. Overall, however, the differences in these situations may be more important than the similarities.

Electric utilities are facing competition because production economies are diminishing generally. Large-scale technologies have suffered disproportionate declines in efficiency. The general trend is toward increasing social cost in electricity, or at least no steady gain in productivity (Joskow, 1986). This situation is just the reverse of what is occurring in telecommunications. This difference gives a whole different flavor to the case of electricity. Under increasing cost conditions all parties are becoming worse off in one way or another. There are no absolute winners such as the new successful high technology firms in telecommunications. We can compare the traditional growth pattern of the utility industry to an increasing pie. Growth brought productivity gains so that the absolute size of each party's benefit (their "slice") grew, without respect to the relative size of the "slices." Now, we have instead what appears to be a most unusual situation in this industry, a declining or at least stagnant pie. Now that the total social cost of electricity production is no longer declining, substantial conflicts can be expected among the various parties.

It is the purpose of this book to develop a feeling for these conflicts. We will ask how they came about, what the cost structure of the industry looks like now, and what the financial and structural alternatives are. We will pose all these questions in the context of specific examples based on the literature of utility planners and regulators. Here is an outline of how we will proceed. Chapter 2 begins with the traditional foundations of economic analysis in the industry. The exposition is based on the presentation in P.H. Jeynes *Profitability and Economic Choice*. Although published in 1968, this folksy textbook has become something of an Old Testament to students of the industry. It represents the world view of utility planners in the declining cost era. We will examine the assumptions about economic analysis and the productivity of capital in the electric utility industry which are fundamental to this world view.

In Chapter 3 we outline the factors neglected in the traditional approach which could no longer be avoided as the cost structure changed. Inflation of fuel prices, capital costs and interest rates all had severe effects on the economics of electricity production. As demand growth slowed, new factors emerged in the utility planning process — reliability, system fuel costs and the environmental effects of new power plants had to be incorporated into the analysis. We will survey these complications to the planning process which has been ignored, neglected, or irrelevant in the declining cost era.

Chapter 4 surveys the basic tasks of price regulation. We contrast the traditional accounting framework with the more modern concern for marginal costs. The former represents the legacy of procedures from the declining cost era. With the cost upheavals of the 1970s came a new concern for marginal costs, and how to incorporate them into the ratemaking process. We illustrate these tensions with reference to data from the 1982 General Rate Case of the Pacific Gas and Electric Company. Particular attention is also paid to inverted residential tariffs (the more you consume, the more each kWh costs). This rate reform represents a complete reversal of the declining cost tariffs from the past.

Chapter 5 examines systematically the subject of marginal cost, introduced in Chapter 4. As competitive pressures increase in the utility industry, it has become increasingly important to understand the marginal cost structure both in the short and long run. A related concept known as "avoided cost" is also examined because of the important role it plays in the pricing and economic viability of independent power production.

Chapters 6 and 7 focus on the alternative power strategy of

conservation and independent power production. These chapters are designed to illustrate the basic economics of these options, and to sketch ways in which they might fit into the long-run future of the electric utility industry. We defer until Chapters 8 and 9 the larger strategic issues concerning how these alternatives compete with one another and with the traditional form of regulation.

In Chapter 8 we address the search for a new paradigm from a theoretical point of view. The rationale for regulation must be thought out again in light of the competing alternatives. If conservation and independent power are economical, does the natural monopoly on production still exist? We take up these questions with an emphasis on the instability of the current markets for electricity. We use stability concepts to characterize the properties of various regulatory strategies. In this light, we pose the policy questions regarding the future of the utility industry.

Finally, in Chapter 9, we return to consider the institutions of the electric utility industry and how they might adapt to the changing economic fundamentals. How might the structure of the industry evolve, and what will be the role of the traditional firm and the traditional regulator?

Chapter 2

Project Decision Rules: Classical Framework

How do planners choose projects? What rules are applied to decide when a particular investment should be undertaken? In this chapter, we will review the traditional approach to these questions adopted by the electric utility industry over the bulk of its history. It is useful to examine the assumptions implicit in this approach and alternative choices that can be made.

The basic challenge of corporate project evaluation is to choose alternatives that make the most money. There are two principal aspects to this problem: first, defining the returns of a given project, which can be done in a number of different ways. We will call this stage the choice of a metric. The second stage involves relating project returns to the financial objectives of the firm. What is the appropriate measure of corporate financial performance?

In the discussion which follows we will introduce many of the concepts associated with both stages of the process. After defining these notions we will describe the logic underlying the traditional practice of electric utility planners. The exposition of this logic closely follows P.H. Jeynes' *Profitability and Economic Choice*. Jeynes was an accountant and engineer for Public Service Electric and Gas of Newark, New Jersey. His book, published in 1968, embodies a lifetime of experience in the engineering economics of electric power, and a concrete, down-to-earth perspective on finance and accounting. It is ironic that at just the time when Jeynes' book appeared summarizing the historic conditions of electricity economics, these conditions changed substantially. Irrespective of subsequent changes, Jeynes' work stands as a codification of the analytic procedures used by utility planners. As recently as 1978, the Electric Power Research Institute based the economic methodology component of its *Technical Assessment Guide* almost exclusively upon Jeynes. Even where modifications have been introduced by more recent writers, the revenue requirements method he expounds remains the dominant mode of utility project planning and evaluation.

To understand the roots of Jeynes' approach it is necessary to take explicit account of the financial marketplace, in particular the stock market. The basic proposition Jeynes demonstrates is that maximizing shareholder profits will produce the most economically efficient outcome for consumers. He argues this thesis with many numerical examples that illustrate *both* a general method of analysis and a particular view about the productivity of technology in the electric utility industry. The thrust of his examples may be summarized in the following simple rules:

1. All projects must meet some minimum rate of return target.
2. These minimum return targets differ among firms and are determined by the stock market.
3. The choice between projects meeting such minimum return targets will usually favor the bigger or more capital intensive alternative, all other things being equal.

Following these rules will maximize shareholder profits and minimize consumer costs simultaneously.

Rules 1 and 2 involve questions of method. It is necessary to understand simple concepts of finance to give a coherent account of these rules. Section 2.1 provides such an introduction. In Section 2.2 we define various concepts of project return including those used by Jeynes, and define the choice criterion favored by Jeynes in Section 2.3. The rule is simply to choose projects that maximize earnings per share. In practice, this rule appears to favor large scale or capital intensive projects, although it is not obvious why this should be so. Indeed it will only be in Chapter 3 that counter examples will be offered. Numerical examples can lend a helpful, concrete tone to the discussion. Those drawn from Jeynes are typical of conditions during the declining cost period, while other more recent data will tend to tell a different story. To illustrate how the Jeynes approach works in detail we outline his revenue requirements methodology in Section 2.4. This method is used to calculate a quantity called the busbar cost of electricity in Section 2.5. (The busbar is the place where the generating unit is connected to the utility grid; thus this is the cost of generating a kilowatt-hour of electricity though it ignores the cost of delivering it to the final customer.) This application represents the most common and easiest way to compare investments in new power plants. We will use it to compare a hypothetical nuclear plant with an oil-fired plant.

Busbar cost is an important concept because it illustrates one of the fundamental flaws in the Jeynes paradigm. This basic assumption is that the project can be characterized independently of the utility system in which it is embedded whereas we will see in Chapter 3 that this separation is not meaningful. Large-scale projects can influence the financial and operating characteristics of the firm as a whole. Jeynes ignored such feedback effects, probably because they were either unimportant or basically favorable during the era he described. In Chapter 3 we will see that they were neither during the transition to increasing cost in the 1970s.

2.1 Introduction to Finance

Financial securities are contractual claims issued or sold by corporations or government agencies which give the purchaser the right to certain future payments. The two most common types of securities are stocks and bonds. In this section we will define the nature of the financial claim represented by each type and introduce methods for valuing them.

Bonds are a specific form of loan in which the issuer receives a sum of money for a specified period of time (usually between 5 and 30 years). At the end of this period the issuer redeems the bond by returning the exact sum borrowed to the holder of the bond. In the interim the bondholder receives interest payments at a rate specified at the time of the loan, called the coupon rate.

Bonds differ from real-property mortgages (which are a more familiar type of long-term debt obligation) because the bond issuer makes no periodic payments against the principal until the very end of the loan term, at which point he pays the entire sum. Mortgages associated with real estate typically require some repayment of principal, called amortization, along with interest over the term of the loan. Bonds are essentially interest-only mortgages with a balloon payment at the end of the loan equal to the entire loan principal. Bonds are also traded on security exchanges after they are issued in what is called a secondary market because the original issuer is not a party to the resale transactions. The corporation that issued the bond pays interest to the current holder, whomever that may be. The existence of a secondary market for bonds involves a mechanism for transferring the basic risk associated with owning bonds — that the market rate of interest will differ from the fixed coupon rate. (Default, which might be expected to constitute a major risk of holding utility bonds, turns out to be a minor factor thanks to regulatory oversight. Even during the Depression, defaults did not increase very much, and bondholders were paid back a large fraction of their investment.)

Stocks represent a claim on the earnings of a corporation. This claim is not fixed in dollar amount, as with bonds, but varies according to the corporation profits. Government agencies can have no shareholders other than the taxpayers, so they can finance investment only with bonds. Private corporations, on the other hand, sell ownership shares in addition to bonds to finance the purchase of assets. Because earnings or profit is the revenue remaining after paying all operating expenses and interest, it can vary with economic conditions external to the firm. This variability, the chance for great gain or loss, makes stock (or equity) financing a more expensive form of finance for a corporation than bonds. Investors must be compensated for the greater risk by earning a greater return.

Defining and measuring the return associated with owning common stock is a complicated and difficult subject. There are several widely used measures, each of which is slightly different in its focus. We will define and discuss three of these concepts without pretending to present a unified account of them.

Return on equity (ROE) is analogous to the interest-rate concepts more clearly associated with bonds. A bond pays a certain percentage of its face value as a coupon interest rate to the owner. The return on equity is found by dividing the earnings of the corporation by the total dollar sum of money paid by original purchasers for shares in that company, i.e. the total common equity (common equity can also include earnings retained by the corporation from previous profits). Return on equity is a fraction, and is easy to compute, but may not be very meaningful if the book or equity value per share is not the same as the market price per share. If a company has a return on equity of 10%, but I can buy a share of its stock for half the book value, then I am earning 20% on my purchase. The difference between accounting or book value and the market price of shares motivates our second notion of return.

The Market-to-Book Value Ratio (MBV) measures the difference between the valuation placed on earnings by the capital markets and the original cost (without adjusting for inflation) of the assets that produce those earnings. If the assets of a corporation are very productive, the stock market will bid up the price of its shares. Electric utility stocks typically had a market-to-book value ratio greater than 1.5 before 1970. At times market-to-book value ratios over 10 have been common. During the period from 1973-1981, however, electric utility shares typically sold for less than book value. This meant that underlying assets were less productive than expected either by original investors, or compared to other current investments (e.g., other stocks). The essential feature of the market-to-book value ratio is that it measures current returns relative to the expectations of the capital market as a whole through an equilibrium process in the capital market that sets stock prices relative to original accounting costs. The ratio of market price to book value shows the deviation of these equilibrium prices from accounting cost. By comparison, return on equity is a simple accounting measure.

The Price/Earnings Ratio (P/E) is another measure of the value associated with shareholder returns which measures the

ratio of current stock price to current earnings. The algebraic
relation among these three concepts is given by

$$P/E = \frac{MBV}{ROE}$$

Most electric utilities today have a price/earning ratio that is
approximately the inverse of the interest rate on long term
debt. If bonds yielded 10%, the P/E of utility stocks would
be about 10. If bonds were to yield 8%, the utility stock P/E
would rise to about 12. Conversely at an interest rate of 12%,
the corresponding P/E would be around 8. This relationship
is approximate. It will vary across utility stocks depending on
special factors. In its more productive period, the shares of
electric utility companies sold at price/earning ratios of 20 or
more. Today, only shares in high growth, high technology
companies sell at such large P/E's.

The price/earning ratio is related to a market capitalization
rate. It says what the current capital value of a firm is in
relation to its expected future earnings. High price/earning
ratios mean that future earnings are expected to be large, so
the current price of a claim on them is high. Underlying this
evaluation of future earnings are expectations of the average
future return of all equity investment in general. These expectations are embodied in a market discount rate (MDR), which
is widely used in equilibrium theories of financial markets,
although not always under that name. A high market
discount rate would imply an expectation that future earnings
on investments will be generally high; a low rate would imply
the reverse. This rate (expressed in percent per year) can be
seen as the time value of money, or the opportunity cost of
tying up capital in a particular investment, thereby being
unable to invest it in another project. The rate is influenced
by returns on competing investments such as bonds, but
because it reflects expectation, the competition is with anticipated future returns rather than with past earnings. MDR is
very hard to measure, in part because it changes constantly in
response to changing conditions. We will say no more now
about market-to-book value ratio except that price/earnings
ratio values for individual stocks must be related (somehow)
to market-to-book value ratio.

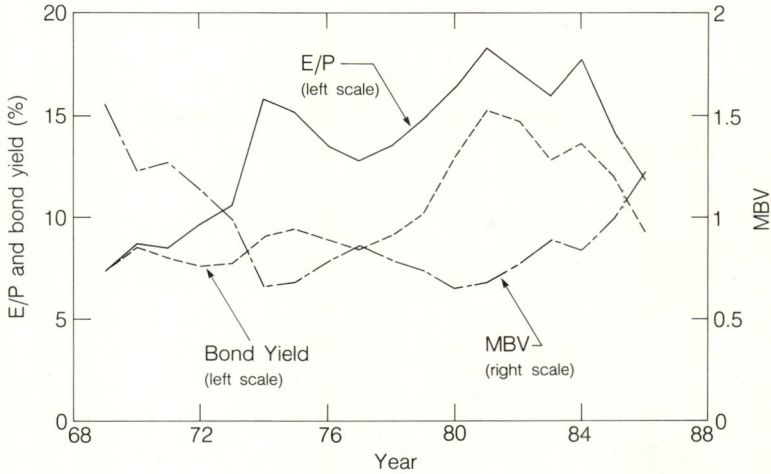

XBL 887-8492

Figure 2-1. Electric utility financial data.

To illustrate the changing nature of interest rates, market-to-book ratio, return on equity and price/earnings ratio we collect data for the period 1970 to 1986 in Figure 2-1. The data represents Moody's Electric Utility Index. Figure 2-1 uses the inverse of P/E, called the earnings yield, to represent the cost of equity capital. Comparing this to the average coupon rate of new AA-rated utility bonds issued in the same year allows calculation of the equity risk premium — the amount by which the return on equity exceeds the return on AA-rated bonds. This difference stems from the fact that equity returns are riskier than bond interest, and averaged 3.0%/yr during this period, although it fluctuated considerably. Finally, for completeness sake we include the annual market-to-book value ratio for the index. It tends to move inversely with the earnings yield.

The interest rate on bonds also depends on their rating. Companies such as Moody's or Standard and Poor's assess the credit quality of firms and assign their bonds a class ranking. The higher the ranking, the lower the interest rate required to sell the bonds because of the lower risk. The interest rate difference between bond ratings is called the

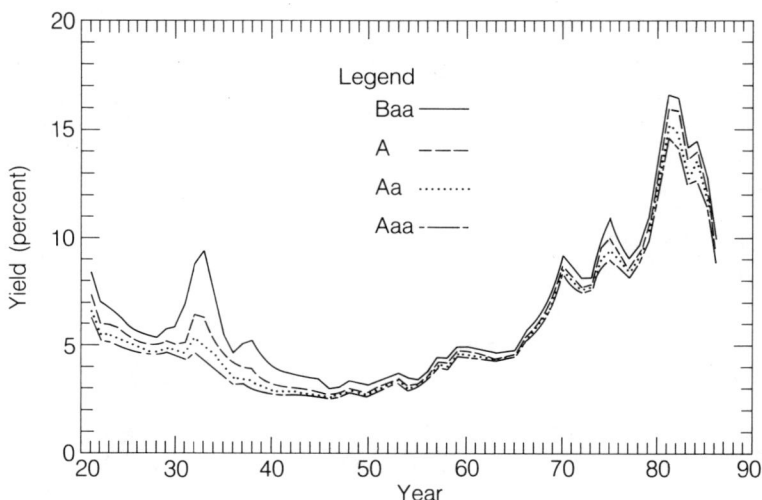

XBL 887-8490

Figure 2-2. Public utility bond yields. (Source: *Moody's Public Utility Manual*.)

yield spread. Figure 2-2 shows variations in bond interest rates from 1930 to 1986 as a function of Moody's ratings from the highest (Aaa) to the medium grade (Baa). Generally speaking, ratings below Baa are too speculative for utilities. These lower-rated securities, sometimes called "junk bonds," have been used extensively in corporate takeovers.

2.2 Project Evaluation: Measuring Returns

Rational investment behavior requires that rules be developed to evaluate projects and decide which ones to accept. The starting point for such procedures is the measurement of returns associated with a given project, a task that can be complicated by a number of factors. First, we focus on the need to discount future benefits. Long-lived projects produce returns many years into the future. The value of nominal dollars generated 10 or 20 years after the time of investment is not as much as the value of dollars required to purchase assets today, both because of inflation and because of the opportunity cost due to not being able to invest that money in another project. The standard methods of accounting for this revolve around the notion of discounting future returns; we will briefly examine two techniques commonly used to do so.

The Internal Rate of Return (IRR) is a popular concept for measuring project returns. It is the annual rate of return that makes the stream of discounted benefits expected from a project equal to the cost of initial investment. Formally IRR is the interest or discount rate defined by the following relation:

$$I = \sum_{i=1}^{n} \frac{R_i}{(1+r)^i} \quad , \qquad (2\text{-}1)$$

where

I = initial investment cost
R_i = return in period i
n = number of periods
r = internal rate of return.

Internal rate of return can only be solved for iteratively (some calculators and spreadsheet programs have this feature programmed into a few keystrokes). When the pattern of returns, the R_i's, includes negative terms, the internal rate of return becomes poorly defined. There are multiple roots and the solution is not unique. As an alternative the **Net Present Value** (NPV) is frequently used to measure the returns of a project.

Net present value is defined similarly to internal rate of return, but the discount rate is chosen at the outset of the analysis, not determined by it. Formally we define net present value as follows:

$$NPV = \sum_{i=1}^{n} \frac{R_i}{(1+r)^i} - I \quad . \qquad (2\text{-}2)$$

Algebraically, when r = IRR, NPV = 0. Usually, however, r is specified in advance as some measure of the cost of capital. Since we have seen that the cost of capital notion can be difficult to capture empirically, there will always be some imprecision, or at least ambiguity, about NPV estimates.

Both Net Present Value and Internal Rate of Return measures depend upon forecasts of future returns R_i over many years. To avoid the tedious process of projecting revenues and expenses over each year, shorthand methods have been developed to reduce the characterization of project returns to a single-year estimate. These engineering/economic formulas are not explicit calculations of returns. Instead, they are estimates of **project revenue requirements** (RevReq) assuming **minimum acceptable returns** (MAR). Jeynes formalizes this approach by defining relations among these notions,

$$\text{Profit Incentive} = \text{Project Revenues} - \text{RevReq} \quad (2\text{-}3a)$$

$$\text{Project Return} = \text{Profit Incentive} + \text{MAR} \quad (2\text{-}3b)$$

The assumption underlying Eqs. (2-3a) and (2-3b) is that investor expectations of minimum acceptable returns can be exceeded by investing in new productive assets. Furthermore, the greatest profit incentive comes from projects which minimize revenue requirements for a fixed revenue level. The notion that this is possible is equivalent to assuming that electricity costs go down and that rates remain stable as the system expands.

We will spend a good deal of effort learning the mechanics of estimating revenue requirements. These are summarized in handbooks such as the 1978 EPRI *Technical Assessment Guide*. Because minimum acceptable returns play such a central role in the project revenue requirements approach, it is important to understand what Jeynes means by it, how it is measured and what use is made of it. In what follows it is useful to rely on his specific examples and generalize from them a little.

First and foremost, minimum acceptable returns is a measure of stockholder's expected return. The simplest formulation is given by Jeynes as

$$MAR = \frac{d_i}{P_i} + \frac{P_{i+1} - P_i}{P_i} \quad (2\text{-}4)$$

where

d_i = dividend at end of period 1

and

P_i = price at the start of period i.

Equation (2-4) says that MAR is the sum of the dividend yield and the percentage capital gain after holding the stock for one period. If we assume that the P/E is constant (a reasonably good assumption over the short term), then we can generalize to the stock price in year $i + 1$ as a function of **earnings per share** (EPS) growth rate g. Formally,

$$P_{i+1} = \left(P/E\right) E_i \left(1 + g\right) . \qquad (2\text{-}5)$$

Using Eq. (2-5) in the second term of Eq. (2-4) we get a more general definition of MAR that is widely used,

$$MAR = \frac{d_i}{P_i} + g . \qquad (2\text{-}6)$$

It is easily seen that the example given in Table 2-1 from Jeynes fits into the formulation of Eq. (2-6). In particular, the dividend yield is 3.2% and the earnings per share growth rate is approximately 5.8%. This yields the estimate of MAR = 9.0%.

That MAR is in some sense the market discount rate which we alluded to earlier is illustrated in Table 2-2 from Jeynes. Here he presents a three period example where the discount rate r = MAR equilibrates future dividends with present stock prices. As in Eq. (2-4), returns are the sum of dividends and capital gains. Formally,

$$P_1 = \frac{d_1}{(1+r)} + \frac{d_2}{(1+r)^2} + \frac{d_3}{(1+r)^3} + \frac{P_4}{(1+r)^3} . \qquad (2\text{-}7)$$

The first three terms reflect the discounted value of the three expected dividends, the final term is the discounted price per share at the end of the third period. To achieve equilibrium, the sum of those must equal the current price of a share. Jeynes shows numerically that for given assumptions about P/E, dividends, earnings and stock prices, r = 9.0% has the property expressed in Eq. (2-7). Applying Eq. (2-7) to the same data produces a dividend yield of 3.5% and in earnings per share of about 5.5% per year.

It is worth examining additional properties of the minimum acceptable returns particularly as optimism about the growth and productivity is reduced somewhat. In Table 2-3 Jeynes considers a company with lower growth and lower price-to-

Table 2-1

Behavior of MAR on common equity

The consensus among investors interested in purchase of the company's stock is as follows. (Optimistic and pessimistic limiting views may also be investigated and given limited weight.)

Year	Market Price (First of Year)	Earnings per Share	Dividend per Share (End of Year)
1	$75.00	$4.00	$2.40
2	79.35	4.23	2.54
3	83.95	4.48	2.69
4	88.82	4.74	2.84

Part I-A. Annual Returns to the Year 1 "Newcomer"

	His First Year	His Second Year	His Third Year
Dividend	$2.40	$2.54	$2.69
Capital gain	4.35	4.60	4.87
Total	$6.75	$7.14	$7.56
In % of $75	9.00%	9.25%	10.08%

Part I-B. Annual Returns to the Year 2 "Newcomer"

	His First Year	His Second Year
Dividend	$2.54	$2.69
Capital gain	4.60	4.87
Total	$7.14	7.56
In % of $79.35	9.00%	9.53%

Part I-C. Annual Returns to the Year 3 "Newcomer"

	His First Year
Dividend	$2.69
Capital gain	4.87
In % of $83.95	$7.56
	9.00%

Part II. Average "First-Year Return to Three Generations of "Newcomers"

1. From Part I-A	9.00%
2. From Part I-B	9.00
3. From Part I-C	9.00
Sum	27.00%

Average MAR on common equity = 27.00/3 = 9.00%

Table 2-2

An estimate of MAR (I)

Based on a reasonable projection of past experience and the opinion of management and financial analysts, together with owners of large blocks of company stock, plus whatever other information may be available, current market opinion is believed to be as follows:

Year	Earnings (End of Year)	Dividend (End of Year)	Price/Earnings Ratio	Market Price (First of Year)
Beginning of Year 1:				
1	$1.75 (est.)	$1.30 (est.)	20 (calculated)	$35.00 (actual)
2	1.85 (est.)	1.35 (est.)	20 (est.)	37.00 (est.)
3	1.95 (est.)	1.40 (est.)	20 (est.)	39.00 (est.)
4	....	....	....	41.00 (est.)

"New comer's" return, Year 1:	
Dividend	1.30
Capital gain	2.00
Total	$3.30/35 = 9.43%

Year 1 Newcomer's Return "Smoothed" Over Next Three Years:
(Try 9% and 9.5% to bracket the Year 1 observation)

Dividend/Trail MAR % = 9.0%		Dividend/Trial MAR% - 9.5%	
$1.30/(1.09)$ =	$1.19	$/(1.095)$ =	$1.19
$1.35/(1.09)^2$ =	1.14	$/(1.095)^2$ =	1.13
$1.40/(1.09)^3$ =	1.08	$/(1.095)^3$ =	1.07
$41.00/(1.09)^3$ =	31.33	$/(1.095)^3$ =	31.23
Total present worth	$35.07		$34.62

Present worth, discounted at 9%, almost exactly duplicates purchase price.
Accordingly, MAR on common equity is currently 9%.

earnings ratio than his previous examples. Instead of growth in earnings per share of 5 to 5.5%, this company projects 2.8%. As expected, dividend yield is much higher in the lower growth case (about 7.7%). This implies MAR = 10.5%. This example suggests that low growth and productivity *increase* the cost of capital and vice-versa.

The example summarized in Table 2-4 tells a slightly different story. Lower expectations of growth in earnings per share reduce the price/earnings ratio (from 20 to 13.3). The resulting lower share prices have the effect of increasing the dividend yield from 3.0% to 4.4%. This increase is less than

Table 2-3

An estimate of MAR (II)

An estimate for another company having slower growth, greater payout ratio, smaller price/earnings ratio, and no preferred stock is:

Year	Earnings (End of Year)	Dividend (End of Year)	Price/Earnings Ratio	Market Price (First of Year)
1	$1.75 (est.)	$1.40 (est.)	10.3 (calculated)	$18.00 (actual)
2	1.80 (est.)	1.40 (est.)	10.0 (est.)	18.00 (est.)
3	1.85 (est.)	1.45 (est.)	10.0 (est.)	18.50 (est.)
4	....	....	....	19.00 (est.)

"New comer's" return, Year 1:

Dividend	1.40
Capital gain	None
Total	$1.40/18 = 7.78%

Year 1 Newcomer's Return "Smoothed" Over Next Three Years:

Try 8% first, based on Year 1 observation: the final conclusion is that the appropriate "smoothed" figure is 9.5%:

Trial MAR% = 8.0%		Trial MAR% - 9.0%		Trial MAR - 9.5%	
$1.40/1.08 =$	$1.30	$/(1.09) =$	$1.28	$/(1.095) =$	$1.28
$1.40/1.08^2 =$	1.30	$/(1.09)^2 =$	$1.18	$/(1.095)^2 =$	$1.17
$1.45/1.08^3 =$	1.15	$/(1.09)^3 =$	$1.12	$/(1.095)^3 =$	$1.10
$19.00/(1.08)^3 =$	15.08	$/(1.09)^3 =$	14.60	$/(1.095)^3 =$	14.47
Total Present worth	$18.75		18.26		18.02

Allowance for Pressure and Selling Cost

A total allowance of $2.00 per share is made. Thus, the company would realize $16.00 per share. The company's MAR on common equity, assuming $16 per share to be acceptable is:

9.5% of $ 18.00 = $1.71 per share
       1.71/16 = 10.7%

the 2% decline in growth in earnings per share (from 7% to 5%). The result is that the minimum acceptable returns *decreases* after the reduction in estimated earnings growth instead of increasing as in the previous examples.

Jeynes gives no account of these contradictions, if that is indeed what they are. We will return to this problem later on. For now, it is important to see how the various project

Table 2-4

**An analyst's prediction of the
future of a stock**

Initial Estimate

Year	Earnings per Share	Price per Share	Dividends per Share
1962	$1.50	$30.00	$0.90
1962	1.60	32.00	0.96
1963	1.71	34.40	1.03
1964	1.83	36.60	1.09
1965	1.96	39.20	1.17
1966	2.10	42.00	1.23
1967	2.25	45.00	1.35
1968	2.40	48.00	1.44
1969	2.57	51.40	1.54
1970	2.74	54.80	1.64

Revised Forecast
(Something drastic happened in 1966)

1967	2.10	28.00	1.23
1968	2.20	30.00	1.32
1969	2.31	32.00	1.39
1970	2.43	34.00	1.45

return concepts can be used in decision rules for accepting or rejecting specific projects.

2.3 Project Evaluation: Decision Rules

A decision rule for project evaluation must involve a comparison of project returns with the financial objectives of the firm. One generic approach to this problem is the **hurdle rate** concept. Projects are evaluated using some return concept and then ranked in decreasing order. The projects' rates of return are then compared to some objective goal called the hurdle rate, and all projects with returns greater than this

hurdle rate are accepted, while all others are rejected. Select-
ing the appropriate level for the hurdle rate is usually an
exercise in estimating the incremental cost of capital.
Minimum acceptable returns has some features of a hurdle
rate, because if a project cannot generate enough revenues to
meet project revenue requirements, then minimum acceptable
returns is not achieved and shareholders are injured by
investment in it.

Jeynes rejects the hurdle rate approach, however, as well as
any other approach based solely on a ranking of project rates
of return. Instead he proposes that maximizing the firm's
earnings per share (EPS), for given revenue increases, is the
appropriate objective for investment decisions. This criterion
gives different results than decision rules based only on project returns and hurdle rates. Let us illustrate the role of
stock market valuation on the acceptability of projects under
the Jeynes rule.

We characterize the firms' returns before any new projects.
The return on equity in the initial period will be called r_1,
and is defined as earnings (E_1) divided by equity capital (C_1).

$$r_1 = \frac{E_1}{C_1} . \tag{2-8}$$

Equity capital is just the number of shares N_1 times the book
value per share PB, that is, $(C_1 = N_1 \times PB)$. So we can
express the earnings per share in this period (EPS_1) as

$$EPS_1 = \frac{E_1}{N_1} = \frac{E_1 PB}{C_1} . \tag{2-9}$$

A new project will have its own return p defined analogously
to Eq. (2-8)

$$r_p = \frac{E_p}{C_p} = \frac{E_p}{N_p P_p} . \tag{2-10}$$

The principal difference between Eqs. (2-8) and (2-10) is that
to finance the new project, the company sells shares at a price
(P_p) that is not necessarily the same as book value. Having
invested in this project, the firm now will have a new earnings per share ratio. We designate the period after the project
has been completed as period 2 and write the expression for

EPS_2 as follows

$$EPS_2 = \frac{E_1 + E_p}{N_1 + N_p} \quad . \tag{2-11}$$

The Jeynes rule says that the new project is acceptable only if

$$EPS_2 > EPS_1 \quad . \tag{2-12}$$

We expand Eq. (2-12) using Eqs. (2-9) and (2-11) as follows

$$\frac{E_1 + E_p}{\dfrac{C_1}{PB} + \dfrac{C_p}{P_p}} > \frac{E_1 \cdot PB}{C_1} \quad ,$$

and simplify to

$$\frac{P_p}{PB} > \frac{E_1}{C_1} \cdot \frac{C_p}{E_p} \quad . \tag{2-13}$$

Equation (2-13) involves only the market-to-value ratio $(=P_p/PB)$, the pre-project return, r_1, and the project return r_p. Substituting these definitions we get a condition on r_p, namely

$$r_p > r_1/MBV \quad . \tag{2-14}$$

Equation (2-14) means that a project is acceptable if its rate of return exceeds the average return on the company's equity adjusted for the market-to-value ratio. This adjustment allows projects to be accepted that have returns below the average return if the company's stock sells at a price greater than book value. Conversely, if the market-to-value ratio is less than 1, then the marginal project must have returns that exceed the average to be acceptable.

A numerical example illustrates Eq. (2-14). Suppose a firm is earning 10% on invested capital. It has three potential projects earning 9%, 10% and 11% respectively. If market-to-value ratio is too low, none of these projects would be acceptable. If the market-to-value ratio were 0.8, for example, a project would have to earn more than 12% to be accepted. Conversely, with market-to-value ratio greater than 1, projects earning less than 10% can be accepted, and for a market-to-

Table 2-5

Project evaluation

(Annual Revenues = $1,200,000)

		Plan (a)	Plan (b)
1.	Minimum revenue requirements		
	Capital investment	4,000,000	5,000,000
	MAR at 6% per year	240,000	300,000
	Depreciation at 2.7185%	108,740	135,925
	Taxes (income and others)	80,000	100,000
	All other expenses	350,000	200,000
		778,740	735,925
2.	Percentage return of project	$\dfrac{240,000 + 0.52(1,200,000 - 778,740)}{4,000,000} = 11.476\%$	$\dfrac{300,000 + 0.52(1,200,000 - 735,925)}{5,000,000} = 10.826\%$
3.	Percentage return of company, post-project	$\dfrac{7,500,000 + 459,055}{100,000,000 + 4,000,000} = 7.653\%$	$\dfrac{7,500,000 + 541,319}{100,000,000 + 5,000,000} = 7.658\%$
4.	Earnings per share, project	$\dfrac{459,055}{80,000} = \$5.738$	$\dfrac{541,319}{100,000} = \$5.413$
5.	Earnings per share of company, post-project	$\dfrac{7,500,000 + 459,055}{2,500,000 + 70,000} = \$3.085$	$\dfrac{7,500,000 + 541,319}{2,500,000 + 100,000} = \$3.093$
6.	Profit incentive per pre-project share	$\dfrac{459,055 - 240,000}{2,500,000} = 8.76¢$	$\dfrac{541,319 - 300,000}{2,500,000} = 9.65¢$

Company Finances Pre-Project

Capital = $100,000,000
Common Stock = $2,500,000 shares
Book Value/Share = $40.00

Market Price of New Shares = $50.00
Annual Earnings = $7,500,000
EPS = $3.00

value ratio of 1.3, projects earning 8% would still meet the criterion. Although Eq. (2-14) looks like a hurdle rate criterion, it is not used that way in practice. Hurdle rate rules focus on rates of return exclusively; maximizing earnings per share yields an ordering among potential projects that depends upon the scale of investments as well as their rates of return. A small project with a high rate of return will not increase earnings per share as much as a larger project with a somewhat lower rate of return; the only requirement is that the large project generate at least the minimum acceptable returns. As is clear, for instance, in Table 2-5, larger scale means more capital intensive. That case involves two alternatives which only differ by their project revenue requirements, and not by the amount of revenues generated. In this example, and all others considered by Jeynes, one alternative has higher capital cost and lower operating cost than the other. The Jeynes criterion will always choose this alternative.

This result bears a striking similarity to the Averch-Johnson thesis that says regulated firms which earn more than the cost of capital have an incentive to (and in fact do) expand capital beyond its socially productive point — sometimes known as "gold-plating." This argument is, in fact, stronger than what can be inferred from Jeynes. The Averch-Johnson model compares the rate of substitution between capital and variable inputs for regulated and unregulated monopolies. In the case of regulation they derive the following relation

$$\frac{-dx_2}{dx_1} < \frac{r_1}{r_2} \quad , \qquad\qquad (2\text{-}15)$$

where

x_2 = variable cost input (quantity)
x_1 = capital input (quanity)
r_1 = cost of capital
r_2 = cost (per unit) of variable.

This equation says that the rate of substitution between variable and capital inputs (that is the decrease in x_2 for a small increase in x_1) is less than their relative costs. A profit maximizing monopoly would choose inputs so that Eq. (2-15) was an exact equality.

Jeynes never offers an example which would satisfy Eq. (2-15). In every case, the extra capital charges, $r_1 dx_1$, are less than the reduction in variable expenses, $r_2 dx_2$, associated with the more capital-intensive alternative. The example in Table 2-5 is typical. Increased annual capital costs, MAR, depreciation and taxes, of \$107,000 in Plan (b), are more than offset by reduced other expenses of \$150,000. This means that the technological productivity assumed by Jeynes is so great that ever increasing capital intensity never leads to an inefficient outcome. This rule of thumb was eventually to be violated in the 1970s.

The examples we have examined so far are all highly simplified in nature. There has been very little specification of the technology underlying electricity production, transmission and distribution. The accounting treatment of fixed costs and economic analysis of variable cost have been only examined in the most sketchy manner. We will correct these deficiencies to some degree by examining the practical implementation of the Jeynes' decision criterion, the minimization of project revenue requirements.

2.4 Revenue Requirements Methodology

In this section we survey in some detail the basic methods of the revenue requirements approach. The fundamental problem in this method is to compare fixed costs and variable costs of alternate projects by reducing each to a single number which reflects varying cash flows in different years. We will begin with examination of fixed costs and then take up the several methods used to treat variable cost.

2.4.1 Fixed Charge Rate

Capital costs are typically annualized by using fixed charge rate (FCR). Fixed charge rate is a fraction between 0 and 1 which expresses the sum of annual requirements for return, taxes, depreciation, and sometimes other fixed overhead costs. The fixed charge rate is calculated by expressing each factor as a percentage and summing these percentages. Symbolically we can write it as

FCR = Return + Depreciation

+ Taxes + Other Overhead   (2-16)

Up to now we have treated the return elements only as equity. In fact, firms typically finance investment with a mix of securities that include bonds and preferred stock in addition to equity. Preferred stock is a hybrid of debt and equity features which pays a fixed percentage return (like bonds) in perpetuity (i.e., it never matures). Dividends on preferred stock, however, must be paid *"before"* dividends or earnings accrue to common stock (hence the name "preferred").

The first step in calculating the fixed change rate from Eq. (2-16) is to expand the return component to reflect the mix of securities which is done using the notion of **weighted average cost of capital** (WACC). The main notion underlying weighted average cost of capital is that firms have a target capital structure which is optimal for their needs, and therefore must be reproduced by the financing of new investment. This target capital structure is a certain percentage each of debt, preferred stock and common equity. The weighted average cost of capital is nothing but the cost of each kind of capital weighted by its share of the capital. It is easily illustrated by example, such as Table 2-6 from Leung and Durning, representing conditions in 1977. The Factor Costs in Table 2-6 are comparable to the yields in Figure 2-1, neither of which includes preferred stock. The estimates are roughly equal for 1977. Some estimates of preferred stock costs show it as less expensive than debt. The 1978 *EPRI Technical Assessment Guide* shows it somewhat higher.

The capital structure illustrated in Table 2-6 is typical for electric utilities since the 1930s. The amount of debt is much greater than the historic norm for unregulated industrial firms which typically have only 30% debt. More recently, take-

Table 2-6

WACC estimate for 1977

Capital Structure Components	Capital Ratio	Factor Cost	Weight Cost
Debt	.55	.080	.044
Common Equity	.35	.114	.040
			.090

overs and leveraged buyouts have raised this fraction. At the other extreme, residential mortgages often constitute 80% of the capitalization of home purchases, and commercial banks are capitalized with about 95% debt. There is no empirically adequate theory of why the capital structure of a given industry takes the kind of values indicated; it is only possible to observe that the amount of debt a firm or household carries increases its risk of default. Optimality is found by balancing increased debt costs against the stability of the cash flows that must pay off that debt.

Depreciation and tax costs may be treated using annuity formulas. Let us begin with depreciation, which is based on the concept that funds must be accrued during the lifetime of a project that will equal the original cost of the plant, thereby allowing for its replacement. This can be modeled as a sinking fund S that earns a rate of return r (the same as the weighted average cost of capital) on balances deposited at year-end. To calculate S we add up annual unit payments plus interest as follows

$$S = \sum_{i=1}^{n} A(1+r)^i \quad , \tag{2-17}$$

where

n = lifetime of project
A = Annual payment.

Since the sinking fund S must equal the original cost of the plant at the end of the plant's useful life, the fraction of the original cost that must be collected each year is

$$\frac{A}{S} = \frac{1}{\displaystyle\sum_{i=0}^{n-1}(1+r)^i} \quad . \tag{2-18}$$

Because payments are made at year-end, the first payment earns its return for $(n-1)$ years. The denominator can be expanded by the formula given in EPRI, p.V-19,

$$\sum_{i=1}^{n} k^i = \frac{k(1-k)^n}{1-k} \tag{2-19}$$

where k is any quantity except 1. We can then substitute $(1 + r)$ for k and insert Eq. (2-19) into Eq. (2-18) to obtain

$$\text{Depreciation} = \frac{r}{(1 + r)^n - 1}$$

(Of course for $i = 0$ in Eq. (2-18), $(i + r)^i = 1$ — which we added to the expansion from Eq. 2-19). It is often useful to combine the depreciation annuity Eq. (2-20) with the return to get the **capital recovery factor** (CRF) as follows

$$CRF = r + \frac{r}{(1+r)^n - 1} \tag{2-21}$$

$$= \frac{r(1+r)^n}{(1+r)^n - 1} .$$

The corresponding annuity for taxes on income is given by the expression

$$\text{Tax} = \left(CRF - SL \right) \left(1 - \frac{di}{WACC} \right) \left(\frac{t}{1-t} \right) , \tag{2-22}$$

where

SL = straight-line depreciation $(1/n)$,
d = debt fraction of capital structure,
i = interest on debt, and
t = income tax rate.

Equation (2-22) is a simplification of other expressions which involve further complexities of the tax laws. These include accelerated depreciation allowances, investment tax credits, and choice of regulatory accounting procedures. Even Eq. (2-20) neglects some factors which are used in complex depreciation and hence tax studies. For our purposes these can be suppressed. Instead we will develop a quantitative feel for these expressions by inserting numbers into Eqs. (2-21) and (2-22).

Let us use Table 2-6 as a starting point. The weighted average cost of capital calculated there can be turned into fixed charge rates for projects by specifying lifetimes and tax rates. Table 2-7 shows examples of such calculations. We assume a combined state and federal tax rate of 52% in these

Table 2-7

Fixed charge rates

Lifetime	Depreciation	CRF	Tax	FCR
5	.167	.257	.032	.289
15	.034	.124	.032	.156
30	.007	.097	.035	.132

calculations, which reflects conditions in the mid-1970s. It is worth noting that for long-lived projects the use of Eq. (2-22) can be avoided by using the tax-multiplier approximation applied directly to WACC which takes advantage of the fact that the capital recovery factor almost equals the weighted average cost of capital for long lifetimes — making the depreciation annuity small. The tax effect is treated by adjusting the taxable portions of the return by the factor $1/(1-t)$. This factor yields the gross revenue required to produce one unit of return after taxes are taken out. For $t = .52$, $1/(1-t)$ is 2.083. Multiplying this by the weighted cost of common equity in Table 2-6 yields a fixed charge rate of 0.127 compared to the value of 0.132 for the 30-year project in Table 2-8. For many purposes the tax-multiplier method is a sufficient approximation to the fixed charge rate. For sensitivity

Table 2-8

Levelization factors

L_f FOR N = 30

Discount Rate

Escalation Rate	$^{(A)}$WAAC = .09	$^{(B)}$WAAC $-$ tdi = .069	(B)/(A)
7%	2.217	2.418	1.091
10	3.368	3.832	1.139

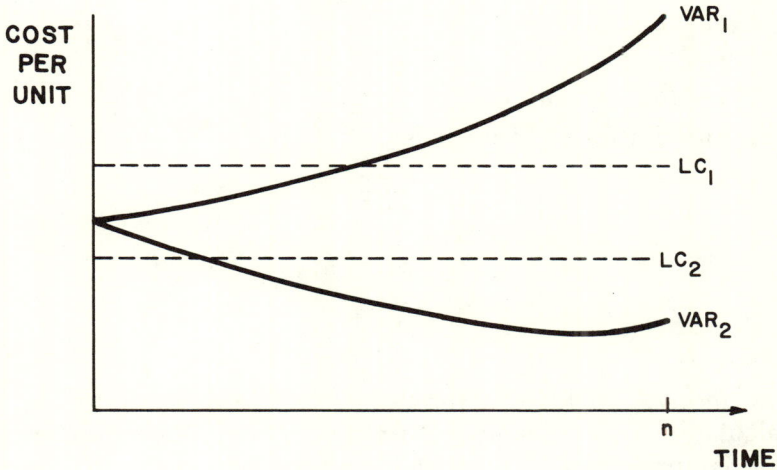

XBL 842-662

Figure 2-3. Variable costs versus time.

calculations on fixed charge rate for the other overhead variables see Gulbrand and Leung.

2.4.2 Levelization of Variable Cost

To value a stream of changing variable costs, the technique of levelization is commonly used. All that is involved in this method is finding a single cost constant, LC, which discounts to the same present value as the stream of variable costs VAR_i over the period of n years being studied. Formally this can be written

$$\sum_{i=1}^{n} \frac{LC}{(1+r)^i} = \sum_{i=1}^{n} \frac{VAR_i}{(1+r)^i} \ . \qquad (2\text{-}23)$$

Graphically the concept is illustrated in Figure 2-3 for the case of increasing cost (VAR_1) and generally decreasing cost (VAR_2).

The EPRI Technical Assessment Guide of 1978 gives a formula for calculating levelized cost (LC) for a stream of variable costs VAR_i which escalate at a constant annual rate e. This formula is designed to compute a levelization factor, L_f, with the property that

$$LC = L_f \ VAR_1 \qquad (2\text{-}24)$$

where

VAR_1 = the variable cost in year 1.

The formula for L_f is given by

$$L_f = CRF \sum_{i=1}^{n} K^i$$

where

$$K = \frac{1+e}{1+r} \ . \qquad (2\text{-}25)$$

The motivation for this formula is best seen by following the calculation of Leung and Durning for the case where escalation is not constant, but varies over the period.

Leung and Durning define levelized cost in a way which illustrates its role as a present-value average of the variable cost stream. In particular, they use the relation

$$LC = \frac{\displaystyle\sum_{i=1}^{n} \frac{VAR_i}{(1+r)^i}}{\displaystyle\sum_{i=1}^{n} \frac{1}{(1+r)^i}} \ . \qquad (2\text{-}26)$$

Equation (2-26) is equivalent to Eqs. (2-24) and (2-25) when e is a constant because

$$CRF = \frac{1}{\displaystyle\sum_{i=1}^{n} \frac{1}{(1+r)^i}} \ . \qquad (2\text{-}27)$$

Equation (2-26) says that the total present-value of the variable cost stream divided by the sum of the future unit annuity payment also discounted to the present yields a constant value for the variable cost stream which satisfies Eq. (2-23). Indeed Eq. (2-26) is identical to Eq. (2-23) when the denominator of the right-hand side is brought over to the left-hand side.

The discussion so far assumes that we are always using WACC for the discount rate r. In fact, there is something of a theoretical debate on this subject. A case can be made for a discount rate which is less than WACC when allowance is made for the tax deductability of interest on debt. Formally, this after-tax discount rate r^* is defined as

$$r^* = WACC - tdi \quad , \tag{2-28}$$

where t, d and i are defined as in Eq. (2-22).

Modern writers on finance such as Brealey and Myers (1981), support the position that for unregulated firms, Eq. (2-28) is the proper discount rate because it more truly represents the cost of corporate borrowing than the weighted average cost of capital.

The argument against Eq. (2-28) is usually made from the regulatory perspective. When the perspective of the consumer is adopted (rather than the utility shareholder), the tax deductability of interest payments is irrelevant if it makes no difference in revenues collected through rates. Recent changes in the tax laws (in particular, the 1981 Economic Recovery Tax Act or ERTA) essentially require regulators to fix rates as if all taxes are paid at current marginal rates. This foreclosed the regulator's option of adopting either normalization or flow-through accounting treatments of tax preferences (see EPRI and Linhart, et al.). Regardless of the debate, it is useful to see how different discount rates affect levelized costs. Calculations in Table 2-8 illustrate this.

Table 2-8 shows that lower discount rates increase levelized variable cost. The net effect of this is to improve the relative attractiveness of projects based on capital substituting for variable costs. Because Eq. (2-28) is not typically used in electric power investment decision-making, but the higher-valued weighted average cost of capital is, it has been argued that no bias to over-invest in capital, a là Averch-Johnson, exists in the industry. Corey makes this argument in his survey of utility practices in 1977. Finally, it is worth noting that Corey, who was a prominent executive with Commonwealth Edison of Chicago, makes the strongest economic argument for the use of Eq. (2-28). Referring to this rate as the "rate of disadvantage," he argues that its use is desirable because the present value of future revenue requirements discounted this way is independent of regulatory or bookkeeping practices (p. 262). This means that truly economic choices can be

Table 2-9
Assumptions for busbar cost comparison

1. Capital Costs	Nuclear	= $2,000/kW
	Oil	= $1,000/kW
2. Fuel Costs	Nuclear: Year 1	= 20 mills/kWh Escalation Rate = 2%/year
	Oil: Year 1	= 50 mills/kWh Escalation Rate = 7%/year
3. Annual Production		= 5000 kWh/kW year
4. Financing Costs	Debt	= 50% of capital, interest rate = 13%
	Preferred Stock	= 10% of capital, interest rate = 13%
	Common Equity	= 40% of capital, cost = 16%
5. Economic Lifetime		= 30 years

made this way without the distortions and constraints of particular rate-making practices. This interesting claim would be more persuasive if it were demonstrated.

2.5 Examples: The Busbar Cost of New Power Plants

To illustrate the revenue requirements method we will compare two alternative hypothetical projects; a nuclear plant and an oil burning plant. In all likelihood neither alternative would be seriously considered by any utility today, but the comparison can be instructive. The quantity we will calculate is the busbar cost per kilowatt-hour (kWh) from each alternative. Busbar cost is the unit revenue requirement for a kilowatt-hour delivered from the generating plant to the transmission network (called the busbar). This figure ignores a number of complications in the total cost of electricity, but is a useful first approximation.

The basic logic of the busbar cost calculation is illustrated by the following relation:

Table 2-10

Calculation of FCR and WAAC

Component	Capital Ratio	Cost	Weighted Cost	Taxable Cost
Debt	.50	.13	.065	.065
Preferred Stock	.10	.13	.013	.027
COMMON EQUITY	.40	.16	.064	.135
	'		WACC = .142	FCR = .227

$$\text{Busbar Cost} = \frac{FCR \; * \; (\text{Capital Cost}/kW)}{\text{Annual Production}}$$

$$+ \text{ Levelized Unit Operating Cost} \quad . \qquad (2\text{-}29)$$

In Table 2-9 we list the assumptions used to make the comparison between nuclear and oil power plants. These assumptions approximately represent conditions in the early 1980s, which was the last time this choice was actively considered. The first step is to calculate the fixed charge rate. Using a total tax rate of 52.5% and the tax multiplier method, the fixed charge rate and the weighted average cost of capital are shown in Table 2-10. The data in Tables 2-9 and 2-10 are sufficient to compute the levelized fixed charges for each alternative. These are given by:

$$\text{Fixed Charges}_N = \frac{0.227 \cdot 2000}{5000}$$

$$= 90.8 \; mills/kWh \text{, and similarly}$$

$$\text{Fixed Charges}_O = 45.4 \; mills/kWh \quad .$$

The magnitude of these costs depends upon the expected annual production (assumed to be 5,000/ kWh per kW-yr). The Table 2-9 assumption is equivalent to assuming that the plants run 57% of the year. Such a number is called the capacity factor. Our assumption that both plants would operate at the same specified level is one of the crucial limitations of this form of analysis. In Chapter 3 we relax this assumption.

Table 2-11
Levelized fuel costs

Escalation Rate	Discount Rate	$K = \dfrac{1+e}{1+r}$	$\dfrac{K(1-K^N)}{1-K}$
N 2%	14.2%	.893	8.065
0 7%	14.2%	.936	12.61

CRF	L_f	Levelized cost (mills/kWh)
N .144	1.16	23
0 .144	1.81	91

Busbar cost is then the sum of fixed costs and fuel costs, i.e.,

$Busbar_N$ = 90.8 + 23
                = 113.8 mills/kWh,

and

$Busbar_0$ = 45.4 + 91
                = 136.4 mills/kWh.

Levelized operating costs are assumed to involve only fuel. In fact, there are also operating and maintainence costs which can be substantial. We neglect this factor and calculate levelized fuel costs using Eqs. (2-24) and (2-25). Table 2-11 summarizes these calculations, and reports the busbar cost for each alternative.

The busbar costs will vary with assumptions about capacity factors, fuel escalation rates, appropriate discount rates (as in Table 2-8), etc. The example illustrates the basic trade-off between fixed and variable costs which is fundamental to electric utility project evaluations. In this example, the extra fixed costs of the nuclear plant more than offset the fuel costs of the oil plant. Based on these assumptions, it is economic to substitute capital for fuel in this case.

Chapter **3**

Modern Complications of the Project Decision Process

This chapter illustrates the difficulties that arose in the 1970s for utility planners. Dimensions of the project evaluation process that were suppressed or neglected in the classical framework became inescapable. Capital costs escalated and project lead times became substantial. These factors had to be incorporated into the evaluation framework. While the fundamental cost conditions for producing electricity were changing, changes in the financial markets began to have a negative effect on utilities. The systems engineering aspects of generation capacity expansion also became more complex. Issues related to reserve margins and bulk power reliability became controversial, requiring more sophisticated modeling and analysis. As the number of factors requiring analysis increased, large scale computer models were introduced to handle the complexity. Even these were inadequate to deal with issues that could not easily be accounted for financially, such as environmental quality or financial risks. Thus the paradigm bequeathed by Jeynes broke down during the economic changes of the 1970s.

The result of the price shocks of the 1970s and the slow adjustment made to them was a substantial mismatch of supply and demand. The evidence of this mismatch is shown in Table 3-1, which indicates the trend in orders for nuclear plants and the cancellation of both coal and nuclear plants from 1972 to 1982. These figures are incomplete and the data are subject to some interpretation, but the trend is clear.

Table 3-1

**Orders and cancellations of new
baseload power plants**

	Orders for Nuclear Plants	Nuclear Cancellations	Coal Cancellations
1972	38	7	
1973	41	0	
1974	28	7	19
1975	4	13	3
1976	3	1	8
1977	4	10	
1978	2	14	2
1979	0	8	4
1980	0	16	2
1981	0	6	6
1982	0	18	

(Source: EIA, 1983a and 1983b).

Many projects which seemed justified under the Jeynes decision rule and cost assumptions before 1974 were found not to
be economically viable in the long run. Many of these cancellations resulted in large losses; the billions of dollars spent
on some projects were ultimately wasted as the plants were
abandoned before completion.

The ultimate impact of these losses has not been sorted out
yet, but their political import is somewhat clearer. Utilities
have been accused of mismanagement and have been penal-
ized financially by regulators. One utility, Public Service of
New Hampshire, has already filed for bankruptcy, and
another, Long Island Lighting company (LILCO), has tottered
near the brink.

A particularly stark situation of this kind involves LILCO's
Shoreham project. Political conflict over safety and evacua-
tion issues associated with the project and enormous increases
in capital cost have undermined the viability of this plant.
Yet regulators never seriously questioned the continuation of
the project until 1983. The chairman of the New York Public
Service Commission from 1974 to 1977 was Alfred E. Kahn,

author of an authoritative 1971 text on public utility regulation. He commented retrospectively in the business press on the regulatory review the Shoreham project received during his tenure.

> We're all victims of creeping incrementalism. At any given time, it was impossible, on the basis of what we knew, to say we shouldn't go ahead ...... Each time, appalled at what had happened before, it was still possible for us to justify continuing. "Nuclear Power Plant Threatens Utility's Future" *Los Angeles Times, March 4, 1984*

Yet despite the support of these regulatory reviews, the project may never operate, an outcome that was wholly unanticipated. How could this happen? What went wrong? In this chapter we will try to answer these questions generally and from a planning perspective. We will discuss the factors which were neglected in the planning paradigm represented by Jeynes but which became important in the 1970's.

In Section 3.1 the evidence of increases in power plant construction cost is reviewed. The increasing amount of time required to build new plants is also illustrated. Section 3.2 introduces a simple model of the economics of premature installation, i.e., the construction of facilities before they are needed to serve demand. Models of this type were used to justify starting large-scale construction projects in advance of demand growth. Section 3.3 discusses the treatment of financing costs for uncompleted construction projects. The fact that regulators tend to impose delays on the recovery of those costs had important effects on the valuation of electric utility stocks. In Section 3.4 the more complex theories of the cost of equity capital cost that were required to explain the stock market of the 1970s are discussed in the context of electric utility cost conditions. Section 3.5 explains the role of reserve margins and reliability in the project evaluation process. In Section 3.6 capacity expansion models are introduced. Section 3.7 explores the particularly difficult case in which non-monetary factors are incorporated into the analysis.

3.1 Moving Targets: Capital Cost Escalation

While it is now clear that fuel costs can change dramatically

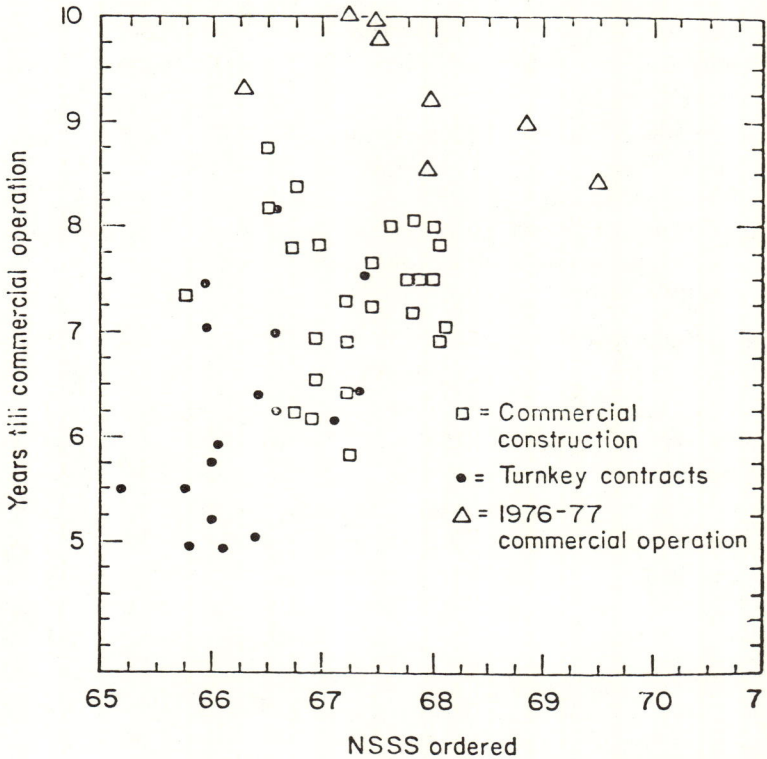

XBL 791-198

Figure 3-1. Nuclear plant construction time.

over time, it became equally clear in the 1970s that capital costs could also change drastically. The direction of change since the 1970s has been toward increases in cost. The sources of these increases involved the internalization of environmental, health and safety costs associated with power production. Labor productivity, management and regulatory factors also played a role.

The problem for project planners is that capital cost escalation is not as easily accommodated to the revenue requirements methodology as change in variable cost. The basic difficulty has to do with the extension of the planning horizon as construction lead-times for power plants increase. It not only became more expensive to build new generation facilities in the 1970s, it also took longer and longer. Lead-time and

Table 3-2
Capital cost escalation: Data

In Service Date	Capital Cost ($/kw)		Change in Handy-Whitman Index of Construction Co.	
	Coal	Nuclear	Coal	Nuclear
1967[a]	185	170	3.1	3.6
			3.8	4.4
			6.3	5.8
			7.2	8.1
1971[b]	162	172	11.1	10.1
			3.7	4.4
			7.5	6.4
			25.1	17.8
1975			9.0	10.8
			6.9	7.9
			6.3	5.9
1978[c]	580	870	10.8	9.3

a) Federal Power Commission, *National Power Survey*, Part II,
     Table 1A (October, 1964) p.178.

b) C. Komanoff, *Power Plant Cost Escalation*, KEA, (1981),
     Table 10, p. 228 deflated to 1971 $ using Handy Whitman
     Index.

c) Generation Task Force, New England Power Planning, 1978.
     (same as (b)).

cost are intimately related since many of the construction
costs of new plants are time-related; it became more difficult
to determine exactly when a project would be completed, or
how much it would cost.

To illustrate the magnitude of these effects it is useful to
examine some of the data on lead times and costs. For the
case of nuclear plants, the increase in construction duration is
illustrated in Figure 3-1. This shows roughly a doubling
(from 5 to 10 years) in the time between the utility's ordering
a Nuclear Steam Supply System (NSSS) from a reactor vendor
and the commercial operation of the plant. Capital cost data
for coal and nuclear plants are displayed in Table 3-2. These

Nuclear Plant Construction Costs: Cost per kW

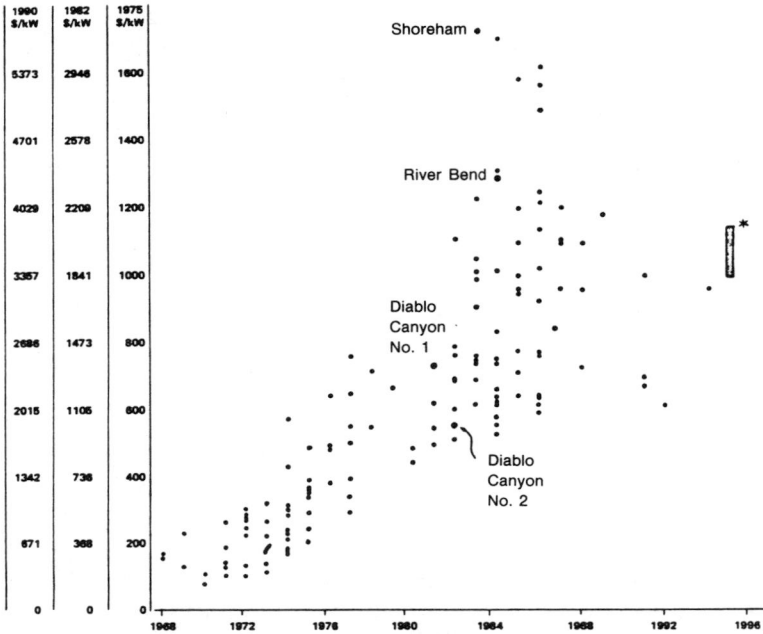

1990 $/kW	1982 $/kW	1975 $/kW
5373	2946	1600
4701	2578	1400
4029	2209	1200
3357	1841	1000
2686	1473	800
2015	1105	600
1342	736	400
671	368	200
0	0	0

- Range of projected costs for additional new plants in 1996, based on Projected Cost of Electricity from Nuclear and Coal-Fired Power Plants. EIA, August 1982.

Includes all costs (both construction expenditures and accumulated AFUDC, where applicable).

XBL 842-663

5-29

Figure 3-2. Scatter plot for nuclear plant construction costs.

costs represent the nominal dollar accounting cost of the plants that corresponds to a rate base valuation, that is, when the plant's costs are incorporated into rates. The Table 3-2 figures represent the investment cost per kilowatt. Figure 3-2 is a scatter plot for nuclear plant construction costs. In a revenue requirements study this cost is the term which is multiplied by the fixed charge rate to compute the annual fixed charges. Table 3-2 also includes data on the average annual change in construction cost factors for power plants. The Handy-Whitman Index is a specialized cost index designed to measure changes in labor and materials prices that is analogous to broader price indices such as the CPI, the GNP deflater or the Producer Price Index. It is useful to com-

Table 3-3

Explained and unexplained cost escalation

	Coal	Nuclear
A. 1978/1971 Costs	3.580	5.058
B. Handy-Whitman Index 1978/1971	2.126	1.994
C. Real Escalation = (A/B)	1.684	2.537
D. Average Real Escalation per year	6.7%	12.3%

pare changes in the construction cost index to changes in plant cost to separate the components of cost escalation. This is done in Table 3-3 for the 1971 and 1978 plant cost estimates.

In Table 3-3 power plant cost escalation is separated into that part which reflects increases in unit labor and materials cost (item B) and another term (item C) that reflects increases due to all causes other than simple inflation. The residual or real cost increase is generally thought to reflect an increased complexity of plant design for environmental and safety controls. That is, extra labor and material requirements for systems not required in earlier plants (for example, flue gas desulfurization in coal plants and backup safety systems in nuclear plants). Other possible explanations for item C include declining productivity and management inefficiency. In fact, there are additional complexities in the data, in particular, scale economics at the plant level. Over the period 1967–1978, the size of new generating units increased substantially (roughly by a factor of 3). All other things being equal, the unit capital costs for a plant are generally observed to decline as size increases. This factor should offset the cost increases attributable to additional environmental and safety controls to some degree. Table 3-2 suggests that between 1967 and 1971 scale economies for coal and nuclear plants were substantial (and unit size roughly doubled in that period). Detailed study of this data is by no means complete. Komanoff's book represents one attempt to untangle the various factors.

One principal conclusion that emerges from these data is that the static view of project alternatives assumed implicitly in the revenue requirements methodology is not appropriate to periods of rapid and uncertain change in unit capital costs. This inappropriateness is most clear when explicit account must be taken of the time dimension. Jeynes' view of project evaluation is one in which investment occurs overnight — time is never a fundamental element. To broaden this perspective we will consider explicitly how the time dimension complicates the problem of project evaluation. The issues involved in this exercise include scale economies, inflation, cost escalation, and lead time.

3.2 Time Dynamics: The Economics of Premature Installation

Leung and Durning provide an example of project evaluation involving the temporal dimension which neatly illustrates how quickly decision rules can break down. The example involves the installation of a transformer serving a residential housing development. The problem involves choosing between a 37 KVA transformer which would be adequate for present demand and a 50 KVA transformer that is projected to be required in 10 years. The capital cost of the smaller unit is assumed to be $60,000 and the larger unit is assumed to cost $90,000. If the smaller unit is chosen today, it must be replaced with the larger unit at an escalated cost of $160,000. Each unit has a salvage value at the end of ten years. This is $15,000 for the smaller unit, and $30,000 for the larger unit installed in year 10. The alternatives are summarized in Table 3-4.

Following Leung and Durning we calculate the present value of all future revenue requirements for alternatives (a) and (b). We assume that there is no difference in operations and maintenance cost, so that we can ignore this element. The analysis concerns only the fixed costs. Let us first calculate the fixed charge rates appropriate to 10-year investments (alternative [a]) and 20-year investments (alternative [b]). These are given in Table 3-5 where the depreciation and tax annuities are calculated using Eqs. (2-20) and (2-22). Additional allowances are made for property taxes (ad valorem), insurance and administrative and general expenses. We call

Table 3-4
Transformer decision

Costs and Values

	Year 1	Year 10	Year 20
i) 50 KVA	9×10^4	16×10^4	3×10^4 salvage
ii) 37 KVA	6×10^4	1.5×10^4 salvage	

Installation Schedule

Alternative (a)	Install ii)	Replace ii) with i)
(b)	Install i)	

Table 3-5
Fixed charge rates (percent)

	10 Year Life	20 Year Life
Return	9.00	9.00
Depreciation	6.58	1.95
Income Tax	2.98	3.18
Other Overheads	3.41	3.41
	21.97%	17.54%

these others overheads. We now calculate the present value revenue requirement for alternative (a). The first step is to discount the 10-year stream of fixed charges on the smaller transformer:

$$PV_{\text{Fixed Charges}} = \sum_{t=1}^{10} \frac{FCR_{10} \cdot \text{Capital Cost}_1}{(1+r)^t} \qquad (3\text{-}1)$$

where

FCR_{10} = the fixed charge rate for a useful lifetime of 10 years,

r = the discount rate, and CapitalCost$_1$ is the cost incurred in year 1, and

$PV_{\text{Fixed charges}}$ = the present value of fixed costs.

Recalling the definition of the capital recovery factor (CRF) as the inverse of the sum of the present worth factors $1/(1+r)^i$, so

$$PV_{\text{Fixed charges}} = \text{Capital Cost}_1 \cdot \frac{FCR_{10}}{CRF_{10}}$$

$$= 6 \cdot 10^4 \cdot \frac{0.2197}{0.1558} \tag{3-2}$$

$$= \cdot 10^4 \cdot 1.409$$

$$= \$\ 8.456 \cdot 10^4\ .$$

Next we subtract the salvage value in year 10, which must be discounted back to year 1,

$$PV_{\text{Salvage Value}} = \frac{1}{(1+r)^{10}} \cdot 1.5 \cdot 10^4$$

$$= .4224 \cdot 1.5 \cdot 10^4$$

$$= \$\ .634 \cdot 10^4$$

The third step is to calculate the present value of the fixed charges on the replacement transformer. This is analogous to Eqs. (3-1) and (3-2), but involves the discounting from year 10 back to year 1. In particular:

$$PV_{\text{Fixed Charges}-\text{Replacement}} \tag{3-4}$$

$$= \frac{1}{(1+r)^{10}} \cdot \frac{FCR_{10}}{CRF_{10}} \cdot \text{Capital Cost}_{11}$$

$$= 0.4224 \cdot 1.409 \cdot 16 \cdot 10^4$$

$$= \$\ 9.523 \cdot 10^4\ .$$

The salvage value of the replacement transformer must also be discounted back to year 1, as follows:

$$PV_{\text{Salvage Value}-\text{Replacement}} = \frac{1}{(1+r)^{20}} \cdot 3 \cdot 10^4 \qquad (3\text{-}5)$$

$$= 0.1784 \cdot 3 \cdot 10^4$$

$$= 0.535 \cdot 10^4$$

$$= \$ \; 5.35 \cdot 10^3 \quad .$$

Finally, then the present value revenue requirement of alternative (a) is the sum of the fixed charges minus the salvage values. This sum can be computed from the results of the equations presented above:

$$(3-2) - (3-3) + (3-4) - (3-5) \quad .$$

$$PV_{\text{Alternative (a)}} = \$ \; 1.681 \cdot 10^5 \quad .$$

In alternative (b), we use the analogue of Eq.(3-1) for projects with a 20-year life. This is calculated as:

$$PV_{\text{Alternative (b)}} = 9 \cdot 10^4 - \frac{1}{(1+r)^{20}} \cdot 3 \cdot 10^4 \qquad (3\text{-}7)$$

$$= \frac{0.1754}{0.1091} \cdot 9 \cdot 10^4 - 0.1784 \cdot 3 \cdot 10^4$$

$$= 14.45 \cdot 10^4 - 0.535 \cdot 10^4 \; \$$$

$$= \$ \; 13.915 \cdot 10^4 = \$ \; 1.3915 \cdot 10^5$$

The conclusion that can be reached from this exercise is that premature installation of the larger transformer saves money in the long run, a conclusion that represents a planning rule of thumb which has characterized the utility industry for many years. The basic business strategy embodied in this example is that building ahead of the load is economical and profitable. To understand how this conclusion emerges and what factors produce the result, we shall generalize and abstract from the transformer example. Note, however, that the projected growth in demand is fundamental to this example. If demand never grows to the 50 KVA level, it would always be preferable to install the smaller unit. The present value revenue requirement in such a case is only $9.37 \cdot 10^4$ ($=1.606 \cdot \$6 \cdot 10^4 - 0.1784 \cdot 1.5 \cdot 10^4$).

To simplify our analysis of the general case we drop the consideration of salvage values. Because of discounting, these are small (5 to 7%) in comparison to original installed cost. Let us call the ratio of FCR to CRF for a given discount rate r and lifetime i, Z_i, that is

$$Z_i = \frac{FCR_{i,r}}{CRF_{i,r}}$$

We will use the index n for the long lived asset and m for the shorter lifetime. To characterize the cost of big and small units we define

S = price per unit capacity of the small unit (e.g., $/KVA)
s = size of small unit (e.g., KVA)
B = price per unit capacity of the big unit (e.g., $/KVA)
b = size of big unit (e.g., KVA)
e = cost escalation rate

We now define Alternatives (a) and (b) in this notation as

(a) $Z_m \, Ss$ $+$ $\dfrac{1}{(1+r)^{n-m}} \, Z_{n-m} \, Bb(1+e)^{n-m}$

$$\left(\begin{array}{c} \text{cost of} \\ \text{small unit} \end{array} \right) \qquad \left(\begin{array}{c} \text{discounted, escalated} \\ \text{cost of large unit} \end{array} \right)$$

(b) $Z_n \, Bb$

(The larger unit is in service for $n - m$ years.) We have introduced cost escalation in the large unit by using a growth rate e in alternative (a). We would like to know when the cost of alternative (b) is less than that of (a). This occurs when the following inequality is satisfied:

$$Z_n \, Bb < Z_m \, Ss + \left[\frac{1+e}{1+r} \right]^{n-m} Z_{n-m} \, Bb \ . \qquad (3\text{-}9)$$

Equation (3-9) can be re-written as

$$\frac{Bb}{Ss}\left[Z_n - \left(\frac{1+e}{1+r}\right)^{n-m} Z_{n-m} \right] < Z_m \quad . \quad (3\text{-}10)$$

The first factor on the left hand side of Eq. (3-10) can be expressed using the definition of scale economy. The total cost of capacity of size x can be expressed as:

$$c(x) = kx^{1-a}, \text{ for } k = \text{constant and } a < 1 \quad . \quad (3\text{-}11)$$

This relation indicates that costs increase more slowly than capacity. For $a < 0$ there are dis-economies of scale — that is the cost per unit increases with size. Using Eq. (3-11) we can re write Eq. (3-10) as:

$$\left(\frac{b}{s}\right)^{1-a}\left[Z_n - \left(\frac{1+e}{1+r}\right)^{n-m} Z_{n-m} \right] < Z_m \quad . \quad (3\text{-}12)$$

Equation (3-12) shows that both scale economies and cost escalation tend to favor premature installation in the model as long as demand continues to grow. What is more interesting empirically is that even with dis-economies of scale, premature installation can still be favored if there is enough cost escalation. The transformer example represents such a combination. The data show scale dis-economies. The large transformer costs 11% more per unit than the smaller one ($1800/kVa vs $1620/kVa). Therefore the parameter a must be less than zero. It is roughly -0.35, so that only the effect of the parameter e allows Eq. (3-12) to be satisfied in this case. (Note that $1+e = (160,000/90,000)1/10$ implies that $e = .06$).

There is considerable historical significance to this illustration. Broadly speaking, the period of scale economies in power generation ended as the era of cost escalation began. A decision rule such as Eq. (3-12) tends to confuse these two phenomena. This confusion is important because, in the long run, cost escalation will end up altering the demand conditions underlying the derivation of Eq. (3-12). The strategy of premature installation of oversized capacity is appropriate only if the need for the larger capacity ultimately materializes. If it does not, or is substantially delayed (m approaches n),

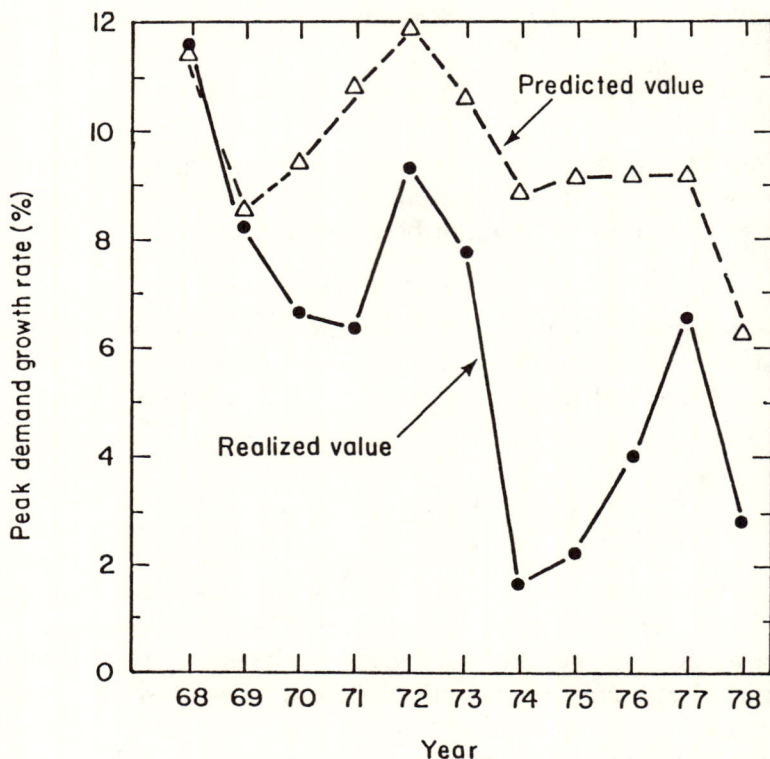

XBL 792-389

Figure 3-3. Planning forecasts of future demand, made one year in advance.

then the logic of early installation breaks down. Yet cost escalation, if it is pervasive enough, will reduce future demand through price elasticity.

This is approximately what happened in the generation segment of the electric utility industry. The capital cost escalation indicated in Table 3-2 was paralleled by increases in fuel costs. Together these effects dominated all other costs in the price of electricity and had the effect of dampening demand considerably. Planning forecasts of future demand did not adapt quickly to these changes (see Figure 3-3) and rules of thumb such as Eq. (3-12) were not abandoned even though they were no longer appropriate. By the 1980s, however, it became increasingly clear that fundamental changes in industry conditions required new decision criteria, which we will explore in some detail later. First it is necessary to examine the consequences of the substantial lag-time in adjustment from a regime of scale economies and declining cost to one of cost increases.

As we have seen, one of the main features of changing power plant construction conditions in the 1970s was the increasing length of the construction period. We now turn to an explicit treatment of the time-related costs imposed by increased construction time and their effects upon utility customers and shareholders.

3.3 Construction Financing Costs

The utility industry developed an accounting practice to deal with construction financing costs which transforms them into capital costs and incorporates them into rate base when the plant comes into service. The guiding legal and regulatory principle at work here is the "used and useful" doctrine with respect to the recognition of plant costs in customer rates. The basic idea is that customers ought not to pay for uncompleted projects until they provide service. Therefore the finance costs associated with such investments should not form part of retail rates. Nonetheless, construction finance costs are real, and must be recovered ultimately if the plant comes on line. To accomplish this they are capitalized.

Comtois provides convenient formulas for calculating how much of the final accounting cost of a plant is capitalized interest. The magnitude is clearly time-related, as is the escalation component of final cost. Numerical examples illustrate that under current lead-time and interest rate conditions, capitalized interest can be a large fraction of cost. From an accounting standpoint, these costs are handled with a convention called Allowance for Funds Used During Construction (AFUDC) on the utility's income statement (an annual summary of revenues, expenses and earnings reported by all companies to their shareholders). The essential idea is that these costs appear as credits to income, even though they do not correspond to actual current cash flows. The 1982 income statement for the Southern California Edison Company (Table

Table 3-6

1982 income statement from the Southern California Edison Co.
(thousands of dollars)

| | | Year Ended December 31 | | |
		1982	1981	1980
Operating Revenues:	Sales	$4,266,950	$4,026,548	$3,631,373
	Other	35,652	27,808	29,744
	Total operating revenues	35,652	27,808	29,744
		4,302,602	4,054,356	3,661,117
Operating Expenses:	Fuel	1,778,553	2,078,393	1,729,552
	Purchased power	449,348	479,813	280,675
	Provision for energy cost adjustments	367,565	(90,273)	361,600
	Other operation expenses	496,585	441,939	392,593
	Maintenance	210,160	193,397	228,269
	Provision for depreciation	220,927	202,182	187,959
	Taxes on income — current and deferred	177,251	197,865	38,683
	Property and other taxes	65,486	59,885	69,652
	Total operating expenses	3,765,875	3,563,201	3,288,983
Operating Income		536,727	491,155	372,134
Other Income and Income Deductions:	Allowance for equity funds used during construction	209,485	162,879	121,488
	Interest Income	34,571	39,025	33,889
	Taxes on non-operating income — credit	100,655	54,261	30,358
	Other	965	13,896	1,524
	Total other income and income deductions	345,676	279,061	187,259
Total Income Before Interest Charges		882,403	761,216	559,393
Interest Charges:	Interest of long-term debt	360,915	281,626	227,163
	Other interest and amortization	59,367	59,351	55,493
	Total interest charges	420,282	340,977	282,656
	Allowance for debt funds used during construction	(93,633)	(69,673)	(40,799)
	Net interest charges	326,649	271,304	241,857
Net Income		555,754	489,912	317,536
Dividends on Cumulative Preferred and Preference Stock		72,396	67,888	60,950
Earnings Available for Common and Original Preferred Stock		$ 483,358	$ 422,024	$ 256,586
Weighted Average Shares of Common and Original Preferred Stock Outstanding and Common Stock Equivalents (000)		94,257	85,610	73,241
Earnings Per Share		$5.13	$4.93	$3.50
Dividends Declared Per Common Share		$3.38	$3.10	$2.84

3-6) demonstrates this treatment of construction financing costs. (See the lines marked "Allowance for equity funds used during construction" and "Allowance for debt funds used during construction.") The utility is allowed to claim as income the amount invested so far in the partially completed plant, multiplied by the utility's cost of capital — that is, its carrying costs on its investment.

The rationale for claiming these funds as income is that the plant will eventually come on line, and the regulators will allow the utility to earn a return on these current carrying costs. The amount which appears now as non-cash income is equal to the present value of these future earnings. By recognizing this discounted stream of future earnings in current income, accountants assert their belief that the earnings will materialize. In fact, there is no iron-clad guarantee that the future earnings will appear. The regulators may disallow some of the proposed AFUDC additions to rate base, or grant a return on them too low to produce the amount now listed in AFUDC. There have recently been revisions in the accounting treatment of AFUDC that require downward adjustments to current AFUDC if there is reason to believe that disallowances will occur or that recovery will be delayed.

Present practice separates AFUDC into two components. The portion listed as "equity funds" refers to the return on stockholder equity, while the portion marked "debt funds" applies to the return to bondholders. For Southern California Edison in 1982 the equity portion was $209 million and the debt portion was $94 million. Together this $303 million represents 55% of the utility's Net Income of $555 million. Since AFUDC is not cash, the reported Net Income substantially over-states the cash position. This distortion can create financing problems for utilities with large construction programs by making capital more expensive because analysts realize that the utility doesn't have as much cash as its income statement would imply. Therefore, in the 1970s proposals for alternatives to AFUDC accounting were made, and in many cases implemented. The principal alternative is called Construction Work in Progress (CWIP) in Rate Base, or CWIP for short.

CWIP is essentially a "pay-as-you-go" method of financing construction. Instead of delaying the recognition of financing costs in rates with AFUDC, CWIP treatment places the direct construction cost in rate base as it occurs. Thus under CWIP rates go up sooner than with AFUDC, but not as much. The AFUDC part of capital cost is eliminated, so that the total plant cost in rate base is lower. To examine and compare these procedures from the perspective of shareholders, we use a simple model developed by Rothwell.

We consider a two-period world starting from zero output. Construction occurs in period 1 and production in period 2. We want to incorporate the prospective nature of the rate-making process, so we will distinguish between estimates of certain variables (indicated by superscript *) and realized values of those variables. We denote the rate of return on capital by r, the construction cost by K and the output by Q. In the case of CWIP the revenue requirement is r^*K^* in period 1. This is a fixed fee which must be paid by all customers without receiving any output. In period 2, the regulator estimates a price $P^* = (r^*K^*)/Q^*$ based on an estimate of output. Actual revenues are P^*Q. For AFUDC, the period 1 revenues are zero. In period 2 the price is set higher than for CWIP because of capitalized interest. We summarize the cash flows as follows:

	Period 1	**Period 2**
CWIP	r^*K^*	$r^*K^*\dfrac{Q}{Q^*}$
AFUDC	0	$r^*\left(r^*K^*+K^*\right)\dfrac{Q}{Q^*}$.

We want to discount these cash flows and compare them. Let us use d_1 and d_2 to denote the discount rates appropriate to each period. These rates are essentially the required rate of return, or the market discount rate to which we have referred previously. Let us calculate the capitalized value of CWIP (CV_c) and AFUDC (CV_a) Cash Flows — the capital value implied by receiving a certain series of annual cash flows, given a discount rate d. We obtain:

$$CV_c = \frac{r^*K^*}{d_1} + r^*K^*\frac{Q}{Q^*} \cdot \frac{1}{d_1(1+d_2)} \qquad (3\text{-}13)$$

and

$$CV_a = r^*\left(r^*K^* + K^*\right)\frac{Q}{Q^*}\ \frac{1}{d_1(1+d_2)} \cdot \qquad (3\text{-}14)$$

Notice that we are capitalizing back to the beginning of period 1, so the period 2 cash flow must be discounted to period 1, then capitalized.

Next we assume that $d_1 = r^*$. This means that the regulator has *correctly* identified the cost-of-capital in period 1 and made it the basis of rates in period 2. This simplifies Eqs. (3-13) and (3-14) to:

$$CV_c = K^* + \frac{K^*}{(1+d_2)} \frac{Q}{Q^*} \qquad (3\text{-}15)$$

and

$$CV_a = \frac{r^*K^* + K^*}{1+d_2} \frac{Q}{Q^*} . \qquad (3\text{-}16)$$

The second term of Eq. (3-15) also appears in Eq. (3-16). We can eliminate it to find when

$$CV_c > CV_a .$$

This occurs when

$$K^* > \left(\frac{r^*K^*}{1 + d_2} \right) (Q/Q^*) ,$$

or

$$1 > \left(\frac{r^*}{1 + d_2} \right) \left(Q/Q^* \right) . \qquad (3\text{-}17)$$

Of course, Eq. (3-17) can be used to find $CV_c < CV_a$ by reversing the direction of the inequality. This means that the value of CWIP or AFUDC depends on whether the estimated rate of return is greater than, equal to, or less than the cost of capital and whether actual output is greater than, equal to, or less than estimated output.

Equation (3-17) says that CWIP is preferred by shareholders when either the allowed return on capital in period 2 is less than required, or actual output is less than estimated output, or both. Conversely AFUDC will provide greater revenue when the return on capital exceeds its cost (the Averch–Johnson condition) or when output (sales) exceeds forecasts, or both. Broadly speaking the conditions making AFUDC favorable to shareholders occurred before 1970, and those making CWIP attractive occurred after. The data in Table 2-1 on the market-to-book value ratio (MBV) of utility stock indicates that returns were generally less than the cost of capital after 1973. The forecast error is estimated for 1968–1978 in Figure 3-3. It shows systematic over-estimates of demand starting in 1970 and growing worse after 1973.

Of course, this evidence is not conclusive. The model yielding Eq.(3-17) is simplified, and even contains ambiguous cases. We cannot tell *a priori* the direction of the inequality when the two ratios have opposite effects, that is, when $r > d_2$ and $Q < Q^*$, on the one hand, or $r < d_2$ and $Q > Q^*$ on the other, PV_c could be greater or lesser than PV_a. Moreover, this model has a project-evaluation framework, where systematic effects of the larger environment are neglected. In the 1970s it became increasingly important to understand such effects as they impinged on the planning environment.

The Livingstone and Sherali paper on CWIP is one example of a broader analytic perspective on the CWIP vs AFUDC evaluation. The more narrow project evaluation style is a multiple-year cash flow comparison of the alternative regulatory treatments. The cash flows are discounted at some appropriate rate and compared. As the preceding two-period model should suggest, the choice of discount rate will have a crucial effect on the outcome. There may also be differences among studies in the accounting conventions used to generate revenue requirement cash flows.

The Livingstone and Sherali paper considers the effect of multiple projects, or more generally, construction expenditures growing at an exponential rate. They find that this changes the results of the typical single-project analysis by making CWIP more burdensome. The basic idea here is that as the utility's construction budget grows, CWIP in rate base weighs increasingly heavily on ratepayers in the early years of the cash flow. Discounting the future AFUDC costs coming from an increasingly remote future provides less and less of a present burden.

This completes our discussion of construction financing costs. The remaining aspects of these issues have to do with market valuation of utility shares as a function of CWIP or AFUDC accounting. The question is how the regulatory choice over the treatment of construction financing costs influences the price of the stock. It is clear from Eq. (3-17) that there ought to be an effect. But the model from which this conclusion follows is so simplified that it may distort or at least over-emphasize the magnitude of the effect. Reviewing the theory of computing the cost of equity capital for utilities and examining some applications will allow us to examine this issue in more detail.

3.4 The Cost of Equity Capital

The evidence on electric utility shareholder returns shows a steady deterioration during the 1970s. Table 2-1 and Figure 3-4 illustrates this general trend. Untangling the forces at work during this period in order to arrive at a wholly satisfactory quantitative explanation is not easy. In this section we review several approaches to this problem and compare their results.

Let us begin with a consideration of interest rate risks. The paper by Haugen, Stroyny and Wichern provides a comparison of the response of utilities and industrial stocks to interest rate changes during the period 1967 to 1975, showing the former to be more sensitive to interest rate changes than the latter. An explanation of this phenomenon can be made

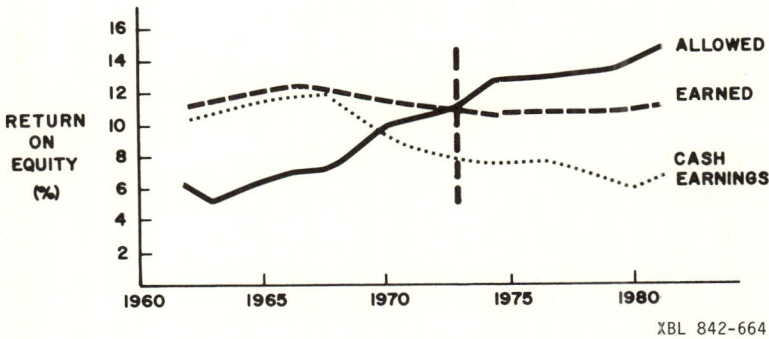

Figure 3-4. Deterioration of utility shareholders returns in 1970s.

by comparing relative lengths of asset lifetimes of utilities and industrial firms. The longer-lived assets of utilities imply a greater change in the present value of earnings as the discount rate changes. Because all asset returns are linked to one another, interest rate changes mean there will be corresponding changes in the discount rate. It can be shown that for an annuity, the partial derivative of present value with respect to the discount rate increases with the length of the annuity period. This result is a special case of the more general phenomenon that the value of long-lived assets shows greater volatility than that of shorter-lived assets. The partial derivative with respect to the discount rate, r, of the present value of an annuity stream can be expressed:

$$\frac{\partial PV}{\partial r} = \frac{\partial \sum_{i=1}^{n} \frac{k}{(1+r)^i}}{\partial r} \tag{3-18}$$

$$= nk \frac{\partial}{\partial r} \left[\frac{1-x^{n+1}}{1-x} - 1 \right]$$

where

$x = \dfrac{1}{1+r}$

k = annuity payment.

n = length of the annuity system (time).

Equation (3-18) can be expanded to produce

$$\frac{\partial PV}{\partial r} = nk \left[\frac{1-(n-1)x^n + nx^{n+1}}{(1-x)^n} \right] \left(-x^2 \right) \tag{3-19}$$

which is larger with increasing n. The simplest generalization of this result is to the case of bonds, which resemble annuities with a balloon payment. In the bond case, it can be shown that longer-term bonds are more sensitive than shorter-term bonds to changes in the market discount rate.

While the downward pressure on utility stocks during the 1970s may be broadly attributed to generally increasing interest rates, this relation is difficult to illustrate with any quantitative precision in specific cases. The goal of security analysts is to understand the particular price determinants of individual stocks. They have therefore constructed statistical models of security prices on more or less ad hoc empirical grounds. A good example of this genre for electric utility stocks in the late 1970s is described in a paper by the Wall Street analyst, Charles Benore.

Benore rejects standard finance theory models such as the discounted cash flow (DCF) model of minimum acceptable returns (Recall discussion of minimum acceptable returns at Eq. [2-6]). In particular, he seeks insight into the dividend policy which will maximize the price of an electric utility stock. Modern finance theory asserts that dividend policy is irrelevant because efficient capital markets look only at the real economic returns and not at details of financial policy such as the dividend payout ratio — the fraction of the annual profits that are paid out as dividends. Since dividends are a large part of the return on utility stocks, however, they may be an important part of the overall valuation. Benore builds a regression model of the market-to-book-value ratio (MBV) in which payout ratio (PR) plays a prominent role. The model takes the form:

$$MBV = a_1 + a_2(ROE \times EPSG) \tag{3-20}$$

$$+ a_3(PR) + a_4(PLANTG)$$

$$+ a_5(FUEL) + a_6(AFCHIGH) \quad ,$$

where

ROE	=	expected return on equity
EPSG	=	expected earnings per share growth rate
PR	=	payout ratio
PLANTG	=	projected growth of gross plant
FUEL	=	fuel mix index
AFCHIGH	=	a binary variable whose value is 1 if AFUDC is greater than 35% of net income and zero otherwise;

and a_1 through a_6 are numerical coefficients determined through regression.

Table 3-7

Expected MBV and cost of equity: Benore model

	Case 1	Case 2	Case 3	Case 4	Case 5
a) Payout Ratio	.5	.6	.7	.8	.9
b) ROE	11.7%	11.7%	11.7%	11.7%	11.7%
c) EPS Growth	5.6%	4.4%	3.2%	2.0%	0.7%
d) MBV	.86	.92	.98	1.04	1.10
e) Div. Yield	6.8%	7.6%	8.4%	9.0%	9.6%
f) DCF Return	14.4%	12.0%	11.6%	11.0%	10.3%

$$d) = a_1 + a(b)(c) + a_3(a) + a_4 (x_4) + a_5(x_5) + a_6 (x_6)$$

$$e) = \frac{ROE}{MBV} \cdot PR$$

$$f) = (c) + (e)$$

All the estimated coefficients in Eq. (3-20) have the expected sign, and all are significant at the 5% level except fuel. Nonetheless, Benore's model is flawed by its wholly arbitrary choice of explanatory variables. The AFUDC indicator, for example, is designed to single out only those companies with AFUDC above the then-current average rate. The coefficient a_5 has the value -0.05. This means that the predicted market-to-book rate goes down 5% for companies above the 35% threshold. Other estimates of the impact of AFUDC on common equity costs will be discussed later. Benore uses Eq. (3-20) to modify the DCF model and find the optimal payout ratio. Using average values for his electric utility sample, Benore constructs an example of the role the payout ratio plays in determining the market-to-book ratio. This is summarized in Table 3-7.

In Table 3-7 we summarize Benore's calculation of predicted market-to-book ratio (line d). While the cases show a linear increase in MBV with increasing payout ratios, Benore warns against extrapolating beyond MBV = 1. At this point, he warns, regulators will reduce the return on equity to prevent excess profits to shareholders. Therefore MBV = 1 must be the maximum, so the payout ratio should be chosen to approach that value. In this case a ratio of 73%, between cases 3 and 4, would be optimal.

Table 3-7 also allows comparison with the DCF model of minimum required returns. The DCF model is Eq. (2-6). In lines (e) and (f) we calculate the dividend yield and DCF return. Line (f) suggests that required returns go down as payout ratio increases. This should not happen in any efficient capital market, because investors are not thought to respond to financial policy changes. Moreover, if they did, there should be some discounting for the increased bankruptcy risk associated with high payout ratios. An equilibrium interpretation of the Table 3-7 data is that the DCF model must be modified to discount earnings per share growth. If we assume that Cases 1 to 5 all imply the same cost of capital, then we can calculate the range of the discount on growth in per-share earnings as follows:

$$2/5 < \left| \frac{\Delta \text{ Dividend Yield}}{\Delta \text{ EPS Growth}} \right| \leqslant 2/3 \ . \qquad (3\text{-}21)$$

Equation (3-21) says that EPS Growth is only worth at most 2/3 of its value in the Benore model compared to the DCF model.

Other models include AFUDC as an explicit determinant of the cost of equity capital. One version of such a model, developed by a consulting firm (National Economic Research Associates or NERA), is formulated as follows:

$$\text{Cost of Equity} \ = \ \frac{ROE}{MBV} + k \ \frac{AFUDC}{NI} \ , \qquad (3\text{-}22)$$

where

$AFUDC/NI$ = AFUDC as a fraction of net income
k = constant estimated by regression = .027.

To illustrate the performance of these various models, we illustrate some market data representative of 1983 conditions in Table 3-8 and analyze it in Table 3-9. The data describe five utilities in very different circumstances. Of these, the New England Electric System (NEES) was generally thought to be in the soundest financial condition. At the opposite extreme was the Long Island Lighting Company (LILCO),

Table 3-8

1983 market data*

Company	Price	Dividend	Div. Yield	Book Value[a]	MBV	AFUDC/ N
SCE	38-3/8	3.52	9.2	37-5/8	1.02	0.54
PG&E	15-1/8	1.60	10.6	16-5/8	0.91	0.44
PECo	16-5/8	2.12	12.7	18-3/4	0.89	0.63
NEES	37-3/4	3.20	8.5	32	1.18	0.31
LILCO	15-5/8	2.02	12.9	19-1/8	0.82	0.88

[a]Value Line data for 1983

[b]Annual Reports, 1982

*As of September 26, 1983

Table 3-9

Projected earnings, dividends and estimated cost of equity

Company	EPS Growth[b]	ROE[a]	PR[a]	DCF	Benore	NERA
SCE	7.5	16.0	0.63	16.7	14.2	17.2
PG&E	7.0	13.0	0.76	17.6	15.3	16.5
PECo	4.0	12.0	0.89	16.7	15.4	14.2
NEES	7.0	16.0	0.66	15.5	13.2	14.4
LILCO	4.0	13.5	0.81	16.9	15.6	18.9

[a]Value Line estimate for 1983

[b]Value Line projection for 1986–1988

whose Shoreham project was a great financial burden. Of the remaining companies, Philadelphia Electric (PECo) was probably the weakest, and Southern California Edison (SCE) was probably the strongest. Pacific Gas and Electric (PG&E) was the median case. These rankings correspond to the MBV ordering of these companies in Table 3-8.

Of the three models for cost of equity used in Table 3-9, Benore's seems to out-perform DCF and NERA, whose predictions seem counter-intuitive. While DCF clearly shows that superior performer NEES has the lowest cost of equity, it does not make sense for PG&E to be judged riskier than LILCO or PECo, both in much poorer financial condition. The weakness of PECo is not captured in the NERA model, nor is the relative strength of SCE. The Benore model seems to get the order of risk (or conversely financial strength) most nearly correct. The relative magnitudes of risk, however, are still difficult to judge.

A final empirical note is necessary on the internal consistency of the Value Line estimates in Table 3-9. Value Line is a popular investor information service which makes widely used forecasts of financial variables. It can be taken as representative of the information generally available to investors. As a check on the ROE estimate, one can use the estimated payout ratio PR, MBV, and Dividend Yield to calculate a ROE estimate. The relations among these variables were used in line (e) of Table 3-9. Performing this check yields a slightly different ROE estimate than the one cited in Table 3-9. None of the qualitative features of Table 3-9 results would change with this variation.

One broad conclusion which emerges from the data and calculations of Tables 3-5 and 3-8 is that large-scale construction (measured for example by AFUDC/NI) has a negative influence on utility share prices and therefore increases the cost of equity capital. To develop such a relation in an equilibrium context, one must resort to a model, such as the one used by Peck, in which returns are measured against a market-required rate of return. The basic relation used for this purpose is given by:

$$MBV = \frac{R}{K} + \frac{\left(R - k\right)}{k} \frac{I}{\left(k + RD\right)K} \tag{3-23}$$

R = allowed ROE (yr^{-1}),
k = cost of equity (yr^{-1}),
D = debt/equity ratio (dimensionless),
I = level of investment ($/yr), and
K = book value ($).

Equation (3-23) says that $MBV > 1$ if and only if $R > k$. But the difficulty with using this equation in practice is that k is so difficult to estimate — Table 3-9 shows that it varies from company to company.

Peck concludes from Eq. (3-23) that with $R < k$, the shareholder should minimize I. But large-scale projects actually allow for little flexibility because construction elements cannot be easily separated. In our small sample of 5 utilities, NEES should have the largest investment program since it has the highest MBV, which is greater than 1. But measured by AFUDC/NI, NEES has the smallest program. The other four companies may have been interested in reducing investment requirements, but are constrained by past commitments. Equation (3-23) would suggest that SCE would be relatively more likely to invest than the other companies since its MBV is about 1.02. In practice, however, it is not possible to distinguish this empirically.

In summary, the financial upheavals of the 1970s have been sorted out in neither theory nor practice. With declining productivity of investment, there is clearly less incentive for capital intensity than in the past. But quantitative measures of this incentive are difficult to come by, and theoretical models only somewhat suggestive. All that can be said with certainty is that the applicability of the Jeynes' decision rule is gone. Project evaluation must be done in the overall context of the firm and not on the limited side-by-side method of the past. How to incorporate firm-level constraints is still a subject of much uncertainty.

We will survey some of the methods which have been used to examine new projects in a systems context. Possibilities include utility influence over the way its customers use electricity, known as demand-side management. Utility programs to encourage conservation, thereby deferring the need for new power plants, fall into this category. Another option is ending the utility monopoly on generation by buying power from independent producers of electricity. We will consider these in later chapters, and begin here with a discussion of reliability and reserve margins.

3.5 Reliability and Reserve Margins

One of the unique engineering features of electric utility systems is the need for reserve capacity. Electricity is not inexpensively stored, so that when random outages occur to generating units, there must be excess capacity ready to pick up the load very quickly. To understand this phenomenon better, and to plan for reserve requirements, utility engineers have developed some numerical techniques to measure power system reliability. The most popular of these is a calculation known as the Loss of Load Probability (LOLP). In this section we will define LOLP, discuss its measurement, interpretation and use in various analytical settings. LOLP is a measure of the aggregate match between generation resources and loads on an electric utility grid. It is an abstract measure which ignores such important practical constraints as the transmission configuration and the causes of generation outages. All generation unit failures are thought of as independent random events. The LOLP for a power system (with $\underline{X}$ representing a random variable) is defined by a relation such as:

$$LOLP = \frac{\sum \text{Prob}(\underline{X} < L)}{n} \qquad (3-24)$$

where

$\underline{X} = \sum_{j=1}^{g} X_j$ which is the aggregate capacity of the generators X_j each of which is a random variable,

g = number of generators,
L = load, and
n = the number of periods per year in which the system configuration differs.

Equation (3-24) is an average LOLP calculated over the n periods per year. During each period, a given mix of generating units is available for service, that is, not on scheduled maintenance. Equation (3-24) is the weighted sum of the probabilities that the load will exceed the capacity of the operating generators.

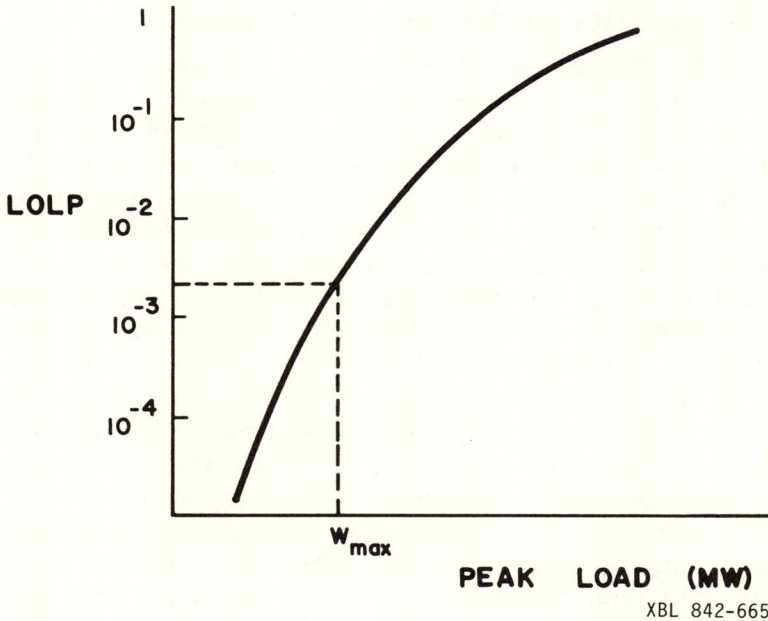

XBL 842-665

Figure 3-5. LOLP versus load, for a given system of generating resources.

The notion of forced outage is a central idea in the LOLP framework. The definition of a forced outage is an event requiring the immediate shutdown of a plant. There are technical subtleties associated with this notion, particularly where partial curtailment of plant output is involved. In many cases a condition will occur at a plant which operators interpret to require a limitation on output. This is called a partial outage (as opposed to a full outage when the entire plant is shut down). As indicated in the definitions associated with Eq. (3-24), maintenance or scheduled (i.e., not forced) outages are treated as a change in the total generation capability.

Because of the abstraction of the LOLP concept, it is useful to illustrate some of its applications. A convenient representation of the LOLP function for this purpose is the graph of LOLP versus load such as Figure 3-5. Note the nearly exponential nature of the function; the vertical axis in LOLP versus load plots is typically scaled logarithmically while the horizontal axis is scaled linearly. A precisely exponential relationship between LOLP and load would result in a straight line on the graph.

Graphs such as Figure 3-5 can provide some insight into the concentration of the LOLP over the year. Some power systems are needle-peaking in nature — their maximum loads are very much above average levels and persist for only very short periods. This can concentrate the risk of generation deficiency. This phenomenon cannot be distinguished from a system which has the risk diffused more evenly, but is still very reliable on the average. Both such systems will have steep rather than flat graphs of LOLP vs. load. This means that small changes in load produce large changes in risk. To distinguish needle-peaking from high reliability, it is convenient to refer to the reserve margin.

The standard definition of reserve margin, which we will denote R_m, is given in the following relation:

$$R_m = \frac{\text{Installed Capacity} - \text{Peak Load}}{\text{Peak Load}} . \qquad (3\text{-}25)$$

Equation (3-25) can be measured for any system without regard to LOLP. To relate the two concepts, planners define a reliability objective. It has been common to specify the objective as some version of the LOLP "less than one day in ten years" criterion. This level defines the minimally acceptable risk of generation insufficiency. There are many ways to apply the notion of one day in ten years to specific calculations. All of them eventually end up associating some maximum peak load, W_{max}, with the acceptable risk criterion as in Figure 3-5. Using this correspondence we can define a particularly interesting reserve margin, the required reserves. Let us call this $R_m Req$. It is defined by:

$$R_m Req = \frac{\text{Installed Capacity} - W_{max}}{W_{max}} . \qquad (3\text{-}26)$$

$R_m Req$ will vary from system to system, even when the same conventions on calculation are used. A common rule of thumb relation is that $R_m Req = 20\%$ corresponds to LOLP = 1 day/10 years. There is, of course, much variation in actual

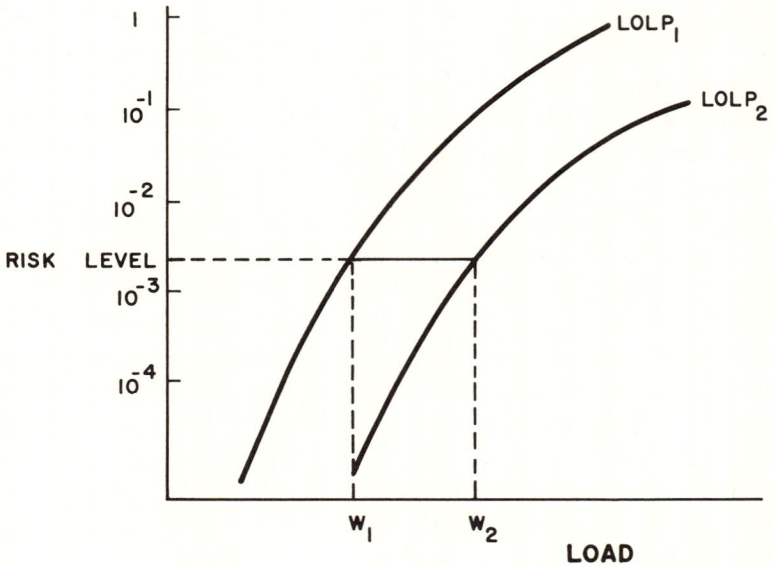

XBL 842-666

Figure 3-6. LOLP curve shifts to the right when new unit is added to power system.

circumstances. Generally speaking, however, the more reliable the generating units in the system, the lower the reserve margin requirement for a given peak load and installed capacity.

Conversely, systems which are unreliable will have a large reserve requirement. Typically, unreliable systems have relatively flat LOLP graphs compared to reliable ones. $R_m Req$ is related to the variance of the available capacity. This increases with high generator-forced outage rates, and in situations where one or two units make up large fractions of total capacity ($> 20\%$). Generally speaking, when $R_m Req$ is high, then the supply variance is high, and so a little more load does not increase risk very much. This means the LOLP curve rises slowly.

For project evaluation purposes, we are interested in incremental LOLP. Different units will have different incremental effects on required reserves. There are many ways to study these effects, but one of the most lucid discussions is the 1966

IEEE paper of L.L. Garver of the General Electric Company. Garver observes that when a new unit is added to a power system, the LOLP curve shifts to the right, as illustrated in Figure 3-6. Unless the incremental unit is perfectly reliable, the incremental load at the acceptable risk level, $W_2 - W_1$, will be less than the maximum capacity of the unit. Garver defines the incremental load, $W_2 - W_1$, measured at the LOLP criterion level, as the effective load-carrying capability (ELCC) of the unit. ELCC is sometimes referred to as effective capacity, as in the Lyons paper, where this concept is incorporated into the busbar cost framework. It can be expressed as a percentage of the unit's maximum capacity, or in megawatts not normalized to any standard.

Garver also introduces an approximation technique which will allow estimation of ELCC in particular cases where a numerical LOLP study has already been performed. His equation for ELCC is given by:

$$ C - m \ln\left[1 - f + f e^{C/m} \right] \qquad (3\text{-}27) $$

where

C = nominal capacity of the new unit,
f = forced outage rate of this unit,
m = system specific parameter, and
e = base of natural log.

Equation (3-27) reduces the ELCC calculation to the process of estimating the parameter m for specific systems. This parameter is related to the slope of LOLP graphs such as Figures 3-5 and 3-6. The estimation requires the transformation of such graphs into LOLP vs. Reserve Requirements. This produces a graph such as that of Figure 3-7.

Figure 3-7 shows how the parameter m is estimated from the transformed LOLP graph. It is clear that such LOLP vs. Reserve Requirements graphs slope the opposite way from those in Figures 3-5 and 3-6. As reserve margin goes up, LOLP goes down and vice versa. The parameter m is just a linear approximation to the incremental reserve sensitivity of the system.

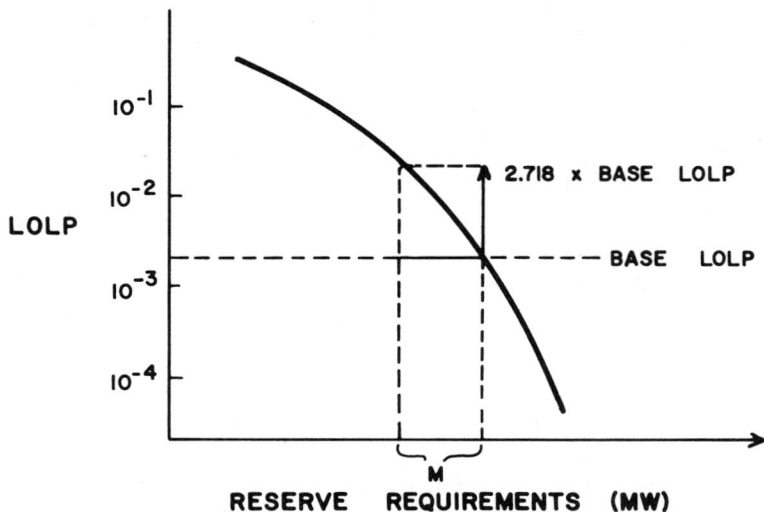

XBL 842-667

Figure 3-7. LOLP versus reserve requirements.

The main application of ELCC calculations is to supplement the highly simplified busbar cost calculation for use in project evaluation. Busbar cost assumes that all generation projects have the same incremental impacts on reserve requirements. This is not true. Examination of Eq. (3-27) shows that ELCC as a fraction of nominal capacity goes down as capacity goes up and as forced outage rate increases. In the 1970s it became clear that generator unit size and forced outage rate were correlated. Large units performed more poorly than smaller units. Thus ELCC gradually became incorporated into project evaluation techniques. The Lyons paper of 1979 is one of the first published examples of this kind of analysis.

Numerous problems remain in the area of reliability assessment. LOLP is a highly artificial concept, ignoring many practical constraints and complexities. Even if the concept were more representative of the actual problem, a reasonable criterion for LOLP is not obvious. Not only is the notion of one day in ten years ambiguous, it is very hard to link with customer values. Economists have tried to place values on the reliability of electric power supply to different users, but surveys show enormous variation. (See, for example, the

National Electric Reliability Study, 1981.) The cost of a 10-minute outage to a household may be negligible; the cost to a word-processing firm may be quite high. Broadly speaking, the U.S. electric utility system is very reliable compared to that of less developed countries — indeed unreliable power supply is often used as an indicator of a low stage of economic development. But if too little reliability is costly, too much can also be expensive. Deciding how to optimize is very difficult.

With respect to reserve requirements and growth, it is not accidental that ELCC became an issue in project evaluation when electric demand growth slowed substantially in the 1970s. The reason for this can be illustrated from some of Garver's original data. He shows ELCC for five successive 600 MW units added to a system. While the first unit has ELCC = 60.4% of capacity, the last has ELCC = 84.7%. Thus for a given-size generating unit, there is an ELCC penalty for the first units of this size. The additional load-carrying capacity depends on the system's initial conditions (as reflected in m), which change with the addition of each new unit. If load growth is high, then many units of a given size will be required to produce a scale economy in ELCC. With declining load growth, only the first one or two units at the highest-capacity level will be installed, and therefore they will have lower ELCC on the average than in the high-growth case.

This discussion illustrates concretely how factors relating to the firm as a whole enter into project evaluation. The 1970s saw a number of such developments. To survey these approaches we must introduce a new type of analysis called capacity expansion planning. This kind of study is considerably more complex than the project evaluations we have seen up to now.

3.6 Capacity Expansion Models

Capacity expansion models are designed to generalize the simple project evaluation methods to a comprehensive consideration of the utility system as a whole. In practice, of course, these models do not focus on all possible effects.

Perhaps the single most important feature of such models is the attention given to total system fuel cost. Oil price increases during the 1970s made much existing generation capacity uneconomic in static cost-minimization terms. This means that if the utility could instantaneously adjust its generation resources to minimize total cost, then coal and nuclear units would replace high cost oil and gas-fired capacity. To calculate the tradeoff between new plant investment and fuel cost reductions, capacity expansion models are used to do complex and tedious production cost computations. We will summarize briefly the nature and results of such computations.

The typical starting point for a production cost model is the load duration curve (LDC). This is plotted on a graph representing all hourly kW demands, sorted from highest to lowest. An example is given in the upper panel of Figure 3-8. The peak load is at the origin of the x-axis and the minimum load is at the extreme right of that axis. Production cost models simulate the economic dispatch of the system's generators to meet the load at minimum cost. Account is taken of scheduled maintenance, forced outages and (often) other engineering constraints. Due to the complexity of the computations, it is difficult to develop an overall picture of the basic cost structure of the utility. To facilitate such a global approximation, a screening curve simplification has been developed. An example is given in Figure 3-8.

Screening curves attempt to approximate the optimal mix of generating units. Different technology types have different proportions of fixed and variable cost in their total busbar cost. A low fixed cost, high variable cost technology, such as a combustion turbine, is better suited to serving peak loads of short duration than base loads which are constant throughout the year. To represent the different proportions of fixed and variable cost factors, we plot total annual revenue requirements versus the capacity factor on the bottom panel of Figure 3-8. Nuclear plants, whose costs are largely fixed, have a high intercept and relatively flat slope on this graph. Conversely, combined cycle (CC) and gas turbine (GT) units have low fixed cost and high variable cost, i.e., low intercept and steep slope.

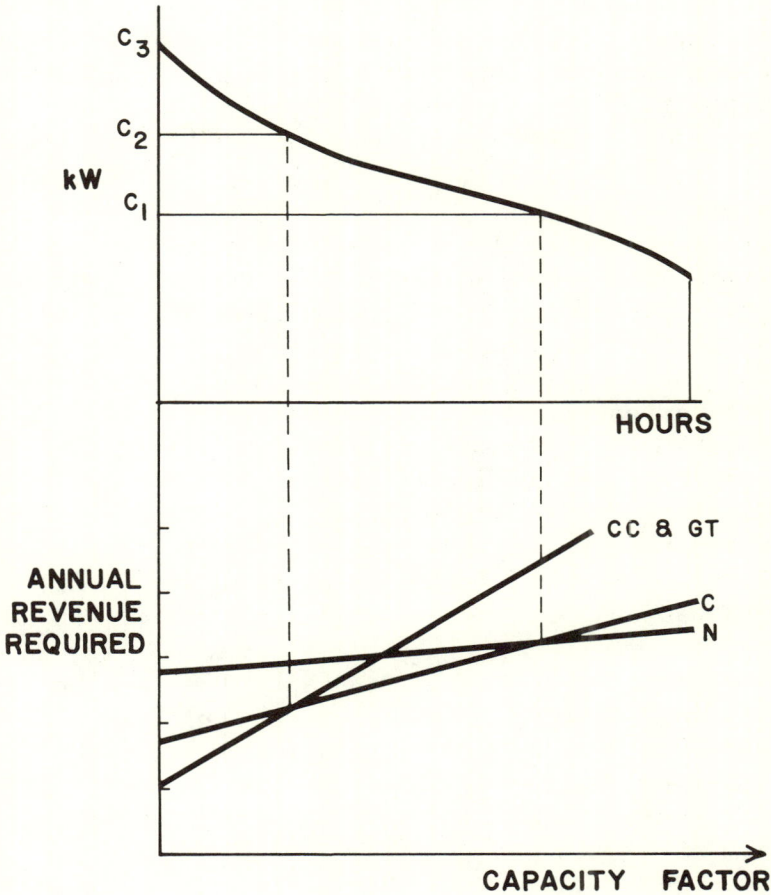

Figure 3-8. All hourly kW demands sorted from highest to lowest.

The keys to minimizing costs are the intersection points of each technology total cost function. By mixing production from peaking (CC and GT) and intermediate (C = coal) generating units for the proper number of hours with the optimal base load generation, cost can be minimized. This will be the envelope of the intersecting curves closest to the x-axis. Where CC & GT crosses C, for example, tells us the maximum number of hours it is least expensive to run peaking plants compared to intermediate plants. Projecting this up to the LDC, we can find the amount of peaking capacity corresponding to this maximum economic running time. This is C_3-C_2. Similarly the amount of intermediate capacity would be C_2-C_1, and baseload capacity would be C_1.

Such calculations provide an indication of the ideal capacity mix. For many utilities in the 1970s, screening curve analysis indicated that they were very far from the optimal configuration. Typically the results suggested that more baseload coal and nuclear units were required to displace oil and gas-fired generation. Simple busbar cost calculations do not capture the value of baseload capacity expansion, because they do not capture the production cost savings associated with approaching a better configuration.

Figure 3-9 is a block diagram representing the structure of capacity expansion models. Taking the load forecast as an input, a generation expansion plan can be specified which will meet anticipated demand and be used in turn as input to both production costing and reliability evaluation. If the LOLP, or other reliability index, does not meet the criterion of adequacy, then the expansion plan must be revised. This revision is represented by the loop in Figure 3-9 between Generation Expansion Plan and Reliability Evaluation. For a given plan, both the investment cost and the production cost must be calculated, both terms being typically calculated at the level of the firm. Investment cost means all fixed costs, such as interest, depreciation, taxes, fixed O & M and return on equity. Production cost is also a systemwide calculation.

There is substantial variation in the way the various steps indicated in Figure 3-9 can be carried out. In principle, all possible expansion paths could be examined and the one involving minimum revenue requirements would be selected. This is computationally complex, so often only a small number of alternative supply scenarios are chosen and then tested. Capacity expansion models differ primarily in how they handle the calculations within each step. Very often the financial detail associated with calculating the fixed or investment cost aspect of corporate revenue requirements is simplified. Many of these models are insensitive to regulatory practices such as the difference between CWIP or AFUDC accounting. Even where financial detail is substantial, the

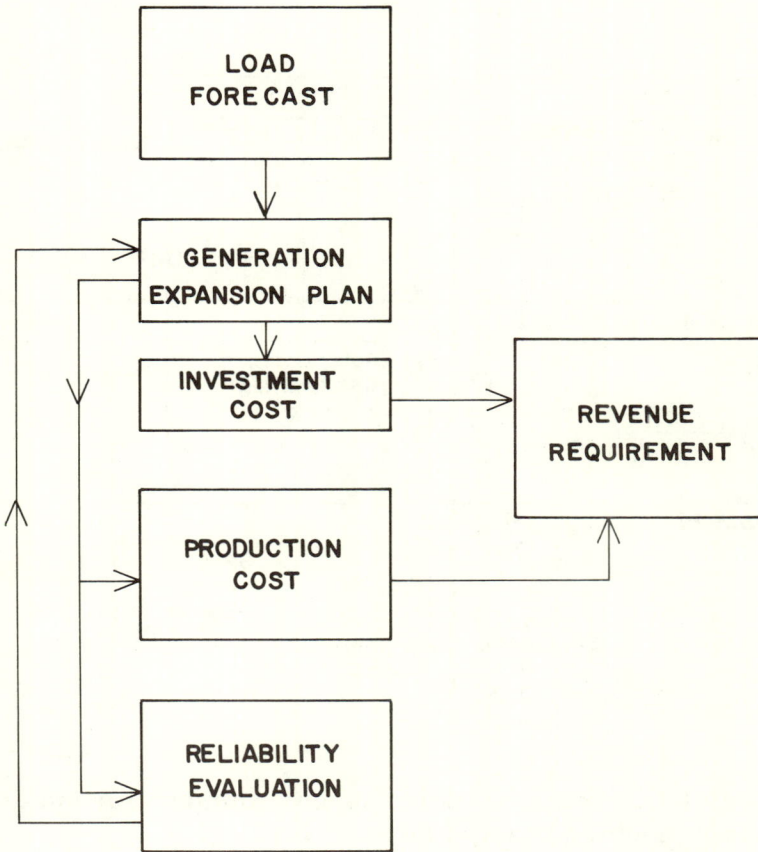

XBL 842-773

Figure 3-9. Capacity expansion model block diagram.

models cannot be run to optimize a financial objective; the most common emphasis in these models is production cost. Caramanis, et.al. (1982) discusses a representative recent package of these models called EGEAS, developed by the Electric Power Research Institute, which illustrates this point.

Regardless of limitations associated with the structure of capacity expansion models, the really practical problem associated with their use is uncertainty of input assumptions. With escalation of capital and fuel costs at varying rates, it is extremely difficult to get a fix on cost functions. Similarly, the uncertainty in future load growth makes it difficult to have

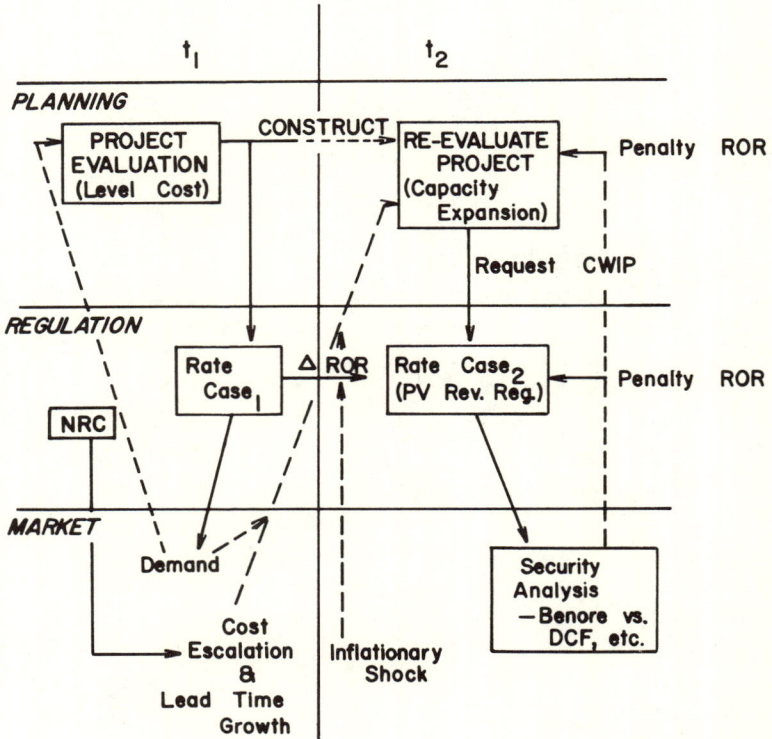

XBL 842-669

Figure 3-10. Characterization of environment surrounding planning method changes in the 1970s.

confidence in a given forecast. With conditions of rapid change, studies based on one set of assumptions soon become obsolete. Indeed, capacity expansion models were often brought into play after projects had been selected by cruder project evaluation techniques, reflecting change in the basic rationale for central station project contruction during the 1970s from growth to fuel cost reduction. When new capacity was *required* to meet future demands, sophisticated capacity expansion models were not needed, and busbar cost was a good enough yardstick to choose among alternative ways to expand capacity. As load growth diminished and reserve margins grew to unprecedented levels, the need for new capacity could no longer have anything to do with reliability.

Instead it was fuel cost reduction which became the critical strategic consideration underlying new construction. In theory, a graph of total consumer cost, including the cost of insufficient capacity as a function of investment level, would show some optimal level of capacity which would minimize total fixed and operating cost. In practice, however, capacity expansion modeling appeared in a dynamic framework schematically illustrated in Figure 3-10.

Figure 3-10 characterizes the environment surrounding planning method changes in the 1970s. Roughly speaking t_1 represents the pre-1974 period and t_2 the post-1974 periods. During t_1 utilities planned for new capacity using simple bus-bar cost methods, based on high-growth demand forecasts, and without much constraint from the regulatory process. Nonetheless, forces set into motion at the end of this period soon began to make planning more complex. Federal regulation of environmental, health and safety risks associated with new plant construction tended to increase lead times and costs to the utility, as we have seen. The effect of rate increases, especially from fuel cost, began to dampen demand growth to the point where projects under construction and planned during the later 1970s no longer seemed quite so necessary.

At this point, capacity expansion modeling came into play, rationalizing new plant construction that was already in progress from the long-run fuel cost savings perspective. To achieve these long-run economies, large rate increases were necessary during period t_2. Regulators typically refused to increase revenue requirements as much as utilities requested. Thus earnings deteriorated, the financial market turned hostile toward electric utilities, and another cycle of rate requests was initiated. To justify construction expenditures during this period, utilities repeatedly appealed to the reduction in long run fuel cost that would eventually benefit ratepayers. In the short run, however, CWIP in rate-base was necessary or the utility stock would fall in value, thereby increasing the cost of equity to ratepayers.

The more elaborate these arguments became as the 1970s drew to a close, the less convincing they became to all parties involved. By the end of the 1970s a substantial dissatisfaction with traditional analytical procedures and assumptions emerged within the electric utility industry. One symptom of this dissatisfaction was a remarkable committee report by the Long Range System Planning Working Group of the IEEE's Power Engineering Society (Platts and Womeldorff, 1980). This group reported a survey of industry planners concerning their attitude about the significance and validity of current assumptions embedded in their standard procedures. Lack of consensus and lack of a clear vision of the future was obvious in every major area. Demand forecasting was acknowledged to be very difficult. Uncertain estimates of future costs made planning uncertain at best. The cost minimization basis for making economic choices was questioned. Regulatory pressures expressing changing societal goals were seen to be transforming the very concept of a utility. Under these conditions even the best computer model is useless.

Another way to illustrate the breakdown in capacity expansion modeling is to focus on newer and more sophisticated techniques designed for the current environment. Two of these modern papers illustrate particular inadequacies of capacity expansion models by proposing ways to treat problems previously ignored. The Keeney and Sicherman (1983) paper tries to model explicitly the way in which utility decision-makers trade off different attributes of projects that are not usually considered equivalent. The Merrill (1983) paper also deals with unequal trade-offs, specifically those of environmental pollution and economic cost. Merrill adopts a social rather than a utility perspective.

3.7 Analyzing Unequal Parameters in Capacity Expansion Decisions

A common critique of economic methods of analysis is that often important social values are neglected because there are no market prices attached to them. Damage to the environment is a widely cited example of this phenomenon, although regulation has internalized these costs increasingly by setting certain maximum impact standards. Nonetheless, social choices are involved in the production of electricity with regard to the type and level of environmental impact resulting from different technology options. These choices are not usually made with a great deal of explicit analysis. Information is difficult to gather in this area, because the processes involved are complex and vary with local conditions. The Merrill paper illustrates some of the difficulties.

Merrill is interested in assessing cogeneration development in the New York City area. Cogeneration is the combined production of heat and power at a site where both products can be used. The waste heat from central station power plants is not typically put to any economic purpose. Heat is expensive to transport and/or store, so it cannot be easily transferred from central station power plants. In New York City, cogeneration by customers is attractive primarily because electric rates are so high that there is a substantial incentive for customers to leave the utility system and produce their own power. A number of other factors, such as local tax policy and environmental regulation standards, also affect the relative costs to potential cogenerators. The Consolidated Edison Company (ConEd), which supported Merrill's research both financially and technically, has publicly opposed cogeneration development in its service territory. ConEd has argued that when cogenerators leave the utility system, the rates of other customers have to be increased to cover the utility's large fixed costs. For this and other reasons, a prominent ConEd executive has referred to cogeneration as a wolf in sheep's clothing (Schwartz, 1981).

Merrill seeks to assess cogeneration development from a broader social perspective than the private interest of ConEd. He focuses attention on three variables: fuel use, air quality and total electricity revenue requirements. To study how these variables change under different development scenarios, Merrill runs standard models for utility production cost, revenue requirements and regional air quality. The total revenue requirements are calculated from the sum of utility costs and cogenerator costs and implicitly account for the revenue shift complained about by ConEd.

To perform a strategic analysis, Merrill makes a large number of model runs. Indeed the number is so large that special procedures are necessary to understand and generalize the functional dependencies implicit in the results. This is accomplished by the use of SMARTE functions — linear

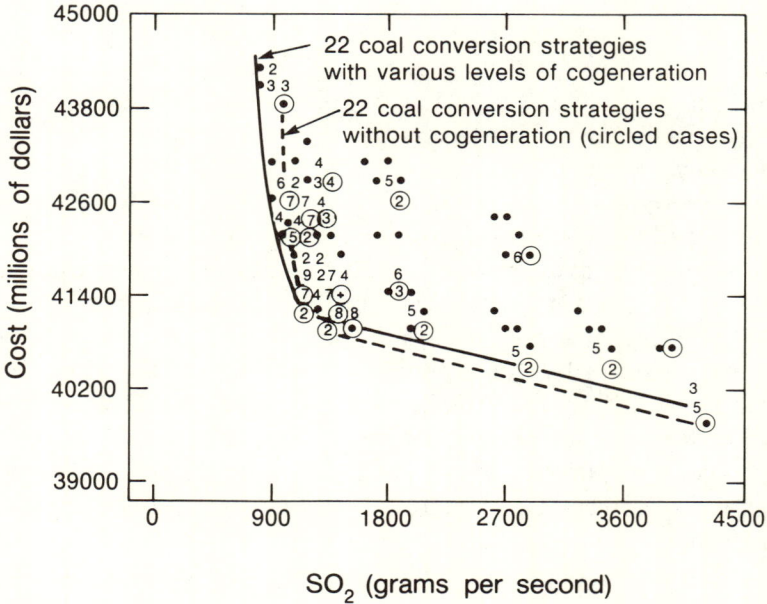

XBL 886-9689

Figure 3-11. Shift in cost versus SO$_2$ trade-off curve as cogeneration alternatives are added. (Note: numbers indicate individual strategies.)

regressions of the decision and exogenous variables on the attribute variables of fuel use, and air quality cost. The SMARTE functions turn the vast output of the simulation scenarios into more tractable summary form, facilitating the analysis of an exhaustive set of scenarios. Scenarios in which attribute, decision and exogenous variables fall into some intermediate range can be explored more systematically and efficiently.

Having generated what looks like a complete picture of all alternatives, Merrill must reduce the results in a way which reveals the best choices. He graphs results for two attributes at a time. The resulting scatter plots generally reveal a trade-off curve that bounds the points in a region of feasible alternatives which minimizes the undesirable value of one attribute with the other fixed. A number of operations can be performed on the trade-off curves or the scatter plot itself to

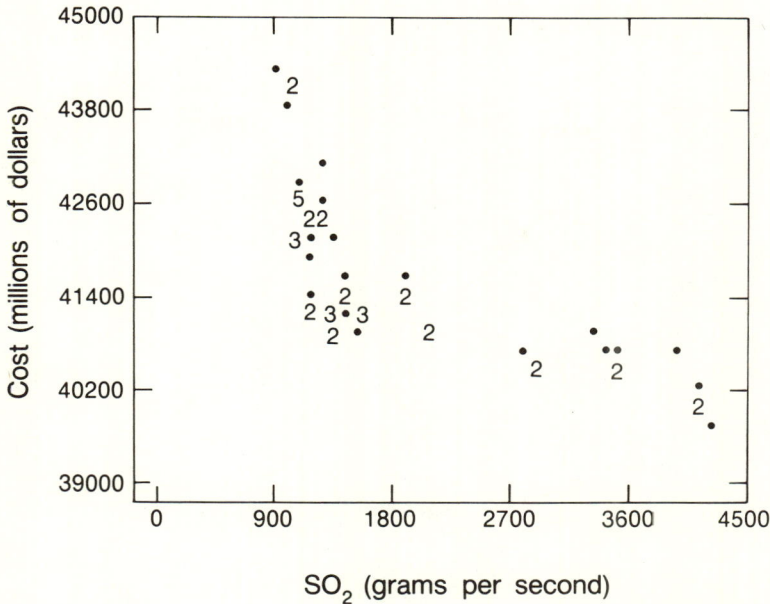

Figure 3-12. **Pareto-optimal strategies in terms of five attributes, projected onto cost/SO$_2$ plane. (Note: numbers indicate individual strategies.)**

illustrate important qualitative features of the decision. We will examine some of these.

In Figure 3-11 Merrill shows a shift in the cost versus SO_2 trade-off curve as cogeneration alternatives are added to an electricity development scenario based on converting ConEd's oil-fired generation units to coal. Compared to coal conversion, cogeneration increases cost (an upward shift) and decreases SO_2 (a shift to the left).

Such qualitative conclusions are still insufficiently explicit to yield a best strategy. Strategies can be eliminated from consideration if, compared to alternatives, the superior values of attribute variables can be found. Therefore, Merrill introduces optimizing techniques such as Pareto optimality.

Formally, if x and y are two strategies and $a(i,x)$ and $a(i,y)$ are the values of the ith attribute associated with x and y, then strategy x is *dominated* by strategy y if

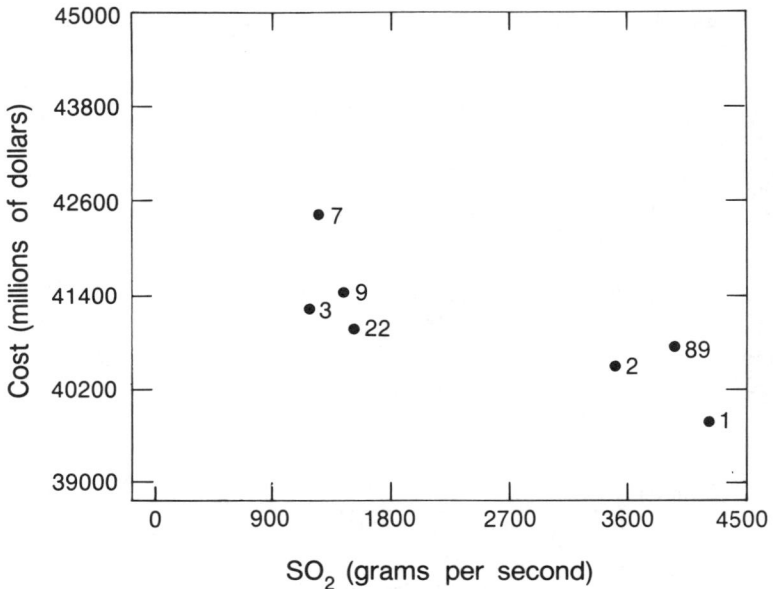

Figure 3-13. **Strongly pareto-optimal strategies in terms of five attributes, projected onto cost-SO_2 plane. (Note: numbers indicate individual strategies.)**

$$a_{i,x} > a_{i,y}, \text{ for all } i \quad . \tag{3-28}$$

A strategy which is undominated is Pareto optimal.

Figure 3-12 shows that many Pareto optima exist for this problem. This does not aid decision-making because there are still too many alternatives. Therefore, Merrill introduces *strong Pareto optimality* and the corresponding notion of *near domination*. The intuitive notion is that many optima are close and so they can be reduced to a single better representative which is nearby. Formally, this requires that a small number Δi be chosen so that strategy x will be nearly dominated by strategy y if:

$$a(i,x) > a(i,y) - \Delta i, \text{ for all } i \quad . \tag{3-29}$$

This definition allows a significant reduction in the number of important strategies which can then be studied in detail.

For this study Merrill reduces the number of strategies to seven. He plots these in Figure 3-13. Examining the results, he excludes three on the grounds of unacceptable SO_2 levels. The remaining strategies involve substantial coal conversion and no cogeneration. Coincidentally, this is precisely the preferred approach of Consolidated Edison management.

From a methodological perspective, the weakest link in the analysis is the strong Pareto optimality notion. The concept is both numerically arbitrary and artificial in its concept of utility. The numerical arbitrariness is obvious since results depend upon the value of $\Delta\ i$. While this is a serious flaw, if the nearness concept were sound, it would be possible perhaps to find a metric for it. Unfortunately, "nearness" as defined in Eq. (3-29), implicitly assumes a highly restricted social utility function. Since the distance defining nearness, $\Delta\ i$, is the same for all attributes, essentially Eq. (3-29) says that all attributes are equally important. If one attribute were worth more than another, then there should be different measures of nearness for each. Merrill's method seems to allow him to escape estimating explicit trade-offs among attributes, by assuming that they are all equally important. This is not really an escape, however, but an arbitrary representation of social utility that has no particular claim to reality. After all, it is the analyst who chooses the attributes in the first place, and assigns them their respective weights.

It is at this point where the Keeney method claims its superiority. The goal of the Keeney-Sicherman paper is to elicit explicitly the decision maker's utility function, including a specification both of the relative weights attached to attributes and the quantitative trade-off among them. This is practical only if the policy of a utility can be articulated by a single decision-making group which can be identified and interviewed in the appropriate manner. For the case study reported in the paper, an interview was conducted with a senior executive of the Utah Power and Light Company, whose expansion decision was to be analyzed. It does not necessarily represent the actual values of the Utah Power and Light Company management, principally because only one executive was interviewed.

The results of the analysis are summarized briefly in Table

Table 3-10
Results of UP&L analysis

Attributes	Relative Weight	Expected Values Coal	Nuclear	Attribute Trade-off −1% Feasibility = 1.6 mills/kWh Coal	Nuclear
Busbar Cost (mills/kWh)	0.34	60.7	47.4		
Feasibility (prob. of completion)	0.54	0.60	0.31	64.3	110.5 Equivalent cost (mills/kWh)
Health and Safety	0.09				
Environmental Impact	0.002				
Expected Utility		0.53	0.40		
Equivalent Cost		125.	157.9		

3-10, which shows the relative importance of attributes, expected impacts associated with the two most important attributes and the trade-off between them. Table 3-10 indicates that considerations other than busbar cost and feasibility are of minor importance. Of all those considered, health and safety impacts have the most weight. To evaluate attributes, Keeney devises impact scales which are used to contrast coal and nuclear plant choices. The economic impact is represented by busbar cost. The feasibility impact is illustrated by probability of completion (i.e., of the plant's not being cancelled). Since feasibility carries so much weight in the decision, it is worth examining it in detail. Keeney identifies nine circumstances which might lead to plant cancellation. The major factor is financing difficulties — the nuclear plant has a 50% probability of cancellation compared to a 25% chance for the coal plant due to the financing difficulties. To aggregate this factor with all others, Keeney uses a multiplicative risk model: if each of n factors has a probability of cancellation P_i, then the overall probability that the facility will be cancelled, p, can be found from the relation:

$$1 - p = \prod_{i=1}^{n} \left(1 - P_i\right) \qquad (3\text{-}30)$$

Eq. (3-30) expresses the probability of completion which is reported in Table 3-10.

Keeney says very little about his concept of financing difficulties except that the nuclear project is perceived to be more capital-intensive and requires greater financing at the beginning of the project. This comment is not consistent with the busbar cost data cited in the paper. Here the nuclear plant is presented as 10 to 15% *less* capital-intensive (total project capital cost). This seeming contradiction brings into question his methodology's supposed ability to clarify and rationalize intuition.

Keeney's real interest seems to be the trade-off of feasibility risk against the nuclear busbar cost advantage. He elicits a trade-off relation from his executive interview. One per cent feasibility reduction equals 1.6 mills/kwh. Applying this estimate of the cost of risk makes the nuclear plant 25% more expensive in equivalent cost than coal. The busbar cost advantage of nuclear power (roughly 21%) is swamped by the feasibility cost. Sensitivity analysis indicates that if the price of risk were to go down by a factor of 3, decision-makers would be indifferent to the choice between coal and nuclear.

What are we to make of this analysis? Is this rational decision-making or a rationalization of inconsistent perceptions? One gets the feeling that this study has found the right answer for the wrong reason. Clearly nuclear plants are riskier than coal plants, and this risk will deter investment. But Keeney has told us little about where the risk comes from, and how it is valued. We do not know how to interpret the trade-off parameters: where they come from or what they mean. As with the Merrill paper, we get the appearance of comprehensive and reasonable consideration of all effects. But when the complexity gets too great, arbitrary simplifications are used to reject most of the data generated so laboriously.

These studies represent the high-water mark of capacity expansion modeling. They embody the end of a line of thought, rather than the beginning. As capacity expansion models reach this level of sophistication, utilities have ceased expanding capacity. The alternatives analyzed by Keeney are no longer the principal activities on the margin of the electricity supply system. Merrill is closer to the spirit of the current climate, where the decentralized choices of electricity users have the dominant effect on utility system development. To prepare ourselves for studying the "post-central station era," it is necessary to develop a systematic understanding of the price regulation mechanics which go into rate-making. This is the next subject to which we will turn.

Chapter **4**

Price Regulation Mechanics

4.1 Introduction

Most of our discussion up to now has focused on aspects of regulation in which the regulator's role is somewhat circumscribed: the determination of revenue requirements either in the context of project evaluation or for the utility as a whole. (The two principal areas we have touched on are: (1) identifying the cost of common equity, and (2) the choice between CWIP and AFUDC accounting.) A larger portion of rate-making activity involves distributing the burden of providing this revenue; the question of which customers will pay what portion of these total revenue requirements. Before entering into a general discussion of what is involved in this process, it is useful to distinguish different perspectives on what rate-making is supposed to do generally.

We can distinguish two broad strands of thought about the rate-making process. One is accounting-oriented and organized around the average cost of service. The other tradition originated among economists and is principally concerned with marginal costs. Economic theory is largely concerned with resource allocation efficiency. The standard micro-economic theories suggest that resource allocation is efficient when commodities are priced at their marginal cost. Marginal cost pricing has never been the practical norm in utility rate-making, because marginal and average costs are seldom identical, and one of the aims of regulation is to ensure a sufficient but not exorbitant return to the utility. Let's say prices were set at marginal cost; then the return to the utility would be too low if marginal cost were below average cost, and too high if it were much above average cost. Nonetheless, the changing nature of the marginal costs of electricity has resulted in increased attention to this concept. The resulting tension between the accounting and economic points of view is inherent in current rate-making practices.

The basic conflict between the accountant and the economist concerns which cost is to be given dominant consideration. There is little argument about the functional components of cost or the need for procedures which go from aggregate revenue requirements to manageable tariff schedules (unit costs) that will produce those revenues. The problem of rate-making amounts to adopting a dominant perspective, then reconciling it with the most important information associated with the less compelling point of view. In order to organize the material concretely in the discussion which follows, we shall emphasize one perspective more consistently than another, but it should be remembered that in practice each point of view will sometimes be dominant. Due to its theoretical importance, we will give primacy to marginal cost.

The practical difficulties of marginal cost pricing are twofold. First the costs must be identified concretely, a task for engineering economics. The technical features associated with small (i.e., marginal) changes in consumption must be determined and then costed. Once the costs have been catalogued and measured, revenue generated by pricing at the calculated level must be compared to revenue required to cover total expenses. In the era of declining costs, this comparison usually resulted in a deficit. (In fact, the condition of marginal costs running below average revenue requirements is a definition of declining cost.) Since no one had an adequate solution to funding this revenue deficit, marginal cost pricing was not widely advocated. In the 1970s and early 1980s the opposite situation has predominated: marginal costs have exceeded average rates, so that marginal cost pricing would result in a revenue excess. In a period of increasing cost, the wish that utility rates should serve a rationing function to limit excessive consumption has led to the revival of interest in marginal cost theory.

In the discussion that follows, we will explore the conditions in the 1970s and early 1980s under which marginal cost exceeded average cost. At this time, rate-making based on marginal cost frequently required this theory to be reconciled with average cost notions of total required revenue. In the mid 1980s the opposite situation emerged. The decline in world oil prices and the glut of generation capacity has created an environment of low marginal costs compared with average costs. Thus the rate-making problem using marginal cost concepts has undergone a dramatic reversal. The situation of the mid-1980s is not a return to the declining-cost era, but a hiatus in a longer-term trend toward higher energy costs. The instabilities created by these dramatic reversals in marginal and average cost trends will be addressed later. Our present purpose is to understand the tasks of rate-making when due account is taken of marginal cost. The underlying concern with marginal costs stems from the resource-allocation benefits associated with marginal cost prices. Focusing on the case where marginal costs are high, we will see how this information can be used to guide the design of prices.

Rate regulation can be characterized as a four-stage procedure. The stages are: (1) determination of total annual revenue requirements, (2) estimation of seasonal and diurnal variation in costs, (3) allocation of costs to customer classes, and (4) design of rate schedules. We will discuss the basic task of each stage, the principal distinctions (or concepts) associated with each stage, and the data used to assess particular circumstances. Controversial issues will be identified and illustrated with examples.

The first stage, *determination of total annual revenue requirements*, can be quite simple in the accounting or average cost paradigm. From the marginal cost perspective, however, the issues become complex. We will review PG&E's estimates made for its 1982 General Rate Case in some detail. Regardless of the perspective, there is commonly agreed to be a *division* of costs according to function among the following categories:

1. Demand-Related Costs
    a) Generation
    b) Transmission (4-1)
    c) Distribution
2. Energy-Related Costs
3. Customer Costs.

In most cases the categories into which costs fall are obvious. Fuel, for example, is an energy-related cost, as are variable operations and maintenance expenses. High-voltage lines are clearly transmission expenses. There are, however, interesting problems concerning costs that fall into more than one category: where to place the boundary between distribution costs and customer costs is one example. While meters are clearly customer costs, the small distribution transformers on low voltage lines may reasonably be assigned to either category. The PG&E example will provide more detail on this particular issue.

The controversial issues in stage one have often centered on the legitimacy or prudence of certain management decisions. If extra expenses were incurred by the utility compared to what a prudent and reasonable course of action might have been, should customers be obliged to pay for these in rates? This issue frequently arises in the case of abandoned construction projects, and has also been raised with respect to fuel supply contracts. If every management action will result in cost recovery, regulation is not providing any incentive for management efficiency. Conversely, if management decisions are continually second-guessed by regulators with the benefit of hindsight, management will either take no risk or lose the financial capability of attracting capital.

The division into functions of generation-demand-related costs can impose some delicate questions. These costs are not necessarily the same thing as the fixed costs of generation capacity. The *NARUC* (National Association of Regulatory Utility Commissioners) *Cost Allocation Manual* recognizes that some part of generation plant investment cost may be energy-related, illustrating this with the example of the hydro-electric storage reservoir. Larger dams result in more water storage. It is the volume of water which is proportional to total energy (kWh). As the height of a dam increases, the water storage (energy) increases faster than the capacity that can be produced (kW or demand-related cost). Therefore some part of the dam's capital cost is energy-related.

It should be noted that the hydro-electric storage reservoir case provides some analogies with that of large baseload thermal plants. As you will recall the ELCC (demand-related capability) of such plants can be quite low; their principal virtue is low energy cost. This subtlety can be obscured in either a marginal cost analysis or in an accounting framework. We will examine this issue in more detail in Chapter 5.

The second stage of the rate-setting process is a characterization of the *time variation of costs*. The cost of electricity production, like other production costs, depends on the supply/demand balance. Costs increase as demand rises closer to the limits of supply, and vice versa. In electric power systems there are consistent seasonal and diurnal patterns in the variation of costs which are studied in the rate-making process. This stage may be characterized by the following tasks:

1. Determination of Costing Periods
   a) Load statistics
   b) Variation in loss of load probability
2. Determination of Generation Capacity Costs   (4-2)
   a) Engineering characterization of capacity response to load changes
   b) Valuation of capacity
3. Compilation of Transmission & Distribution Demand Data (T&D)
4. Establishment of Energy-Related Costs.

To simplify analysis it is common to divide the year into time periods so that conditions within each period are more or less homogeneous. The qualitative difference between peak and off-peak periods is quantified in this first task. Either load statistics, LOLP variations, or both are used to define a small number of costing periods. The cost associated with the functional categories listed in (4-1) are then assigned to costing periods by engineering analysis. Analysis of the loss of load probability is used increasingly to break up the year into seasons and to divide days in each season into periods of peak and partial-peak demand. Average or accounting costs methods are typically less sophisticated. Transmission and distribution demand is typically studied in less detail than generation-related demand. Here the marginal and average cost allocation procedures are not too different. Because the problem of estimating marginal impacts on the T&D system is so difficult, only simple rules of thumb are possible. For energy-related costs, some form of production cost model is used to match cost changes to specified time periods.

The third stage in the rate-making process is to *allocate costs to customer classes.* This is usually done by first specifying the load characteristics of each customer class. These load characteristics can then be valued (or costed) by using the previously defined costing periods. This makes class allocation fundamentally a load study problem in which the revenue responsibility of each class is determined. Of course, if we knew *when* each customer consumed electricity, as well as how much they consumed, we wouldn't need to allocate revenue responsibility by class of customer. But for most customers, metering of this nature is not economically feasible. Often, however, other issues are brought to bear upon this stage. Questions of competition, price elasticity and price discrimination often affect these allocation procedures. One mechanism through which this occurs is the definition of customer classes.

Although all utilities have residential, commercial and industrial rate classes, there is a wide variation in the number of sub-categories within each broad class. In theory, it is possible to define very small, homogeneous customer groups based on some common characteristic. The main impetus to do so usually stems from outside forces such as competition or political pressure. For example, utilities commonly provide special lower rates to electric heating residential customers. While it is generally claimed that these low residential rates are cost-justified due to more off-peak consumption, it is also true that these customers are more price-elastic — that is, likely to reduce consumption as price increases — than is the residential class as a whole. Therefore, the utility has an economic incentive to discount to them to optimize total revenue. If electric heating rates were too high, the utility would lose sales as these customers switched fuels.

A similar situation exists among some price-elastic industrial customers. Here the motive to discount is often phrased as a desire for regional economic development. If electric rates are so high that they make local industry uncompetitive, the regional economic loss can be large. This will eventually be reflected in lower energy sales and a shift of fixed-cost responsibility onto non-industrial customers. To avoid this, it is considered better to keep rates to price-elastic industrial customers low. An example of this is the aluminum industry in the Pacific Northwest. Here, if costs associated with abandoned or mothballed projects were passed on to the aluminum refiners, they could force those plants to close—thus forcing residential and commercial customers to shoulder a larger fraction of the system's fixed costs through higher rates. Similar arguments for discounting to large customers involve the possibility of those customers bypassing the utility by producing their own power via on-site cogeneration.

The last stage of rate-making is the construction of *unit cost tariffs*. This is the culmination of the three previous stages and brings together all the previous issues and more. Usually this is an iterative process in which first approximations are refined by successive consideration of other factors. Broadly speaking, the tasks of this stage can be characterized as follows:

1. Determination of Preliminary Rates
   a) Unit costs = revenue allocated/sales estimated
   b) Revenue reconciliation
2. Tariff Design
   a) Demand charges vs. meter cost
   b) Rate tiers
   c) Base rates vs. fuel adjustment.

$$(4\text{-}3)$$

The first task is designed to develop a rough estimate of the unit costs, defined as the ratio of the previously developed class revenue allocation and the sales forecast. If the marginal cost approach has been used, the revenue requirements found must be adjusted, using the accounting cost perspective to prevent over- or undercollection of revenue. This may be performed at either the class-allocation stage or the tariff-design stage. There are several ways to make this adjustment, and even different definitions of the conditions that imply it has been achieved. We will examine PG&E's discussion in detail.

Actual tariff design requires a specification of the metering technology. In many cases, it is economic to meter both demand and energy consumption (kW and kWh); in other cases the cost of metering outweighs the benefit. In this situation, rate tiers are often adopted to provide price discrimination for different kinds of consumption. In the era of declining costs for instance, residential rate structures often had declining prices as consumption increased. We will study inverted bloc rates in which price increases with use to ration customer demand.

Finally, it is important to distinguish how particular revenues are recovered. Fuel costs are typically collected through automatic adjustment procedures in which there is relatively little regulatory review. Fixed costs, which determine shareholder earnings, are subject to much more review and controversy. Administratively these base rates are determined in general rate cases separately from fuel adjustment. (In some states, such as California, an Energy Rate Adjustment Mechanisms account is maintained so that if the utility's earnings differ from the allowed rate of return one year, the deviation can be accommodated in allowable revenues the following year.) The tariff design may have different fractions of fuel cost and base rate in each component. Deciding how to apportion these is usually more a matter of art than science.

This general outline does not convey the level of complexity involved in rate-setting. To illustrate the process in detail we will flesh out each stage in the procedure with concrete examples. We will begin with Pacific Gas and Electric Company's testimony on marginal cost in their 1982 General Rate Case.

4.2 Marginal Costs for Pacific Gas and Electric Company

Although economists have long advocated the marginal cost approach, there has been much ambiguity about the manner in which these costs should be identified, a situation which has led to much confusion. To resolve the ambiguities, California electric utilities, regulatory agencies and interested parties formed study groups to forge a consensus or methodology. The goal was to develop an approach that would allow practical estimates of marginal costs. PG&E's general rate case testimony presents their version of the resulting general approach. This can be summarized in the following two equations:

$$MC = \frac{\Delta C(R)}{\Delta L} + \frac{\Delta C(0)}{\Delta L} + \frac{\Delta C(I)}{\Delta L} \qquad (4\text{-}4)$$

where

$$\frac{\Delta C(I)}{\Delta L} = \left[\frac{\Delta FC}{\Delta I} + \frac{\Delta C(O)}{\Delta I} + \frac{\Delta C(R)}{\Delta I} \right] \left[\frac{\Delta I}{\Delta L} \right] \qquad (4\text{-}5)$$

where

$C(\ )$ = the cost function for R, O, and I,
R = reliability,
O = operations,
I = investment,
L = load, and
FC = fixed costs.

As Eq. (4-4) shows, marginal cost is a function of reliability, operations and investment. The first term is the change in reliability costs in response to a load change, assuming no change in utility operations or investments. This term, often called the marginal shortage cost, is essentially identical to the generation-related demand cost identified in (4-1). The basic idea here is that system reliability must be maintained to avoid a shortage (or system outage), therefore the cost of preventing a change in reliability is the relevant measure. The second term of Eq. (4-4) is the marginal energy cost. It can be calculated from production cost models in a way that will be indicated below. The final term is the marginal investment cost. This term is expanded in Eq. (4-5).

The marginal investment cost expressed in Eq. (4-5) is the sum of the changes in three marginal costs with respect to investment, multiplied by the marginal investment response to load changes. Of the three bracketed terms, only the first is typically positive — fixed costs always go up with new investment. The second term is often called fuel savings, i.e., the (typical) reduction in total system operating costs resulting from new investment. The last term is the change in shortage costs with the new investment. This is roughly the extra load-carrying capability, times the value of capacity.

PG&E's witness, Fiske, the sponsor of this testimony, discusses and interprets Eq. (4-5) because it had been the subject of controversy and misunderstanding. He begins by focusing on the term in brackets which he calls the net resource cost. This cost can be negative, zero, or positive. Suppose, he suggests, it were negative. This would mean that PG&E's resource planners should add such investments to the system, since they would lower total costs. In fact, the planner should increase this type of investment until it has zero cost, or until some constraint limits expansion. Negative net-cost resources are not abundant, however. Even if some projects may appear to have negative costs, non-financial costs may limit their development. Coal plants, such as the proposed, then abandoned, Allen-Warner Valley System, are examples of this phenomenon. The utility argues that such plants would lower costs in the long run, but are too risky to be built.

Fiske goes on to argue that Eq. (4-5) is in fact always zero. If a resource had negative net cost (the bracketed terms), then the investment would occur without respect to load changes. This means that $\frac{\Delta I}{\Delta L} = 0$. If a resource had positive net cost, the planner would also reject it as a response to load changes. Again, $\frac{\Delta I}{\Delta L} = 0$. This term, which Fiske calls the capacity response factor, is only positive when the net resource cost is zero, which is true of the many marginal or deferrable resources. But for these Eq. (4-5) is also zero. Therefore, the investment term is always zero, and marginal cost is equal to the shortage cost plus the marginal operating cost.

By this argument Fiske has avoided identifying new generation projects as the marginal cost, and has placed the primary burden on marginal energy costs and shortage. Although his argument rests on unrealistic assumptions of perfect knowledge by utility planners and equilibrium among investment alternatives, it is useful in helping us to avoid a discussion of new power plant costs in the context of rate-setting.

Table 4-1

Annual marginal costs of equivalent supply

Year	Electric[1] (mills/kWh)	Gas[2] (mills/therm)
1981	92.3	637
1982	103.5	739
1983	113.1	820
1984	123.0	910
1985	134.3	1010
1986	147.5	1121
1987	162.2	1245
1988	180.3	1382
1989	197.7	1534
1990	216.5	1702
1991	235.1	1873
1992	254.2	2060
1993	275.4	2266
1994	299.6	2493
1995	307.3	2742
1996	344.6	3016
1997	343.9	3318
1998	385.4	3649
1999	432.8	4014
2000	453.6	4416
	After year 2000, escalated at 8% per year	After year 2000, escalated at 10% per year

(1) From PG&E-16, Chapter 1 workpapers; 1982 marginal cost is the combined cost per kWh of energy and demand at the secondary distribution level.

(2) From PG&E-16, Chapter 2, Table 2-B.

If long-run investment choices had to be considered, the uncertainties would be far greater than warranted by a rate case's short time horizon (one or two years). A consideration of possible investment decisions would require a forecast of oil prices many years into the future as part of the forecast of marginal energy costs — an exercise that cannot be carried out with great confidence. PG&E's own estimates of marginal cost illustrate the volatility characteristic of oil cost projections even before the price crash of 1986. Tables 4-1 and 4-2 show

Table 4-2

Calculation of marginal cost of equivalent supply
Societal Perspective
1982–2002

Pacific Gas and Electric Company

Year	ERI	Annual Adjusted Shortage Cost	Annual Transmission & Distribution Cost	Total Annual Capacity ($/kW)	Total Annual Capacity Cost (mills/kWh) (×1,000)	Marginal Energy Cost Secondary Voltage Level	Annaul Marginal Cost of Equivalent Supply (mills/kW)
1982		73.31	103.51	176.82	20.185		
1983		79.17	111.79	190.96	21.799		
1984	.37	31.20	119.06	150.26	17.153	66.45	83.603
1985	.42	37.71	126.80	164.50	18.780	71.64	90.420
1986	.38	36.34	135.04	171.38	19.564	80.01	99.374
1987	.26	26.48	143.82	170.30	19.441	86.26	105.701
1988	.31	33.63	153.17	186.80	21.324	93.61	114.934
1989	.41	47.36	163.12	210.48	24.027	102.30	126.327
1990	.52	63.98	173.73	237.71	27.136	112.79	139.926
1991		131.04	185.02	316.06	36.080	122.56	158.640
1992		139.55	197.04	336.59	38.424	123.74	164.164
1993		147.22	207.88	355.10	40.337	138.30	178.837
1994		155.32	219.31	374.63	42.766	155.40	198.166
1995		163.87	231.38	395.25	45.120	170.69	215.810
1996		172.88	244.10	416.98	47.600	193.84	243.440
1997		182.38	257.53	439.91	50.218	208.08	258.298
1998		192.42	201.69	464.11	52.981	223.28	276.731
1999		203.00	286.64	489.64	55.895	233.28	289.175
2000		214.17	302.40	516.57	58.969	252.85	311.819
2001		225.95	319.03	554.98	62.212	273.95	338.162
2002		238.37	336.58	574.95	65.634	295.32	360.934

the change in expectations over a two-year period.

Table 4-1 presents an estimate produced for PG&E's 1980 General Rate Case (CPUC Appl. No. 60153). The figures in both columns represent the sum of the marginal energy cost and the shortage cost. Table 4-2 is a more detailed breakdown of the same concept from the 1982 General Rate Case. The detail in Table 4-2 indicates that the annual capacity cost is a small percentage (on the order of 20%) of the total marginal cost. Although the calculation of shortage cost used to produce the figures in Table 4-1 is somewhat different than that used to produce Table 4-2 (in ways which will be discussed below), this cost is still a small part of the whole.

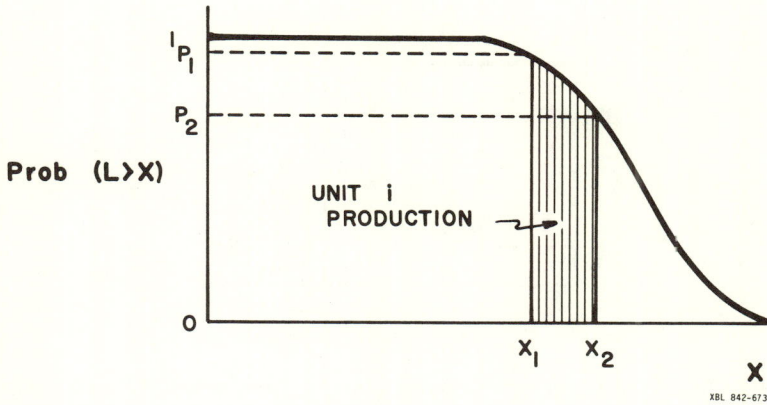

XBL 842-673

Figure 4-1. Contribution of unit *i* to marginal energy cost.

Therefore in the long run, the difference between these estimates reflects changing perceptions of the oil market, since oil
at this time was expected to be almost always PG&E's marginal fuel. For 1990, the estimate made in 1980 was 55%
above that made in 1982, and for 2000 it was about 45%
higher.

With this kind of long-run price uncertainty, it is difficult to
take Fiske's assertions about net resource costs and marginal
investment cost literally. It would be an interesting exercise
to use Tables 4-1 and 4-2 to value PG&E's Diablo Canyon
project, which was under construction during this period.
Clearly the lower marginal costs would diminish Diablo
Canyon's value. Such an exercise would require a capital cost
estimate, which is itself uncertain. The multiple uncertainties
would make this a controversial analysis.

For rate-making purposes it is not necessary to make long-
run forecasts of marginal cost, at least with respect to energy.
All that is necessary is the short-run marginal cost which can
be estimated from standard production-cost models. The procedure is illustrated in Figure 4-1. This figure illustrates the
use of the inverted load duration curve in production costing
for marginal production by a particular generating unit *i*.
(This is the same load representation as in the upper panel of
Figure 3-8, only rotated so that minimum loads are here

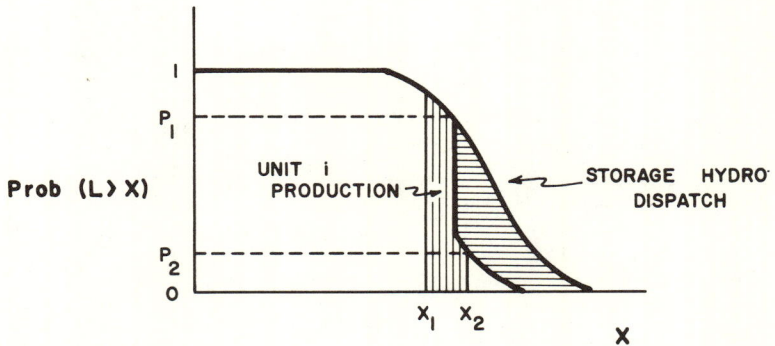

XBL 842-674

Figure 4-2. Storage hydro dispatch produces a dominant marginal unit.

represented as Prob $(L > \text{minimum}) = 1$.) The shaded region represents the energy produced by the ith unit. Baseload units serve below units such as i which here is shown to be on the margin for loads between x_1 and x_2. Since units are dispatched in the order of increasing production cost, loads above x_2 will have higher marginal cost than those served by unit i. We can calculate the mean marginal cost for the period represented by the load duration curve in this manner. The cost of marginal units such as i is weighted by the fraction, $P_i = P_1 - P_2$, of time the unit is on the margin. Formally, for marginal cost MC, we can write:

$$\text{Average } MC = \sum_j C_j \cdot P_j , \qquad (4\text{-}6)$$

where

C_j = production cost of the jth marginal unit,

and

P_j = fraction of time the jth unit is on the margin.

As will be discussed later, it will subsequently become necessary to spread the marginal cost calculated by Eq. (4-6) over the costing periods. The marginal cost-curve for systems like that of PG&E with substantial amounts of hydro storage has a special characteristic resulting from the geometry of Figure 4-2. By convention, the dispatch of storage hydro is used to

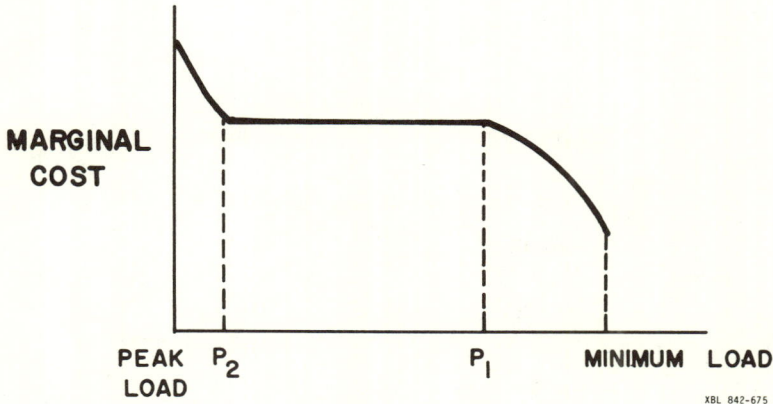

Figure 4-3. Marginal cost curve corresponding to Figure 4-2.

shave the peak of the load duration curve as illustrated by the horizontally shaded area in Figure 4-2 (see for example, Zahavi [1981]). The resulting change in the shape of the load duration curve creates an unusually large fraction of marginal time for the unit nearest the perturbed curve. The corresponding marginal cost curve is shown in Figure 4-3. More detail on such calculations appears in Chapter 5.

Monthly variations in estimated marginal energy costs for 1990 are shown in Figure 4-4. These are based on simulations for the 1982 General Rate Case. They illustrate the effect of hydro resource variation on marginal cost. Curves are labeled with month number and hydro condition (average, A; wet, W; or dry, D). The normally wet spring months (March = 3 and April = 4) can result in long periods of near-zero marginal cost in wetter-than-average years (curves 3W and 4W). If conditions are dry, however, marginal springtime costs can be higher than average-condition costs in September (compare 3D with 9A).

The next problem is estimating the generation shortage cost. Fiske divides this into the two stages indicated in item (2) of Eq. (4-2). First, there must be an engineering characterization of system reliability changes in response to load changes. Second, there must be a valuation of these reliability changes and the capacity response to them. PG&E proposes a method

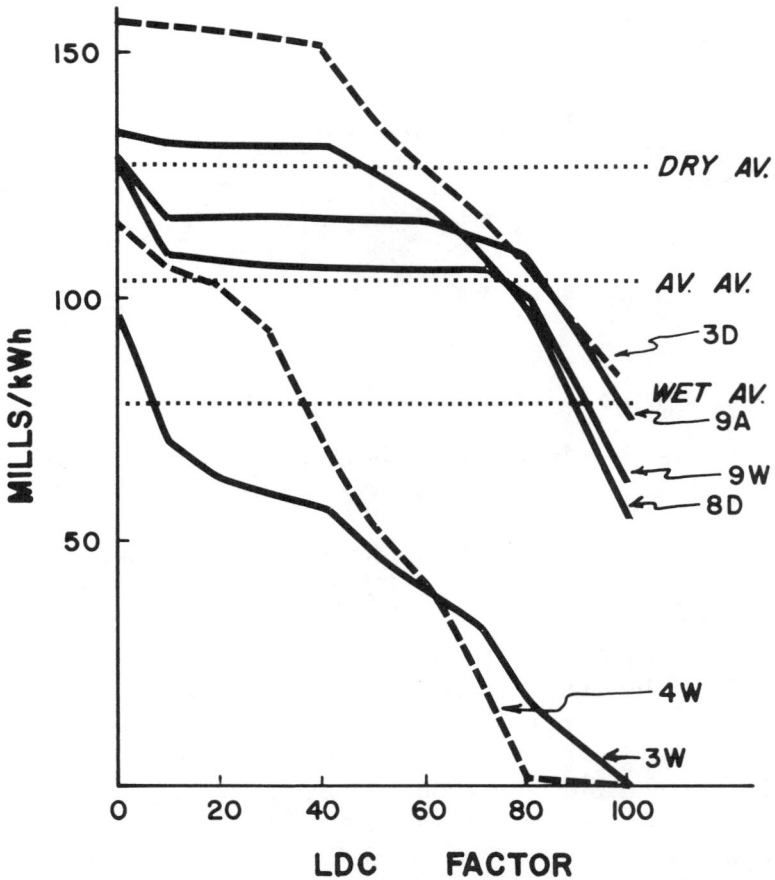

XBL 842-676

Figure 4-4. Estimated monthly marginal cost curves, 1990.

for measuring reliability changes that extends the ordinary
LOLP calculation. The basic idea is to examine the effects of
emergency voltage reduction and load-shedding actions that
would be necessary in an actual shortage situation. The effect
measured is the total kWh reduction associated with kW load
reductions required by specific emergency procedures. This
calculation produces a measure called the Energy Reliability
Index (ERI). Formally ERI is defined by

$$ERI = \sum_i \left[Prob \left(EA_i \right) \right] \cdot \Delta L_i \qquad (4\text{-}7)$$

where

EA_i = emergency action i,

ΔL_i = load change associated with each EA_i, (kW)

$Prob(EA_i)$ = expected frequency of EA_i (hr/yr).

Notice that $Prob$ (EA_i) is equivalent to a certain number of hours of the year, so that ERI is measured in units of energy (kWh) and not capacity. The greater the power system reliability, the smaller the ERI. PG&E expects relatively large reserve margins in the mid-1980s to early 1990s with the added capacity from Diablo Canyon and new, privately owned power plants. Under these circumstances, the ERI will be smaller than it was when LOLP met the one-day-in-ten years criterion. Therefore PG&E argues that the shortage cost must be lower than the standard value associated with conditions when LOLP equals one-day-in-ten years.

The valuation of reliability is widely recognized to be a very difficult problem. It basically involves comparison of the utility-functions of all electric customers where the values involved are not all quantifiable or expressed in financial terms. To simplify this problem, California utilities and regulators typically adopt the gas-turbine proxy. Gas turbines are the least expensive capital investment response to increased generation demand. Its capital cost is a proxy for the aggregated social value of reliability. PG&E proposes to discount this proxy cost using changes in the ERI to account for high reliability in the 1984-1990 period. The magnitude of this effect is illustrated in Table 4-2 under the column labeled ERI. For the years 1984–1990 a fraction between .26 and .52 is calculated from estimated changes in the ERI relative to LOLP = 1d/10yrs. This fraction is then multiplied by the gas turbine capital cost for a given year to yield the adjusted shortage cost, measured in dollars per kilowatt.

The methods used for estimating marginal T&D and customer costs, simple one-variable regression equations applied to highly aggregated data, are qualitatively much cruder than those embodied in Eqs. (4-6) and (4-7). PG&E takes annual changes in T&D demand and number of customers and fits these to annual expenses for these categories. The slope coefficient of this equation is identified as the marginal cost.

There is no attempt to represent any engineering detail.

The estimation of marginal distribution costs is complex for several reasons. First, a boundary must be defined between demand-related distribution costs and those which are customer-related. This boundary is essentially arbitrary. It depends upon a concept of a minimum distribution system that is neither intuitively motivated nor derived from engineering principles. Its importance is conceptual, stemming from the need to allocate capital costs to the two intuitively distinct functions. Distribution costs are also separated into primary and secondary levels, which refer to the voltage at which particular customers take service. Industrial customers, for example, typically take service at the higher-voltage primary level. This distinction is made because it will be important for the class allocation stage of rate-making.

4.3 Time Variation of Costs

Having estimated annual total costs (either marginal or average embedded) it is necessary to account for time variation in cost. The purpose of this task is to demarcate the peak periods of each season and estimate the fraction of costs that should be borne by those who consume electricity during each of those periods. First, the planner must delineate the boundaries of peak, partial-peak, and off-peak periods for the utility system in question. The practical realities of pricing make it necessary to specify a small number of periods for analysis and price (or cost) differentiation. Each period should be relatively homogeneous with respect to its cost characteristics, so that within a period it will be reasonable to average variations. Since it is useful to have one set of costing periods for all functions, it would be desirable if the periods selected were meaningful for both energy-related and demand-related costs. This inevitably introduces some circularity into the definition of relevant time periods.

PG&E illustrates four measures used to define its six costing periods. The measures are (1) daily load curve variation, (2) hourly marginal energy cost, (3) hourly LOLP and (4) excess load probability (defined as the probability of an hourly load above the mean load). The most important of these are the

Table 4-3

Hourly marginal energy costs for four typical days
(Mills/KWh)

Pacific Gas and Electric Company

1984

	SUMMER				WINTER	
Hour	Weekday Average	Week Average			Weekday Average	Week Average
1	52.29	51.62			55.90	54.59
2	48.51	46.65			52.63	48.96
3	45.71	43.77			50.58	46.03
4	44.71	41.86			51.03	44.95
5	47.14	41.86			51.03	44.95
6	53.65	41.36			61.88	49.67
7	60.63	44.31			65.94	54.89
8	**61.77**	**53.79**			67.37	61.45
9	61.92	59.41			67.37	61.45
10	62.20	60.97	Partial		68.12	65.44
11	62.63	61.36	Peak		68.09	65.62
12	**62.91**	**61.54**			**67.83**	**65.60**
13	63.45	61.56			67.88	65.08
14	64.14	61.56			67.91	64.90
15	64.69	61.58	Peak		67.89	64.59
16	64.79	61.67			**67.72**	**64.77**
17	64.72	61.75			67.96	65.98
18	**64.10**	**61.75**			68.97	66.62
19	63.06	61.68	Partial		69.29	67.16
20	62.57	61.73	Peak		**68.57**	**66.98**
21	62.57	61.83			67.65	66.50
22	**61.88**	**61.64**			**66.97**	**65.00**
23	61.53	59.96			65.21	62.44
24	58.78	53.92			61.34	56.56

hourly marginal cost and LOLP, the quantities used to allocate costs to time periods. The data presented for typical days are instructive.

Examination of the marginal energy cost estimates in Table 4-3 shows reasonable correspondence between changes in hourly loads and changes in cost. But the changes are so smooth and so small (about 30% from high to low) that it is difficult to differentiate any clear boundary that would help define precise costing periods. There is even some question about how the marginal costs in this table can be produced from a load duration curve production simulation. Figures 4-1 to 4-4 do not completely represent the simulation process; when allowance is made for the forced outages of generating units, the link between chronological loads and the marginal cost duration curves is broken. The resulting average marginal costs are then difficult to assign to particular hours. To produce the estimates in Table 4-3, it is necessary to approximate the linkage between costs and hours. These approximations are not conclusive, and make it more difficult to discern the kind of cost differentiation that is useful for rate averaging.

Hourly LOLP is more conclusive than the cost/hours linkage, but we would expect from a nearly exponential function, LOLP is quite volatile. The costing periods defined by PG&E do exhibit substantial jumps in hourly LOLP at the boundaries, although the precise boundaries are not well-defined, and are therefore open to interpretation. Table 4-4 shows a summer peak from 12:30 to 6:30 P.M., and a partial peak at 8:30 A.M. to 12:30 P.M. and 6:30 to 10:30 P.M. weekdays. All other hours are off-peak. For winter, the peak is 4:30 to 8:30 P.M. Even in this case, however, it is not entirely obvious why the summer peak is not an hour shorter or the winter peak is not even more narrow. The boundary between partial-peak and off-peak is reasonably well-defined by hourly LOLP, although even here the winter partial peak might end an hour earlier.

Having defined costing periods, PG&E summarizes the hourly LOLP analysis into allocation factors for generation and transmission demand-related costs. These allocation factors are percentages of total annual cost that can be attributed to each costing period. The resulting estimates reflect a somewhat more diffuse distribution of LOLP over the costing periods than the typical day tables. For example, 68.9% of the annual LOLP falls within the summer peak (Period A = May 1 to September 30), compared to 23.7% during the Period A partial peak. Typical summer weekdays display an hourly LOLP in the peak almost four times that of the

Table 4-4

Hourly LOLPs (×1000) for 4 typical days

Pacific Gas and Electric Company

1984

	SUMMER			WINTER	
Hour	Weekday Average	Weekday Average		Weekday Average	Weekday Average
1	0.00000	0.00000		0.00000	0.00000
2	0.00000	0.00000		0.00000	0.00000
3	0.00000	0.00000		0.00000	0.00000
4	0.00000	0.00000		0.00000	0.00000
5	0.00000	0.00000		0.00000	0.00000
6	0.00000	0.00000		0.00000	0.00000
7	0.00000	0.00000		0.00000	0.00000
8	**0.00000**	**0.00000**		0.00001	0.00000
9	0.01242	0.00000		0.00267	0.00000
10	0.05022	0.00000	Partial	0.00690	0.00000
11	0.13946	0.00000	Peak	0.00521	0.00000
12	**0.21379**	**0.00000**		0.00204	0.00000
13	0.35991	0.00000		0.00618	0.00000
14	0.52574	0.00000		0.01090	0.00000
15	0.65216	0.00000		0.01507	0.00000
16	0.68659	0.00000	Peak	**0.01425**	**0.00000**
17	0.66564	0.00001		0.02302	0.00000
18	**0.53691**	**0.00000**		0.06623	0.00002
19	0.27291	0.00000	Partial	0.06903	0.00177
20	0.12200	0.00000	Peak	**0.03008**	**0.00002**
21	0.15256	0.00000		0.00021	0.00000
22	**0.00013**	**0.00000**		**0.00000**	**0.00000**
23	0.00000	0.00000		0.00000	0.00000
24	0.00000	0.00000		0.00000	0.00000

partial-peak period. Similarly the summer peak appears to have almost twenty times the LOLP of the winter peak (Period B) in the typical-day data. Five percent of annual LOLP falls within the winter peak; about 1/14 of the summer peak allocation.

Presumably the detailed PG&E simulations support the final allocation, but precise evidence of this is not offered directly

in the testimony. Such technical fine points are usually settled in the work papers underlying quantitative studies.
Often these work papers are extensive, and may be computer
programs with complex inputs and outputs.

Having allocated costs to time periods, the next task of
rate-making is to assign these costs broadly to customer
classes. This step is one of the most controversial and difficult.

4.4 Class Allocation of Revenue Requirements

In principle, load research should be sufficient to go from
costing periods to class allocation. The main customer classes
would be assumed to be homogeneous enough so that some
sample of their demand characteristics would allow allocation
of cost. In practice, however, difficulties arise; they appear in
different ways for the marginal cost approach and the average
embedded cost or accounting approach. Let us consider the
marginal cost approach first.

The approach to calculating marginal costs described above
(allocating them to time periods for energy and demand and
summing them with customer costs) yields too large a revenue requirement: marginal costs are greater than average
costs. Since regulators are unwilling to charge marginal cost
prices, they must come up with a procedure which will result
in revenues equal to the average cost revenue requirement.
The discrepancy between the two perspectives must be reconciled by some procedure that is not totally arbitrary, and it is
this reconciliation which creates the problem. The PG&E case
provides a concrete setting in which to examine the issue.
The magnitudes involved are summarized in Table 4-5 along
with the results of using one reconciliation rule.

The "Marginal Cost" column on the left-hand side of Table
4-5 shows that total marginal costs exceed CPUC Revenue
Requirements based on traditional accounting procedures.
Marginal costs exceed the overall revenue requirements by
roughly the total marginal customer costs. The remaining
three columns of the table show class revenue requirements
for residential and industrial customers — only two of

Table 4-5

Marginal cost reconciliation and class allocation for PG&E

	Marginal Cost[a] (10^3)		Revenue by Class	
			Residential	Industrial
Energy	1853			
Demand	945	EPMC		
Customer	909	w/o customer	949	734
Total	3707	costs		
CPUC	2867	MC[b]	1713	735
Rev. Req.		fraction of total	.462	.198
Marginal Cost		EPMC	1324	568
w/o Customer	2798	total MC		
Component				

(a) Testimony of R. Howard, EX. PG&E-20, Table 2-3, CPUC Appl. No. 82-12-48.

(b) Marginal Customer Costs × Number of Customers

	MC/Customer	Customer Total
Industrial	$1048	969
Residential	251	3,044,000

PG&E's several customer classes. The first row shows required revenue scaled so that the responsibility of each class reflects its percentage of marginal cost. This is called the Equal Percentage of Marginal Cost Method (EPMC). With customer costs excluded, residential customers are responsible for about 34% of total revenue requirements; industrial customers for about 26%. This is approximately the share of each class in forecast kWh sales.

When marginal customer costs are included in determining the fraction of costs to be allocated to each class, residential customers account for 46% of the total, and the industrial share drops to about 20%. The resulting revenue responsibility is shown on the last line of the table. Given the substantial differences in cost allocation, it is important to understand the considerations given to including or excluding marginal customer costs.

At first glance, the exclusion of marginal customer costs seems arbitrary. If the marginal cost perspective is so important, why can one component of it be neglected? The best answer to this was given by Bonbright (1961), who emphasized the arbitrary nature of the calculation of marginal customer costs. Bonbright is another of the legendary figures in the history of electric utility regulation. Although he was an academic economist, Bonbright's wide experience in rate-making issues gave him a firm practical sense of the engineering constraints and information limits that restrict the freedom of regulatory control. His *Principles of Public Utility Rates* is a classic treatment of historical issues in rate-making and a sensitive discussion of marginal cost principles. While Bonbright generally favors the use of marginal cost information in setting rates, he advocates flexibility in its use and valuation.

Bonbright observes that marginal customer costs are a somewhat theoretical construct since they are commonly defined with respect to a hypothetical minimum distribution system. However unreal this construct may be, it at least attempts to isolate cost changes which do *not* respond to demand changes at the margin. Therefore, neglecting them is not important from the resource allocation point of view. The main argument economists use in favor of marginal cost pricing is its value in guiding consumption decisions. Even if it were useful to consider marginal customer costs in principle, there are important network density questions which affect estimation of these costs in practice. The cost of adding new customers varies substantially with location. New developments such as suburban subdivisions can be expensive. Denser urban sites with networks in place have low marginal customer costs. Instead of reflecting these differences poorly in general rates, it would be better to charge new customers their marginal cost of connecting to the system.

Industrial customers, of course, would prefer the allocation which lowered their rates; under the circumstances described above they would advocate full marginal cost allocation. Indeed, marginal cost principles are often invoked by industrial customers to argue for lower rates. For now, however, we will exclude marginal customer costs, and shift our attention to dividing demand-related costs among customer classes.

In the early and mid 1970s, marginal cost theory supported a rule known as the peak responsibility method for allocating demand related fixed costs. The basic logic, supported (with some important reservations) by Bonbright, was that peak demand growth drives new investment. Therefore, those classes which contribute most to peak loads should bear capacity costs in proportion to that contribution. It was not uncommon then, and even today, to treat all fixed costs of capacity as demand related. Even under conditions of steady growth in demand and the need for new supply, this approach fails to account for the choice of generating technology, ranging from capital-intensive baseload units to low-cost peakers. Bonbright accepts the argument that any generation capital costs above those associated with gas turbines reflect a substitution of capital for fuel and so should be allocated to energy costs. An equivalent result has emerged in a modern revival of a traditional allocation procedure known as the Average and Excess Demand (AED) method.

The AED method attempts to allocate fixed demand-related costs (here usually identified with all fixed capacity costs) to customer classes on the basis of class load characteristics. Unlike the peak responsibility method, AED also weighs the average demand, i.e., the class share of total energy requirement. Following the recent leading exponent to AED, Eugene Coyle (1982), we can write an expression for a customer class share of fixed costs as:

$$S_c = LF_c \cdot PK_c + PK_c \left(1 - LF_{sys} \right) \quad , \qquad (4\text{-}8)$$

where

S_c = share of *class* c,

LF_c = load factor of *class* c, = $\dfrac{\text{average demand}}{\text{coincident peak demand of } class\ c}$,

PK_c = fraction of coincident peak due to *class* c,

LF_{sys} = load factor of entire utility system.

Table 4-6

AED vs. peak responsibility

Class	PCT PK	LF	Pct. kWh	AED Share
Residential	.35	.40	.27	.287
Industrial	.26	.66	.33	.281

System Load Factor = .58

The first term expresses the class share of total kWh sales and the second expresses the class share in excess system kW-demand above the system average. Older versions of the AED method, such as those discussed in the NARUC Manual, emphasize class non-coincident peaks, such as those which are used to allocate distribution demand over time periods. Non-coincident peaks are meaningless for generation-related demand cost allocation. What matters is the coincidence of class loads with the system peak, because only this affects marginal costs.

The application and effect of Eq. (4-8) is illustrated by an example in Table 4-6. The data is representative of California utilities. This example shows that AED tends to equalize class allocation between residential and industrial customers, compared to coincident peak responsibility. AED in this version has become more popular as the economic rationale for new plant investment has increasingly become more oriented to fuel mix optimization (i.e., oil savings) and not peak load growth.

AED, as embodied in Eq. 4-8, represents a kind of marginalism in the accounting cost framework, which works against the interest of industrial customers; usually marginal cost theory favors large users in one way or another. We will return to this theme in the context of Ramsey pricing in Chapter 8. For our current purposes of surveying price regulation mechanisms, it is necessary to turn to tariff design: the mechanics of constructing rate schedules to produce required revenues allocated to class.

4.5 Unit Cost Tariffs

Unlike commodities to which simple unit prices are applied, electricity is typically priced by a schedule of tariff charges from which a total bill is derived as a function of usage characteristics. There is no one price per unit, but usually more than one applicable price, reflecting the multi-dimensional nature of electric power service. As we have seen, the demand (kW) and energy (kWh) dimensions are the most important cost features. It is not surprising therefore that tariffs would be designed to bill customers for each feature separately. The only limitation on such billing is the cost of meters to measure both kW and kWh. With current technology, this turns out to be economic only for larger customers. Since the relevant load data is often not available in detail for residential customers, sometimes summary statistics such as the customer class load factor are used to justify rate design in terms of cost. To illustrate typical rate design problems we will start by examining demand charges for different kinds of large users.

Linking demand charges and marginal costs is the notion of a coincidence factor. Demand charges are based on the maximum demand recorded in a given costing period. These maximum demands may or may not occur at the same time as actual system peak demand. Furthermore, individual customers are not routinely evaluated separately for the degree of coincidence between their maximum demand and that of the system. Therefore rate designers use a class coincidence factor defined as follows:

$$\text{Class Coincidence Factor} = \frac{\text{Class Coincident Peak}}{\text{Total Class Maximum Billing Demand}} . \quad (4\text{-}9)$$

We illustrate the use of the coincidence factor in determining marginal cost of generation and transmission demand for industrial customers of PG&E, and compare this to proposed tariff charges in Table 4-7.

Table 4-7 compares the marginal generation and transmission cost revenues for PG&E's industrial customers with pro-

Table 4-7

**Marginal generation and transmission costs
and proposed demand changes**

PG&E Industrial Customers

Billing Demand[a] (mw)	Period A	Period B	Revenue at $2.80/kW
Sch. A-22	6,777	9,129	$44.54 × 10⁶
Sch. A-23	5,759	7,987	38.49 × 10⁶
	12,536	17.116	$83.03 × 10⁶

Marginal Costs			Total MC Revenue
Average Monthly Demand[b]	2,507	2,455	
Coincidence Factor[a]	.764	.746	
Coincident Demand	1,915	1,824	
Marginal Cost[c] ($/kW-Period)	$48.30	$3.78	
MC Revenue	$92.49 × 10⁶	$6.89 × 10⁶	$99.3 × 10⁶

(a) Work papers for Ex. PG&E-20 in CPUC Appl. No. 82-12-48.

(b) Period Billing Demand/Months Per Period.

(c) Table I-29, Ex. PG&E-13 (Fiske) at the Primary Dist. Level.

posed demand charges. The proposed demand charges are only intended to cover marginal distribution costs; the rate design neglects the other cost factors in the interest of keeping the demand charges low. The motivation of this tariff design was to avoid the incentive for increased consumption that high demand charges represent; when this rate schedule was designed, PG&E had an economic motivation to encourage energy conservation. Since the demand charge is based on peak consumption, once it is incurred there is no dis-incentive to additional off-peak consumption. Note that the revenue associated with demand charges is only about 11% of the revenue requirement for industrial customers (compare Table 4-7 with Table 4-5). This corresponds roughly to PG&E's marginal cost structure, dominated by marginal energy costs. Other utilities which are less dependent than PG&E on oil and gas will typically have much larger demand charges for industrial customers. It is not uncommon for these rates to be three or even four times the $2.80/kW-month level proposed by PG&E.

A particularly interesting demand charge tariff is the rate for stand-by power for cogeneration customers. Cogeneration is the combined production of electricity and heat for useful (often industrial) purposes. We will discuss the economics of cogeneration in some detail in Chapter 6. Although the cogenerator produces the major part of its electricity requirement on-site, back-up power is needed during forced and scheduled equipment maintenance. Rather than incur the cost of complete back-up on-site, it may often be desirable to purchase back-up power from the utility on a stand-by basis. The key issue is the price for this service, which depends upon the load characteristics of back-up customers. The central fact to be determined is the extent of diversity in back-up requirements for cogeneration. It may be argued plausibly that this diversity should be great, and hence coincident demand low. But without load data, the class coincidence factor is unknown. Table 4-8 shows three estimates of annual demand charge revenues required per kW for stand-by service on the Consolidated Edison system (ConEd) in 1980.

You will recall that ConEd is opposed to cogeneration development on a number of economic and environmental grounds. It is not surprising that their rate proposal (Monsees, estimate #2) projects the largest revenue requirement. ConEd uses the high embedded costs as its basis for valuing service (same as Arnett). Furthermore, ConEd chooses coincidence factors which are identical to those estimated for the customer class (large commercial) from which most cogenerators are expected to come.

The other witnesses who testified on this issue rejected the ConEd coincidence factor assumptions. Arnett, who testified on behalf of a state agency, proposed coincidence factors of

Table 4-8

Stand-by demand charges
cost estimates for Consolidated Edison

	Cost $/kW	Coincidence Factor HV	Coincidence Factor LV	Annual Cost HV	Annual Cost LV
1. Arnett: Average Embedded Cost					
Production	123.80	0.10	0.10	12.38	12.38
Transmission	34.57	0.10	0.10	3.46	3.46
Primary Dist.	41.09	1.00	0.68	41.09	27.94
Secondary Dist.	32.60	—	1.0	—	32.60
Customer Cost	8.80	1.00	1.0	8.80	8.80
				65.70	85.18
2. Monsees					
Production		0.40	0.37	49.52	45.81
Transmission		0.40	0.37	13.83	12.79
Remainder:					
Same as (1)				113.24	127.94
3. Beach: Marginal Cost					
Production	3.26	0	0		
Transmission	21.00	0	0		
Primary Dist.	32.79	~1	~1	31.96	
Secondary Dist.	31.96	0	~1		62.36

10%, a judgment on his part based on his assumption of substantial diversity among cogeneration outages. Arnett then
applied this assumption to the embedded cost values, resulting in revenue requirements that are 58-66% of those proposed by Monsees of ConEd. Beach was the witness of the
Public Service Commission (PSC) Staff. She adopts marginal
cost values for each function and zero coincidence for generation and transmission. Notice that ConEd's marginal costs
were below their average embedded costs. The very small
value for generation reflects ConEd's large reserve margin.
The resulting estimate is 48–73% of Arnett's.

The New York PSC ended up endorsing Beach on this
issue, though the evidentiary basis of that decision was weak.

The only real evidence offered was an LOLP study done for ConEd by consultant Ebasco Services, which purported to yield the result assumed by Monsees on coincidence, but only under the unrealistic assumption that all cogenerators should have an LOLP of 10^{-4}.

In California, the CPUC adopted a cogeneration stand-by demand charge of $0.75/kW-month in the early 1980s. This is about 27% of the then current industrial demand charge and implies a correspondingly low coincidence factor. There has not been a load study on this service since the rate was instituted several years ago. PG&E estimates $3.8 million in revenue under this rate in 1984.

Load characteristics of smaller customers typically cannot be incorporated in tariffs by using demand charges because of the high transaction costs associated with metering smaller loads. Since load information is available for small users, however, it would be useful to incorporate it into tariff design. It is common to combine customer load characteristics into one figure, know as the coincident load factor. (Recall its use at the class level in the discussion of the AED allocation method.) The coincident load factor can also be used at the tariff level to justify the general shape or level of the tariffs designed with a class. Generally speaking, high load factors imply lower cost loads. The logic is the same as at the class allocation level: if one subclass of residential customers can be shown to have higher load factors than another, then they ought to have lower rates. One application of this principle is the generally lower price level associated with electric space-heating tariffs compared to ordinary residential tariffs. Another application of the principle can be made with regard to the differential pricing of different blocs of consumption, which constitutes the structure of rate.

In the declining-cost era of the utility industry, residential rates often exhibited a volume discount in the form of a lower unit price for use above a certain kWh level. The rationale for declining bloc rates was usually related to scale-economy through growth — it did not have much to do with load factors. In an increasing-cost environment, the opposite kind of rate structure, an increasing or inverted bloc tariff, has become more popular. Figure 4-5 illustrates a three-tier version of

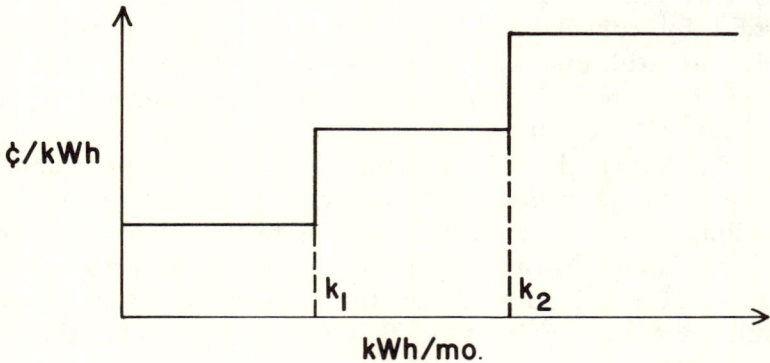

XBL 842-677

Figure 4-5. Three-tier inverted bloc-tariff structure.

this structure. It has been argued that inverted rates, or "life-line" rate structures as they are sometimes called, are cost-justified by load factor considerations; Table 4-9 gives results of one load study supporting this proposition.

The data in Table 4-9 date from the period 1974–1977, and may not be representative of conditions generally. A decrease in the load factor correlates with an increase in average monthly consumption but the use of air-conditioning also seems to be an equally important factor contributing to declining load factor. It is difficult to support a particular tariff structure from data such as this. To understand why rate structures such as that illustrated in Figure 4-5 have been adopted and how they are designed, we will consider the specific example of PG&E's residential lifeline rates and the on-going process of reform in these tariffs called baseline rates.

4.5.1 Lifeline and Baseline Rates:
The Case of Pacific Gas and Electric

Residential rates in California were modified to the structure shown in Figure 4-5 following implementation by the CPUC of the Miller-Warren Energy Lifeline Act of 1975. There was a substantial political impetus behind the adoption of lifeline rates. A number of political constituencies coalesced behind this kind of rate reform as the optimal response to increases in electricity costs. They felt that the lifeline concept both

Table 4-9

Average monthly system load factors

Cincinnati Gas and Electric

Group	Average kWh/month	Average Monthly Load Factor	Summer Average Monthly Load Factor
1 Non Air	329	86.3	100.0
2 Non Air	483	69.5	68.2
3 Non Air	665	72.2	63.8
4 Non Air	1095	76.1	72.2
5 Non Air	2400	66.4	66.1
1 Air	477	65.0	53.4
2 Air	1125	65.0	51.1

promoted conservation and reduced the impact of utility rate increases on low-income consumers. The first goal appealed to environmentalists who sought to reduce the need for new power plants. The second goal appealed principally to consumer groups with an interest in income redistribution.

The California Public Utilities Commission was not initially in favor of lifeline rates. Members appointed by then-Governor Ronald Reagan thought that subsidized prices for low levels of energy use were neither justified by cost nor really achieved any income redistribution. Douglas Andersen, in his book, *Regulatory Politics and Electric Utilities* (1981), cites the frank opinions of these commissioners.

> Lifeline is a fraud. No one gets lifeline because it causes higher rates for business and they pass on more than that cost of business to consumers. It's good for PR and nothing else. They tried to push it as conservation, but that's pure unadulterated b____ s____.
>
> Vernon L. Sturgeon, President, CPUC

A somewhat more philosophical statement of this view was made by Commissioner William Symon, Jr. after a new CPUC majority succeeded in adopting lifeline rates.

> We've become a welfare agency — giving it to people who don't deserve it. We've gotten completely away from the cost-of-service idea. Now it's just like throwing darts at the wall.

These expressions of dismay reflect the substantial changes in rate-making procedures brought about by adopting lifeline rates. Because the impetus for the change was political, there were many technical issues to be settled during implementation that had not been given extensive examination before or during the policy debate. We will examine some of these questions with reference to data describing the Pacific Gas and Electric system.

In the discussion which follows we will survey the major PG&E residential tariff schedules in effect during 1982 and 1983. The problem of forecasting revenues under inverted rates is introduced by describing the sales frequency distribution data. We then describe the reform of the lifeline rate structure into the somewhat simpler baseline form. Frequent changes and adjustments in the rate have made possible many variations on the inverted block-rate structure. It is useful to understand the mechanics of such changes so that the business of predicting and collecting required revenues allocated to consumers can be more completely understood.

Exploration of these technicalities is also useful as more and more utilities are being encouraged to adopt some version of lifeline or inverted rate structure. The California experience in this regard is likely to be repeated elsewhere. Decisions in favor of inverted rates based on social policy considerations alone are often made independent of much analysis or even contrary to studies about its income distribution efficiency. This was essentially the orientation of the CPUC majority which eventually implemented the first lifeline rate structure in 1975. Andersen cites the candid expression of Jim Cherry, legal assistant to Commissioner Leonard Ross, who led the pro-lifeline majority.

> People who kept saying, "But lifeline doesn't help the poor," just didn't understand the issue. The issue is: What is the basic amount society can afford to give you and me? I'd keep explaining that, but they'd come right back and ask what it did for the poor. They didn't understand the broad-based political support for lifeline without restrictions on income.

In 1975, California was the only state to adopt the inverted-rate structure and while it remained the only one adopted for several years, gradually more and more states adopted some form of inverted-rate structure. A 1981 NARUC Survey indicated that 14 states had moved in this direction. One particularly interesting question about inverted rates concerns the price elasticity effects of different tier prices. This can be especially important during the first transition to an inverted structure. In Section 4.5.2 we will examine such a case based on data describing Detroit Edison, but will begin here with an overview of the PG&E lifeline tariff schedules.

The original California lifeline concept is based on a notion of minimum individual needs. These needs were supposed to be reflected in Tier 1 allowances which vary according to a number of factors. The size of Tier 1 is determined by (a) climate zone, (b) appliance holdings, (c) type of dwelling—apartment, single-family home, etc, and (d) special factors, such as rate experiments, or the need for life-support equipment. Fifty-two rate schedules are required to take into account only the first two items. Table 4-10 shows 1982–83

Table 4-10

**Sales from major
residential electric rate schedules
5/82–4/83**

$(10^6$ KWH)

Climate Zone	Appliance Code	Summer	Winter	Total
T	B	1231	1431	
	C	153	208	
	H	84	145	
	W	45	51	
		1513	1835	3348
X	B	2021	2287	
	A	673	559	
	B	924	852	
	C	558	585	
		4176	4283	8459
	C	142	213	
	A	180	227	
	B	396	562	
	C	102	154	
		820	1156	1976

Table 4-10 continued

Climate Zone	Appliance Code	Summer	Winter	Total
	H	91	170	
	A	22	27	
	B	29	42	
	C	32	56	
		174	295	469
	W	62	72	
	A	97	95	
	B	122	132	
	C	26	28	
		307	327	634
WA	B	419	304	
	C	26	30	
	H	13	11	
	W	20	18	
		478	363	841
Y	B	19	18	
	C	74	95	
	H	3	4	
	W	24	24	
		120	141	261
V	B	48	63	
	C	14	20	
	H	1	1	
	W	15	19	
		78	103	181
Direct Control				
X	B			
	A	89	81	
	B	53	59	
	C	19	21	
		161	161	322
				16,491

Appliance Codes:

B = Basic; C = Combined space and water heating; H = Space heating only;
W = Water heating only.

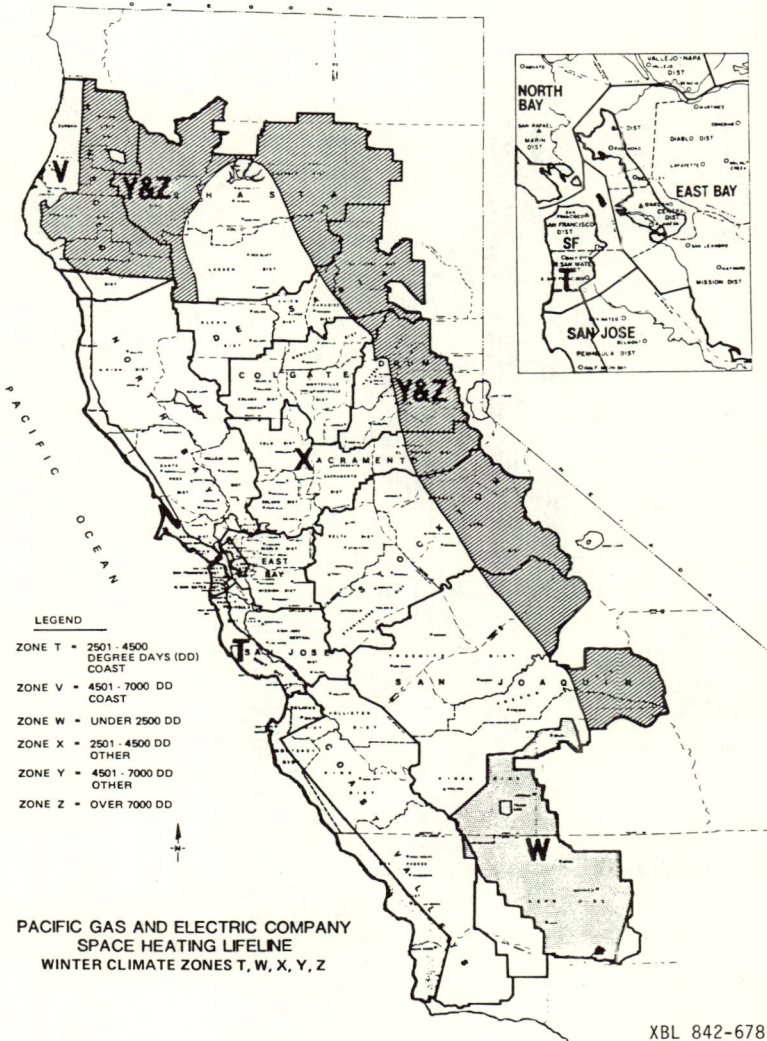

LEGEND

ZONE T = 2501 - 4500 DEGREE DAYS (DD) COAST

ZONE V = 4501 - 7000 DD COAST

ZONE W = UNDER 2500 DD

ZONE X = 2501 - 4500 DD OTHER

ZONE Y = 4501 - 7000 DD OTHER

ZONE Z = OVER 7000 DD

PACIFIC GAS AND ELECTRIC COMPANY
SPACE HEATING LIFELINE
WINTER CLIMATE ZONES T, W, X, Y, Z

XBL 842-678

Figure 4-6a. Present air-conditioning and space-heating lifeline zones for Pacific Gas & Electric: map of winter climate zones.

kWh sales for the major PG&E residential tariff schedules representing 85–90% of residential consumption for this period. Table 4-10 distinguishes climate zones (T, X, WA, Y and V), air-conditioning sub-zones (A, B and C of zone X)

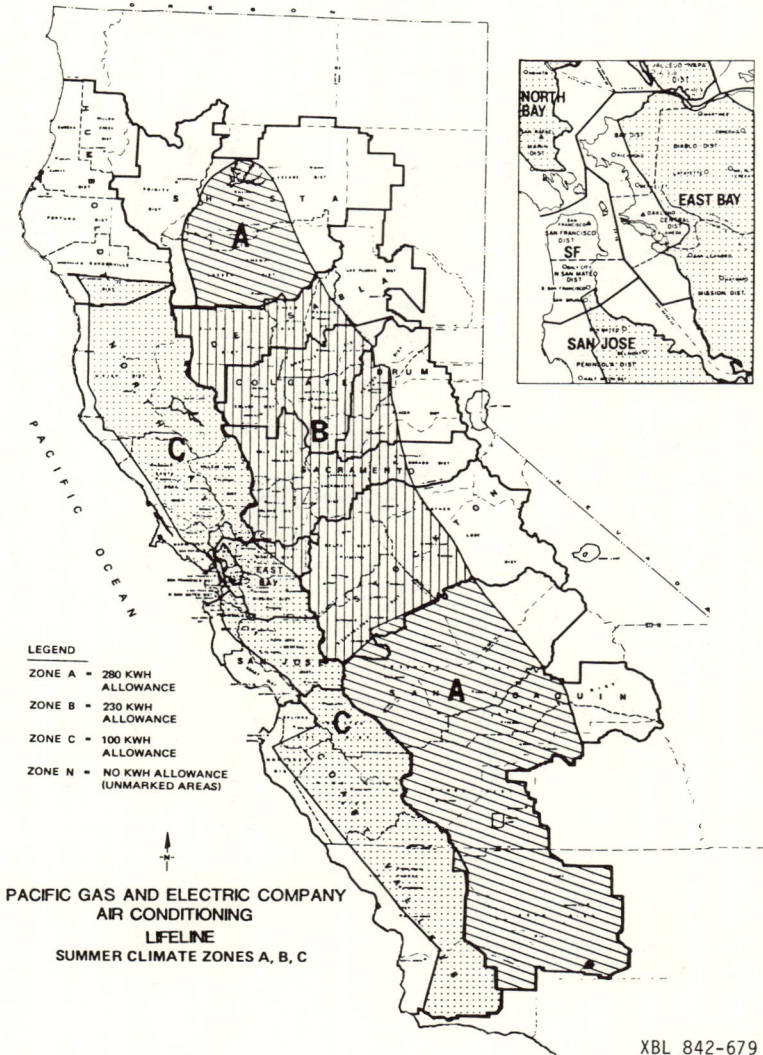

LEGEND

ZONE A = 280 KWH
         ALLOWANCE
ZONE B = 230 KWH
         ALLOWANCE
ZONE C = 100 KWH
         ALLOWANCE
ZONE N = NO KWH ALLOWANCE
         (UNMARKED AREAS)

PACIFIC GAS AND ELECTRIC COMPANY
AIR CONDITIONING
LIFELINE
SUMMER CLIMATE ZONES A, B, C

XBL 842-679

Figure 4-6b. Present air-conditioning and space-heating lifeline zones for Pacific Gas & Electric: map of summer climate zones.

(see Figure 4-6 a&b) and appliance holdings (B, C, H, and W). Since there are different allowances for summer and winter consumption, these are also treated separately. The Tier 1 allowances range from 240 to 1550 kWh per month.

The size of Tier 2 has been the subject of much dispute. The one rule that has been agreed upon is that the Tier 2 allowance would be the lesser of 300 kWh or 2/3 the size of the Tier 1 allowance.

Forecasting revenue for lifeline tariffs is not a trivial exercise. Total revenue for such a tariff is given by an expression of the form

$$\text{Revenue} = \left[\sum P_i \, F_i \right] \text{Sales} \qquad (4\text{-}10)$$

where

P_i = rate for Tier i,

and

F_i = fraction of total sales in Tier i.

The problematic part of Eq. (4-10) is forecasting F_i and total sales issued which are, in fact, connected. To provide an example of this problem with some degree of concreteness, we will examine a form of billing data known as the sales frequency distribution.

The sales frequency distribution is a way of figuring out what fraction of the kilowatt-hours bought by customers in a particular class fall into the first consumption tier, what portion into the second, and so on. We demonstrate the construction of this sales frequency in two examples, given in Table 4-11a. In the first, simpler example, we start with a distribution where each 10-kWh interval of consumption (given in column A) is represented by five customers. For instance, the consumption by the 20-kWh customers is the number of customers (five) multiplied by their consumption (20 kWh), and is given in the second line of column D. The same can be done for the customers at each interval, giving the total consumption by this class as 750 kWh.

The quantity in column E is closer to what we're after. It represents the number of kWh consumed that fell in the first, second, third, etc., 10 kWh of consumption. For a consumption level k_i, we find it by taking the total number of customers with bills of at least k_i, and multiply by the interval between consumption levels, in this case 10 kWh. For k_i = 30 kWh, we take the number of bills of 30 kWh or more (15 bills) and multiply by 10 kWh, to get 150 kWh, as appears on

Table 4-11a

Construction of Sales Frequency Density

Example 1: Uniform Bill Frequency

A	B	C	D	E	F
Interval	# of Bills	Cum Bill	(a)*(B)	(SUM-Cum)*10	(E)/SUM
10	5	5	50	250	0.33333
20	5	10	100	200	0.26667
30	5	15	150	150	0.20000
40	5	20	200	100	0.13333
50	5	25	250	50	0.06667
SUM			750	750	1.00000

Example 2: Lognormal Bill Frequency

A	B	C	D	E	
Interval	# of Bills	Cum Bill	(A)*(B)	(SUM-Cum)*10	(E)/SUM
10	1	1	10	4270	0.07582
20	3	4	60	4260	0.07564
30	9	13	270	4230	0.07511
40	15	28	600	4140	0.07351
50	20	48	1000	3990	0.07085
60	24	72	1440	3790	0.06729
70	26	98	1820	3550	0.06303
80	27	125	2160	3290	0.05842
90	27	152	2430	3020	0.05362
100	26	178	2600	2750	0.04883
110	24	202	2640	2490	0.04421
120	23	225	2760	2250	0.03995
130	22	247	2860	2020	0.03587
140	20	267	2800	1800	0.03196
150	19	286	2850	1600	0.02841
160	17	303	2720	1410	0.02504
170	15	318	2550	1240	0.02202
180	14	332	2520	1090	0.01935
190	13	345	2470	950	0.01687
200	12	357	2400	820	0.01456
210	11	368	2310	700	0.01243
220	10	378	2200	590	0.01048
230	9	387	2070	490	0.00870
240	8	395	1920	400	0.00710
250	7	402	1750	320	0.00568
260	6	408	1560	250	0.00444
270	5	413	1350	190	0.00337
280	4	417	1120	140	0.00249
290	3	420	870	100	0.00178
300	2	422	600	70	0.00124
310	2	424	620	50	0.00089
320	1	425	320	30	0.00053
330	1	426	330	20	0.00036
340	1	427	340	10	0.00018
SUM	427		56320	56320	1.00000

the third line of column E. The density is the fraction of total sales that fall into a particular interval, and is given in column F. Mathematically, we construct the following equation to find the density r:

N = total number of bills,
k_t = the number of bills with sales of at least t kWh/mo,
$\Delta k_{n,t}$ = $N - k_{t-n}$ for any integer n,

then

$$r(\Delta k_{n,t}) = \frac{n \, \Delta k_{n,t}}{\text{Total Sales}} \, . \qquad (4\text{-}11)$$

Notice that as t increases, k_t approaches zero. The higher the level, the lower the number of bills at or above that level.

Table 4-11b
Sales frequency density functions
Summer 1982
Pacific Gas and Electric

Single Family, Zone X, Summer Zones A,B, and C

	IXBS	AIXBS	BIXBS	CIXBS
40	.09300	.06843	.07723	.07294
80	.09170	.06769	.07607	.07255
120	.08870	.06634	.07403	.07162
200	.07921	.06159	.06771	.06767
280	.06701	.05470	.05944	.06116
320	.06046	.05088	.05499	.05721
360	.05383	.04700	.05046	.05301
400	.04733	.04313	.04597	.04858
440	.04105	.03935	.04152	.04407
520	.02981	.03233	.03316	.03512
600	.02095	.02624	.02590	.02796
680	.01442	.02119	.01991	.02043
840	.00684	.01393	.01165	.01138
1000	.00335	.00931	.00690	.00636
1200	.00148	.00575	.00367	.00322
1350	.00078	.00388	.00224	.00188
1550	.00041	.00248	.00129	.00105
Av. kWh.	426	576	510	545

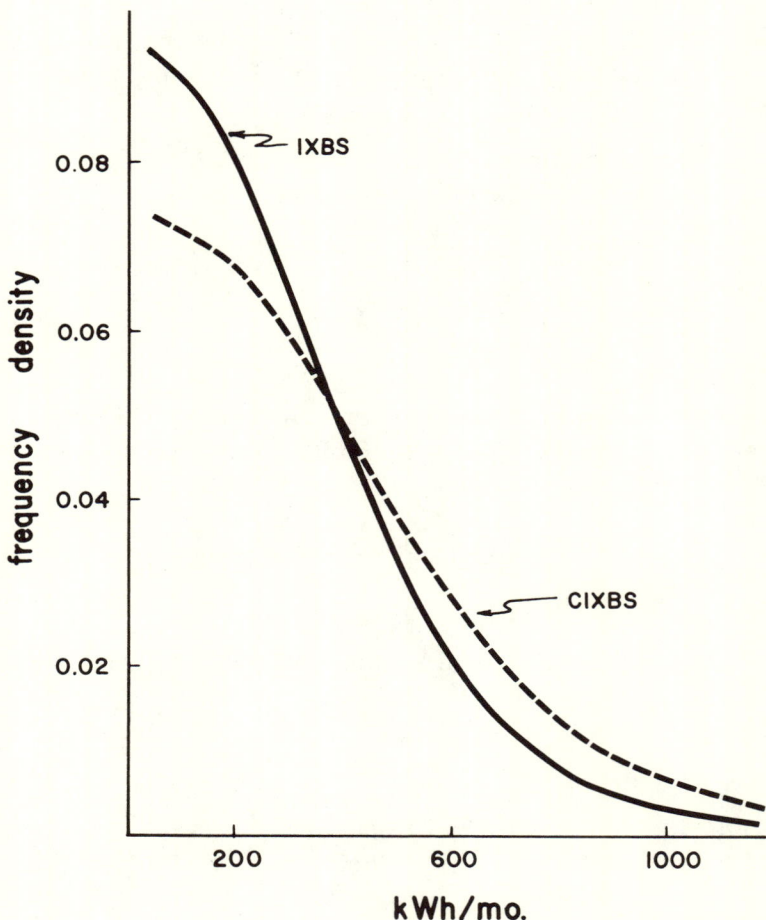

Figure 4-7. Graph of sales frequency density.

Since k_t approaches zero as t increases, so does $\Delta k_{n,t}$ for any n and therefore both $\Delta k_{n,t}$ and $r(\Delta k_{n,t})$ are monotonically declining. The second example in Table 4-11a shows the construction of the function $r(\Delta k_{n,t})$ for a more typical bill frequency distribution which is approximately log-normal. Table 4-11b and Figure 4-7 are examples of the function r for $n = 40$ kWh/mo corresponding to the total sales for these tariff schedules identified on Table 4-10 as Climate Zone X, Summer B, Air Conditioning Zones A, B, and C.

Table 4-12

Sales frequency cumulative distribution
Summer 1982
Pacific Gas and Electric

	IXBS	AIXBS	BIXBS	CIXBS
40	.0930	.0684	.0772	.0729
80	.1847	.1361	.1533	.1455
120	.2734	.2025	.2273	.2171
200	.4370	.3284	.3662	.3548
280	.5734	.4414	.4894	.4806
320	.6378	.4923	.5444	.5378
360	.6917	.5393	.5948	.5908
400	.7389	.5824	.6408	.6394
440	.7800	.6217	.6823	.6834
520	.8450	.6898	.7527	.7581
600	.8910	.7452	.8080	.8161
680	.9229	.7900	.8507	.8601
840	.9598	.8556	.9083	.9176
1000	.9776	.8991	.9422	.9496
1200	.9880	.9342	.9611	.9710
1350	.9918	.9512	.9764	.9798
1550	.9948	.9669	.9850	.9869

The density function r defined in Eq. (4-11) is used to define the term F_i in Eq. (4-10). This is done simply by transforming the density into a cumulative distribution function, which we will call C_i. Formally,

$$C_i = \sum_{t=o}^{i} r\,(\Delta k_{n,t})$$ (4-12)

where the summation is up to the consumption level i. We now let $t = a$ represent the boundary between Tiers 1 and 2 and $t = b$ between Tiers 2 and 3. Then we define

$$F_1 = C_a \quad ,$$

$$F_2 = C_b = C_a$$ (4-13)

and

$$F_3 = 1 - C_b \quad ,$$

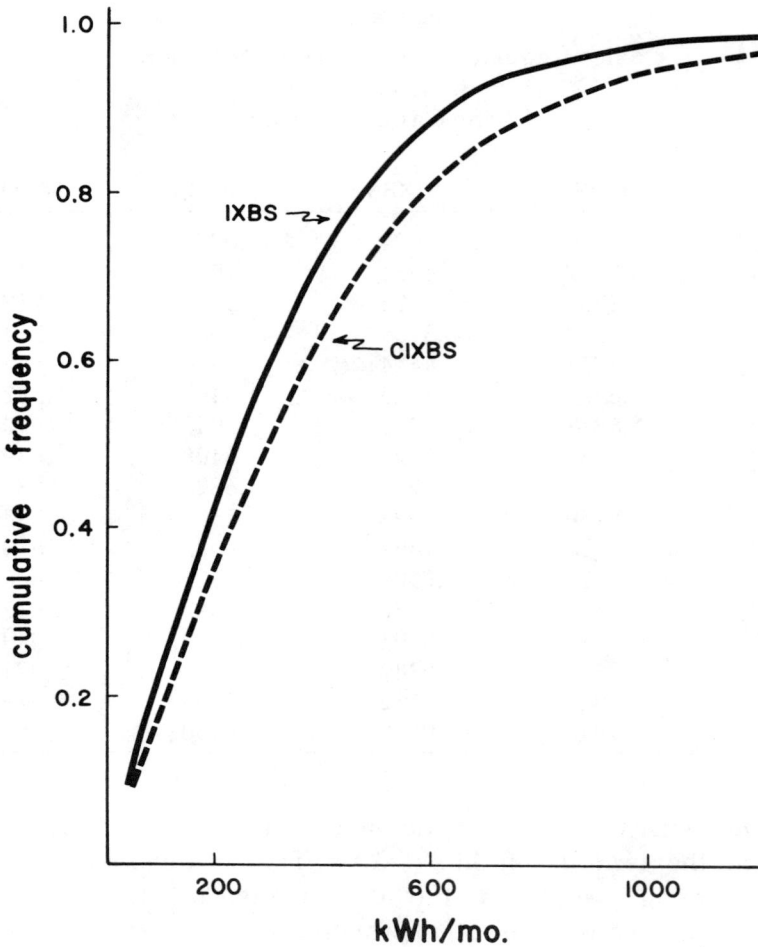

XBL 842-681

Figure 4-8. Graph of cumulative sales frequency distribution.

where each tier is identified as the appropriately numbered subscript.

In Table 4-12 we give selected values of the function C_i corresponding to the data in Table 4-11. Figure 4-8 is a graph of two of the tariff schedules represented in Table 4-12.

A basic property of sales frequency distributions is weather sensitivity. Both electricity and natural gas sales exhibit

Table 4-13

Cooling degree days in climate Zone X
May 1 to September 30

City	1982	1981	10-year Average
Stockton	1161	1685	1440
Sacramento	726	1162	1112
Fresno	1637	2281	1805

seasonality in their variation. At times of greater climatic extremes, residential consumers use more energy than at other times. The amount of seasonality varies with the climate and the stock of appliances. We can observe weather sensitivity cross-sectionally in Table 4-11b. Climate Zone X has hotter and cooler regions. Air-conditioning Zone A, for example, includes Fresno, which averages over 50% more cooling degree days than Sacramento, in Air Conditioning Zone B. Table 4-11b shows higher average use in A compared to B (576 vs. 510). This translates into a slightly different looking shape for the sales frequency density function. In general the relationships illustrated in Figure 4-7 hold. That is, the function describing frequency density for tariff classes with lower average sales have greater intercepts and slopes, but shorter tails than tariff classes with higher average sales.

The practical implications of weather sensitivity involve the time dimension. What conditions represent an appropriate average upon which to base allowances for average or minimal consumption? The 1982 data averages in Tables 4-10, 11, and 12 represent a cooler summer than the average of the late 1970s and early 1980s. Using cooling degree days between the beginning of May and the end of September (PG&E's Period A) we can see the variations for three cities in Climate Zone X in Table 4-13. It is clear from these data that 1982 was a cool year and would not be a reasonable choice on which to base an estimate of typical climate. 1981 appears to deviate from the average in the opposite direction; it was too hot. Nonetheless, it appears as if PG&E relied upon the 1981 data to set the baseline allowance levels that are being

Table 4-14
Summer 1981 sales frequency statistics
Climate Zone X

Tariff Schedule	Climate Zone Mean	Tariff Class Mean (kWh/mo)	55% of Cumulative Tariff Sales	Baseline
1XBS	479	473	305	375
A1XBS	773	712	569	500
B1XBS	709	615	399	500
C1XBS	611	593	356	375

proposed to replace the lifeline system of allowances. The work papers to PG&E's testimony on this subject contain some summary statistics on 1981 sales frequency distributions used to develop the baseline quantities. We reproduce some of this data in Table 4-14 along with the proposed baseline quantities for the tariff zones in question. Among other simplifications associated with baseline is the elimination of Tier 3, and the merging of some tariff classes to reduce the number of tariffs.

It is difficult to reconcile the data in Table 4-14 with public statements made about the nature of the baseline concept. The reform of lifeline represented by this change in tariff structure was intended to simplify and reduce the number of tariff classes. The legislation mandating these changes was designed to set the baseline quantity equal to 50-60% of average residential consumption in a given climate zone. The term "average" is ambiguous in this context, because sales frequency distributions are all highly skewed. This skew distribution is observed with enough regularity that one may generalize its occurrence in the following empirical rule:

Sales Frequency Skew Distribution:
The cumulative distribution of sales
(C_i) is approximately ($\pm 5\%$) equal to .75
at the mean level of consumption.   (4-14)

For all symmetric frequency distributions, $C_i = .50$ for $i =$ mean. In the case of sales frequency distributions, which are not typically symmetric, there are two possible interpretations of the term "average:" it may be understood as either the mean or the median (the point where C_i = .50) of the distribution. In PG&E's testimony on this subject, they interpreted the language of the statute to mean that Tier 1 should be set at the level corresponding to 55% of all sales in a given climate zone. This latter definition would appear to require the merging of tariff schedules within a climate zone (B with W and C with H) to produce a distribution from which the baseline amount would be calculated.

It is not clear from Table 4-14 what procedure was used to arrive at the Tier 1 baseline quantities. In some cases (e.g., BIXBS) they are above 55% of cumulative tariff class sales, in other cases (AIXBS) below. Although the baseline approach removes some of the arbitrariness and complexity of lifeline, it does not itself seem particularly transparent or consistent. Although elimination of the third tier would help utilities estimate revenue more accurately, there would still be problems in estimating the fraction of sales in each tier as a function of total sales. One of the principal residual difficulties lies in understanding how price effects associated with relative tier prices affect the distribution of sales. The nature of this problem, which we may call tier-specific price elasticity, will be illustrated with data from another context, that of Detroit Edison.

4.5.2 Conservation Effects of Inverted Rates: The Transition to Lifeline for Detroit Edison

When substantial changes occur in the rate structure, total sales will deviate from forecast sales. When rates go from a relatively flat structure to a severely inverted one, revenue collected will decrease from that predicted under a flat rate because consumption will decrease. A well-documented example of this phenomenon occurred in the transition to lifeline rates in September, 1981, for residential customers of Detroit Edison. The changes in tier sizes and prices are summarized in Table 4-15. The rate design rationale underlying Detroit Edison's lifeline structure does not distinguish climate variations or appliance holdings. Instead a principal distinction is made between households of one to two persons, and

Table 4-15
Residential tariffs
September 1981
Detroit Edison

	OLD		NEW	
		Block Size		
		1–2 persons/	3+ persons/	
Block Size	Price	household	household	Price
(kWh)	(c/kWh)	(kWh)	(kWh)	(c/kWh)
First 400 kWh	6.31	0–360	0–510	6.045
Next 400 kWh	6.91	360–630	510–810	8.89
Excess	7.61	631 +	811 +	11.82

those with three or more. These two customer classes are allowed different quantities in Tiers 1 and 2 as indicated in Table 4-15.

Due to the direction of the price changes, we would expect declines in the Tier 2 and 3 sales level and a slight increase in Tier 1. Moreover, the percentage decline should be larger in Tier 3 than Tier 2, since the percentage rate increase is roughly twice that in Tier 2. Quantitative assessment of these changes is difficult, however, because one must estimate what would have happened without the rate structure change. Detroit Edison Company has made such an analysis in an application to recover "lost revenue" due to the introduction of the inverted bloc rates (Michigan Public Service Commission Case No. U-6590-R, May, 1983). We will show how the utility makes this argument using sales frequency distribution data, and a particular method for adjusting these data.

The utility's position is summarized in Table 4-16 which shows how actual residential sales were spread over the old rate tiers, compared to how they would have been spread had consumption increased at the rate anticipated and lifeline had not been introduced. The first step in Detroit Edison's (DE) analysis is to predict the total sales without lifeline. This is done on a use-per-customer basis, normalized for weather and other exogenous factors such as regional employment. DE estimates use per customer before lifeline at 492

Table 4-16
Actual vs. estimated residential sales
(10³ kWh)

Tier	Sales w/Lifeline	Frac$_i$	Sales wo/Lifeline	Frac$_i$
0–400	5,568,481	.6827	5,622,102	.6679
401–800	1,942,665	.2382	2,072,788	.2463
801 +	645,033	.0791	722,205	.0858
Total	8,156,179		8,417,095	

Table 4-17
Detroit Edison ogive curve for lifeline analysis

Cumulative Sales Frequency Distribution (KWh/Month)	Cumulative	% Use Per Customer
40	.0798	
80	.1585	
120	.2353	
280	.5084	
320	.5656	
360	.6179	.727
400	.6653	.808
440	.7077	.888
480	.7454	.969
520	.7785	1.050
560	.8073	1.131
600	.8323	1.212
640	.8537	1.292
680	.8722	1.373
720	.8879	1.454
760	.9014	1.535
800	.9129	1.616
840	.9228	1.697
880	.9313	
920	.9386	
960	.9448	
1000	.9503	

kWh/month and after lifeline at 476 kWh/mo. This difference, multiplied by the number of customers, produces the
261 million kWh sales loss that appears in Table 4-16. The
next problem is to spread these sales estimates over the rate
tiers.

DE relies upon the cumulative sales frequency distribution
shown in the first column of Table 4-17. The average
kWh/mo. of this distribution is 495.3. The column labeled
Percentage Use Per Customer indicates what fraction of this
average Use Per Customer corresponds to each sales level.
To adjust the distribution for a different level of average use
per customer, the following approximation is used. The original or base sales frequency distribution is retained, but the
tier boundaries are adjusted to produce new sales fractions for
each tier. The adjustment is made by a proportional change
in Percentage Use Per Customer (UPC), which is then
translated into a new cumulative fraction. Formally this procedure amounts to:

$$UPC_n = \frac{M_b}{M_n} UPC_o \quad , \qquad (4\text{-}15)$$

and

$$D_n = \sum_{i=0}^{n} UPC_i \qquad (4\text{-}16)$$

where

M_b = mean use per customer of *base* sales frequency,

M_n = mean use per customer of the *new* sales forecast,

UPC_o = fraction of average use corresponding to the upper
           boundary of the tier in the *base* distribution,

UPC_n = fraction of average use corresponding to the upper
           boundary of the tier for the *new* forecast sales level,

D_n = cumulative distribution function, i.e., Eq. (4-12).

The logic of this procedure is illustrated by our example.
Consider the case in which M_n is less than M_b, i.e., average
use declines. We know from considering sales frequency
curves that this means that a greater fraction of sales will
occur in Tier 1. To represent this increase, we raise the upper

boundary of the tier. This is equivalent to shifting the curve downwards. The amount we raise the tier boundary is proportional to the ratio of the base sales frequency mean and the new expected mean. Conversely, when M_n exceeds M_b we want to decrease the Tier 1 fraction, which is what Eqs. (4-15) and (4-16) will achieve.

This procedure represents the traditional method of estimating revenue changes given non-linear rate schedules, based on empirical estimates made in the 1930s (Hanks, 1934 and Zuck, 1936). A detailed description can be found in the American Gas Association's *Gas Rate Manual*. More modern mathematical treatments can be found in Liittschwager (1971) or Kahn and Levy (1982).

4.6 Avoided Costs

The concept of avoided cost was introduced formally in the federal Public Utilities Regulatory Policy Act of 1978 (P.L. 95-617), known as PURPA for short. PURPA requires that state regulatory commissions establish tariffs under which electric utilities will purchase power from certain kinds of private producers known as Qualifying Facilities (QFs). Such tariffs are designed so that consumers will be unaffected by these transactions, i.e., there will be no change in revenue requirements as a result of QF sales. Congress delegated to FERC (the Federal Energy Regulatory Commission) authority to set regulations for the implementation of these principles by the states.

Most of the concepts and issues that appear in the context of marginal cost also arise in the context of avoided cost. Indeed, avoided cost may be thought of as a specialized subset of marginal cost — those costs that would be incurred but for the purchase of QF power. In the case of Transmission & Distribution Demand Data (T&D) costs, marginal T&D costs clearly exist and can be estimated (however crudely), but no T&D costs are likely to be avoided by small power production. There may be some changes in the utilization of the T&D system as a result of small power purchases, but on the average use cannot be expected to decrease. Therefore there should be no T&D component in avoided cost prices.

Energy costs are clearly avoided by utility purchase of QF power. The relevant cost is the short-run marginal energy cost, so long as QF output represents only a very small resource. As long as costs are examined on a year-by-year basis and any change in conditions can be corrected by a revised energy value, then marginal cost can be a reliable reflection of the avoided energy value. As we have seen, however, long run expectations about future energy costs are subject to uncertainty and revision (recall Tables 4-1 and 4-2).

This uncertainty creates an important problem for QFs because they need to have assurances about the future price of their output. To finance a QF project, there must be reliable information about future revenues. PURPA does not require utilities to make binding projections of future avoided costs; only to publish tariffs for current prices. Like any other rate, these tariffs can change as conditions change. The issue of long-run energy avoided costs is a complicated one, and is the subject of ongoing adjudication before the state regulatory commissions. Before examining these issues in detail, it is useful to consider the treatment of avoided generation-capacity costs and their translation into QF payments.

It is important to note in valuing capacity that the value changes from year to year. For example, Fiske's marginal cost study assigns an annual dollar value to generation capacity. This value is a function of both the cost of a gas turbine in that year, and the need for capacity (measured by the ERI) in that year. In California, QFs have been offered payment for the generation capacity aspect of their output on either an as-available basis or on a specified contract term basis. In the former case, the capacity is given a time-of-use allocation according to the relative LOLP (Fiske, Table 1-27). This allocation spreads the annual value over costing periods. Let us calculate the 1984 Period A capacity payment for on-peak delivery on an as-available basis:

Period A On Peak as Available

$$= \frac{(\$/kW - yr)^* \text{Allocation Factor}}{\text{On Peak Period A (Hours/yr) Capacity}}$$

$$= \frac{(\$31)^*(.689)}{636} \, ,$$

$$= \$0.0336/kWh \quad . \tag{4-17}$$

California utilities also offer long-term capacity contracts. In this case payment is made on a levelized annual cost basis subject to certain performance standards. Let us first focus on the levelized annual capacity value. You will recall from Table 4-2 that PG&E's shortage cost (i.e., capacity value of generation) estimated in the 1982 General Rate Case increases significantly after 1990. To reflect this increase the annual values can be levelized over the term of the contract. As long as the discount rate is the utility's cost of capital, ratepayers will be indifferent to the levelization. Table 4-18 summarizes these calculations. Table 4-19 illustrates the method for one particular circumstance, a ten-year contract starting in 1984.

The calculations in Table 4-19 use the definition of level cost Eqs. (2-26) and (2-27) and the definition of CRF (Eq. 2-21). The value reported in Table 4-19 differs from that in Table 4-18 by about 10%.

Once a levelized capacity payment has been determined as a function of project start date and contract length, a payment procedure must be determined. The basic problem is to specify a performance standard which will be sufficient to warrant payment. The CPUC has accepted the 80% capacity factor standard. This means that QF output in a given month must be 80% of its maximum under the contract to receive that month's capacity payment. There are small adjustments to this formula for maintenance. Further, there is a bonus for performance above 85% and reductions for less than 80%.

Because levelization involves overpayments in the early years of a capacity contract, provision has been made to have the QF refund payments if contract capacity must be reduced. This is only fair to ratepayers, who are ultimately the party at

Table 4-18

Firm capacity price schedule
(Levelized $/kW year)

Pacific Gas and Electric Company

Contract Life

Operating Date Year	1	2	3	4	5	6	7	8	9	10	11	12	13	14	15	20	25	30
1984	28	31	31	30	30	31	34	40	46	50	54	58	61	64	67	77	84	89
1985	34	33	31	31	32	35	43	50	55	59	63	67	70	73	75	86	93	99
1986	33	29	29	32	36	46	53	59	64	69	73	76	79	82	85	95	103	109
1987	24	27	31	37	49	58	65	71	76	80	84	87	90	93	96	107	114	120
1988	30	36	42	58	68	76	82	87	91	95	99	102	105	108	110	121	129	135
1989	43	51	71	82	90	96	101	105	109	112	115	118	121	124	126	137	144	151

Table 4-19

**PG&E ten-year levelized capacity
Contract price ($/kW)**

Year	Shortage Cost	PV (at 13.5%)
84	31	27
85	38	29
86	36	25
87	26	16
88	34	18
89	47	22
90	64	26
91	131	48
92	140	45
93	147	41

$$\text{Level Cost} = \text{CRF}(10, 13.5) \times \sum PV$$
$$= .188 \times 297$$
$$= \$55$$

financial risk in levelized capacity payments. If too much has been paid for QF capacity delivered, the loss does not accrue to utility stockholders, who are un-involved with the transaction. The basic dynamics of this situation are paralleled in the ongoing CPUC hearings concerning long-run contracts for energy produced by QFs.

The basis for levelized capacity payments is the gas-turbine proxy for the social cost of shortages. A commonly proposed analogy for long-term energy contracts is the coal plant proxy. In this case it is argued that the economic costs of a coal plant are less than the discounted sum of future avoided costs. Formally, the assertion is

$$\text{PV}\begin{bmatrix} \text{Coal} \\ \text{Busbar Cost} \end{bmatrix} < \sum \text{PV}\begin{bmatrix} \text{Avoided} \\ \text{Costs} \end{bmatrix} . \qquad \textbf{(4-18)}$$

Notice that this is similar to the argument used by Fiske to assert that the net resource cost term of Eq. (4-5) is less than zero for a coal plant. Supposing that Eq. (4-18) is satisfied, its importance lies in the different timing of cash flows. Since busbar cost is a levelized (or largely levelized) cost, it will start out at a value above year 1 avoided energy cost, assuming that avoided energy cost increases. But the only way Eq. (4-18) can be true is for avoided energy cost to increase over time.

Now suppose we accept this argument and decide that long-term energy contracts should be priced using the coal plant proxy. As with capacity contracts, price should increase monotonically with contract term length. Now suppose a QF contracts under this basis for a 25-year term. If this QF ceases production at any time before the 25 years are up, the ratepayers will lose some amount of overpayment. Why is this more serious than the analogous situation with levelized capacity contracts? The answer lies in the larger magnitude of the costs involved, and the relative seriousness of the failure to live up to contract terms.

Let us consider the failure to deliver contract capacity. Such failures do not imply that the QF project has ceased production totally. Instead it may just be that output is not produced at the appropriate time. In this event, the QF will still be receiving energy payments, and capacity refunds may be subtracted from that revenue. Furthermore the magnitude of capacity payments relative to avoided energy costs is rather modest. One kilowatt of capacity, operating 60% of the year, will generate $262.80 at $0.05/kWh. The corresponding capacity payments through 1990 are never more than 25% of that amount. Therefore the risk to ratepayers is small for capacity compared to energy. Conversely, long-term energy contracts based on the coal plant proxy place considerable risk on the ratepayers. This is the reason that the proposal is controversial.

The long-run avoided-energy cost question takes us outside the domain of rate-making with its traditional focus on short-run issues, and introduces resource planning questions. These questions are inevitable under the changing cost structure of the utility industry, but cannot be accommodated easily to the framework of a general rate case, where the basic task is to define tariffs for consumers. In the chapters which follow, we will undertake a more systematic investigation into marginal and avoided cost definition, and explore the resource planning choices facing the electric utilities. Rate-making issues will inevitably arise in this context as well.

Chapter **5**

Marginal and Avoided Cost

In Chapter 4 we addressed the definition of marginal cost primarily from the perspective of rate design. This perspective does not require a very high degree of precision, because the information is only used in a qualitative sense. But new applications of marginal cost and related concepts have begun to pervade the resource planning process. As new kinds of alternatives are evaluated by planners and regulators, their marginal impact on the utility's cost structure becomes important. We will explore the use of these concepts in the economic evaluation of privately owned independent power production facilities in Chapter 6 and demand-side interventions in Chapter 7. Compared to rate design, both of these applications require a longer-range view in which the distinction between short-run and long-run marginal cost becomes important. Resource planning applications of marginal cost concepts also tend to involve a more detailed specification of the cost structure — how the cost varies with time and with the amount consumed. System constraints are important and linkages among various cost elements also play an increasingly important role. In this chapter we provide a general discussion of marginal energy and capacity cost and the related notion of avoided cost (discussed briefly in Chapter 4). To illustrate the practical problems of calculation of capacity and avoided costs, we will conclude with general discussion of production cost simulation models.

5.1 Definitions

Implementing practical definitions of marginal cost requires that we pay attention to the distinction between "small" and "large" marginal changes. This distinction is related to but different from the traditional economist's distinction between short-run and long-run marginal costs. The short run is defined as that period of time in which marginal changes in demand cause only changes in the utilization pattern existing capacity: short run is the period during which capacity can be treated as fixed. At some point it becomes economical to expand capacity. This point is defined as the point of transition to the long run. To provide background for these concepts, it will be useful to review our discussion of the economics of generation capacity expansion again, explicitly invoking marginal cost concepts. This is the subject of Section 5. 2 below.

Although the transition from the short-run to the long-run perspective involves changes which are intuitively "large," it is often necessary to consider changes that do not involve the short- to long-run transition but are still large in some appropriate sense. The essential point here is that even in the short run, the cost structure can exhibit discontinuities. While most textbooks treat marginal costs as infinitesimal changes, usually expressed by writing derivatives of cost functions that are assumed to be continuous, this treatment is not appropriate where cost discontinuities in the short run exist. Indeed, our discussion of production cost models in Section 5.3 will show that such discontinuities generally occur.

The term "avoided cost" has no history in the economics literature, but was invented in the legislative arena. It was coined in the Public Utilities Regulatory Policy Act (PURPA) of 1978, which opened the electricity market to private unregulated production. PURPA set down some general guidelines for pricing this electricity, stipulating that utilities should pay a price equal to the costs they would avoid by making a purchase of privately-generated power. In one set of circumstances, this avoided cost would be reasonably identical with the infinitesimal short-run marginal cost. At the opposite extreme, avoided cost could be identified with the long-run marginal costs of expanding capacity. There is a very large range in between these two extremes. In Section 5.4 we examine this range and discuss the transitions between the extremely different characterizations of avoided cost.

To narrow the field of inquiry as much as possible, we will ignore transmission and distribution, and will focus exclusively on the power generation system, distinguishing between generation capacity (or system shortage) costs and energy (or production) costs. As Chapter 4 indicated, there are other costs that are sometimes considered in marginal analysis. Indeed, the total cost of electricity can be divided into a demand-related component, an energy-related component, and a customer-related component. This same functionalization applies, in principle, to marginal costs. In most resource planning applications of marginal cost concepts, the customer-related costs are not relevant and can be neglected. Among the demand-related costs, distribution system costs and for the most part, transmission system costs, are typically neglected. There are logical and practical reasons for this. Logically, neither customer cost nor distribution costs change due to the resource alternatives that are being considered. While in some cases there may be transmission costs associated with a particular project, these can be accounted for including them in the general category of other project costs. As a practical matter the estimation of marginal customer and distribution demand costs is extremely difficult and subject to great uncertainty. Therefore since it is difficult to have confidence in the methods and there is little need for the estimates, it is best to neglect these elements.

5.2 Capacity Expansion and Long-Run Marginal Cost

The textbook illustration of optimal capacity expansion is shown in Figure 5-1. It consists of a set of marginal and average cost curves as a function of increasing demand for power. As output increases from the level Q_A, cost increases along the short-run marginal cost curve $SRMC_1$, and the short-run average cost curve $SRAC_1$. A new resource addition will lower marginal costs to the curve $SRMC_2$. This reflects

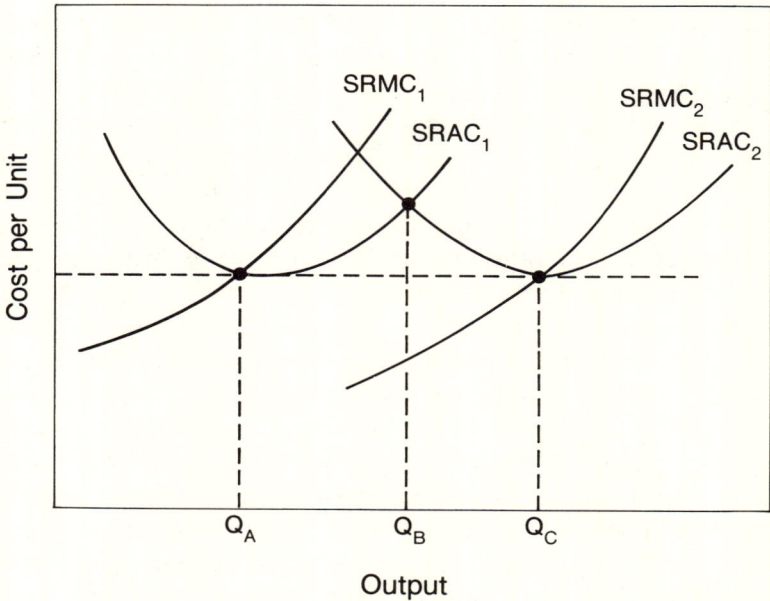

XBL 886-9691

Figure 5-1. Optimal timing of resource additions. (Cost is in $/kWh and output is in kWh.)

the operating cost savings due to the addition of a new plant. From the viewpoint of total or average cost, however, these economies are offset by the fixed costs of the new resource. For output marginally above Q_A the fixed costs dominate. This is shown by the short-run average cost curve $SRAC_2$. $SRAC_2$ declines as output increases, but it is still above $SRAC_1$ until the demand increases to the point we have labeled Q_B. At Q_B average costs decline along $SRAC_2$ but continue to rise along $SRAC_1$. This means that Q_B is the optimal output level for adding a new resource. At this level average costs would be the same whether or not the new resource is added, but marginal costs would be sharply lower. As output increases beyond Q_B, the average cost would decrease and marginal cost would increase. The output level Q_C corresponds to the point Q_A.

Figure 5-1 suppresses many details of the capacity expansion decision. Reliability or shortage costs at the generation level are not explicitly represented. Nothing is indicated about the operational characteristics of the new capacity that is added. Is it "base load" or "peaking" or something in between (recall the discussion surrounding Figure 3-8.) Also, the time dimension is ignored. The operational economies induced by new capacity are realized over many years and these long-term economies are needed to pay for the added fixed costs. Under standard rate-making procedures in which capital costs are depreciated over time, rate increases do not coincide with the realization of operational economies for several reasons: first as depreciation accumulates, the plant's revenue requirements diminish, even though it is still allowing the system to function more efficiently; second, as load continues to grow, the capacity will be used during a greater fraction of the year, increasing its load factor and thus the operational economies it offers; and third, rising fuel costs will increase the economies provided by a new generating unit that uses less (or cheaper) fuel to generate electricity than the older units. This mismatch is indicated to some degree in Figure 5-1 by the declining short-run average cost curves, $SRAC_1$ and $SRAC_2$. These curves show average costs declining as output increases. These output increases can be thought of as occurring over time; that is, as reflecting a load growth trend. Despite its limitations Figure 5-1 does suggest what the short-run marginal cost pattern would look like over time. It is essentially a repeating "saw-tooth" characterized by gradually increasing levels over time followed by discontinuous drops at the point where new facilities are added in discrete lumps of capacity.

Given a picture such as Figure 5-1, it is natural to ask how the definition of long-run marginal cost can be incorporated into this general framework. The simple answer is that long-run marginal cost is just the cost of the new facility that is added when the system is expanded. While this is correct as far as it goes, it does not give the whole picture.

Figure 5-1 suppresses the substantial uncertainties associated with the timing of resource additions. If we knew future fuel costs and demands with certainty, then it would be straightforward to solve the resource addition timing problem. When the present-value of the fixed costs of a new resource become exactly equal to its fuel savings and reliability benefits, then it would be optimal to add it to the supply system (this is the meaning of Eq. 4-5). However, because the future price of fuels and demand cannot be known with certainty, the correct time to add a new resource is very difficult to judge. The definitive answer can only be known many years after the fact, long after such knowledge would have been useful for planning. The only practical procedure is to make decisions based on the best available information about the uncertain variables and on one's tolerance of risk. As the discussion in Chapter 3 indicated, large-scale and long-lead-time projects increase the risk of error.

If we assume that the timing of future resource additions is optimal, then it is reasonable to use the costs of the next plant as a proxy for long-run marginal cost. (If a particular resource were added too early, its costs would overestimate the long-run marginal cost, because its costs would be nearer in time and therefore discounted less.) The costs of the marginal facility consist of the total revenue requirements associated with the capital and operations of the plant. This is essentially the busbar cost defined in Section 2.5 above. To divide these total costs between long-run marginal energy and capacity costs it is necessary to specify some allocation procedures.

There are two kinds of allocations involving the capital costs of the marginal facility. First, there is the question of whether the capital costs are all representative of capacity or shortage costs. Second, and independent of the answer given to the first question, is how to allocate the capital costs over time. In discussing the competing views on these allocation questions, a significant part of this discussion will draw on literature developed to formulate long-run prices for private power producers under the assumption that they avoid new power plant construction.

Allocating the capital costs of new facilities to capacity and energy is particularly important when the facility involved is a capital-intensive resource such as a base load coal plant. One theory used in making this allocation is the "energy-related capital" (ERC) approach. This theory states that the extra capital costs of a coal plant beyond the cost necessary to build a combustion turbine should all be allocated to energy. The rationale for this allocation is that the marginal cost of capacity in the long run is just the lowest-cost technology required to meet peak loads, which is typically a combustion turbine. Choosing to invest beyond this level is justified not on capacity grounds, but on energy grounds. That is, the extra capital cost of a coal plant allows the utility to use a low-cost fuel and avoid higher-cost fuels. The ERC method has been adopted by the California Public Utilities Commission for pricing private power in the long run (CPUC, 1986). Arguments in favor of this method were reviewed in Chapter 4; additional discussion can be found in NERA (1977).

The theory contrary to ERC is simply an allocation of all capital costs to capacity. This position is not without advocates, but it does lack an easily articulated rationale. It has been adopted in Texas, again in the context of implementing PURPA pricing rules. In the Texas case, an argument can be made that peak load periods are so long in duration that combustion turbines are not the cheapest method of satisfying capacity requirements. By recalling the "screening curve" illustrated in Figure 3-8, it can be seen that a "flat" load curve might argue against low-capital-cost technologies to meet peak requirements. Such arguments are specific to individual circumstances. In a region such as Texas with long air-conditioning seasons and substantial winter peak requirements, they might be appropriate.

However the capital costs of the marginal plant are allocated between energy and capacity, their allocation over time is also an issue. Traditional rate-making practice creates a declining pattern as the rate base depreciates. Replicating this pattern in PURPA pricing schedules is unattractive to utilities for a number of reasons. The PURPA producer may not supply power for the same period as the utility would have generated power in its avoided plant, and the private producer certainly lacks the industry's regulatory constraints (such as the obligation to serve).

An alternative pattern for allocating capital costs over time is based on a theory known as the "economic carrying charge

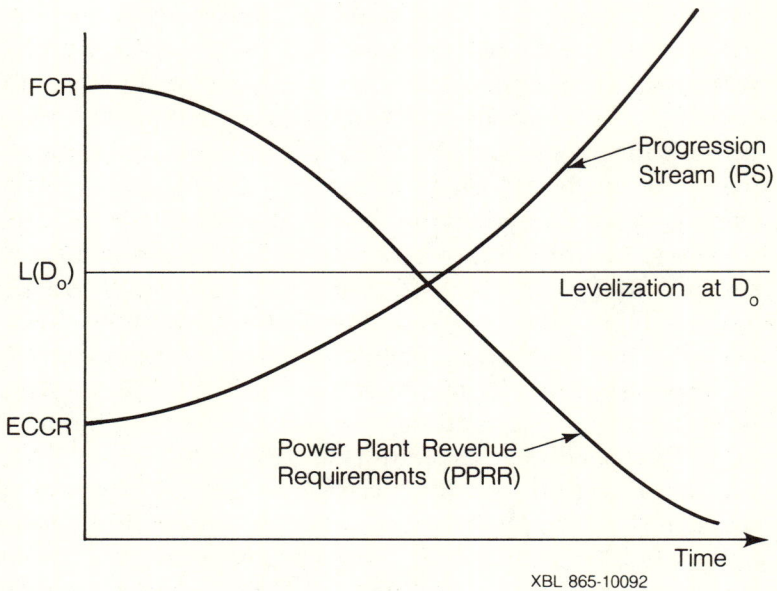

XBL 865-10092

Figure 5-2. Economic carrying charge rate, levelization, and present rate. (FCR = fixed-charge rate, L(D$_o$) = levelized rate at discount rate of D$_o$, and ECCR = economic carrying charge rate.)

rate" (ECCR). This method is illustrated in Figure 5-2 in comparison with the traditional rate-basing approach and the levelization concept discussed in Chapter 2. The ECCR method of allocating capital costs over time produces a stream of payments that increase at a constant rate. The present value of this stream is intended to be identical with the present value of the levelized stream or the revenue requirements stream. The rate of escalation associated with the ECCR method is usually the anticipated rate of inflation. In some versions of this method, adjustments in the rate of escalation are made for tax effects or anticipated technical progress. The basic rationale for the ECCR approach is an effort to simulate competitive market outcomes under conditions of inflation.

In competitive markets the price charged by a firm does not depend on the age of the facility producing a given product, but rate-making based on declining revenue requirements over time does impose such age-dependent prices. A move in the direction of marginal cost pricing must eliminate the accounting conventions of regulation and approximate conditions in which prices are set by market forces. In a market without inflation, it is reasonable to expect stable prices for all products over time except for the effect of technical progress. Under these conditions a levelized price would adequately reflect the indifference of the market to the age of production facilities. Inflationary expectations alter market pricing dynamics. The best way to consider this effect is to examine the costs of entering a given market over time. A producer entering a market at a later date will expect to pay more for equipment and have higher costs of production than a producer who purchased equipment earlier. If the later entrant is the marginal producer, then its costs determine the market price. In such a scenario, the market price for the product will rise over time. The rate of increase will be at the rate of inflation.

This scenario illustrates the economic rationale for the ECCR method. Capital cost recovery for investment in a facility is constant in real dollar terms, but increases in nominal dollars to account for general price level escalation. For this reason the ECCR method is sometimes referred to as the "real carrying charge" method. To implement it, one develops the present value revenue requirements for a facility in the standard manner and then computes the first-year value under ECCR by using the weighted average cost of capital (WACC) minus the inflation rate as the carrying charge. The revenue requirement in every subsequent year is escalated at the inflation rate. (See Table 5-1 for an example.)

The ECCR method has also been used to provide a more operational characterization of the transition from short-run marginal cost to long-run marginal cost. This transition is particularly important in the estimation of avoided-cost prices for PURPA producers. Figure 5-1 shows this transition very abstractly. The time dimension is not explicit in this representation, and the indifference point in short-run average cost, i.e., the intersection of the SRAC curves, contains no information on the issue of how to count the fixed costs of

Table 5-1

Present value revenue requirements

Rate of Return = 0.11 Year 1 Value of Progression Stream From NERA
Escalation Rate = 0.04
Total = Return + Depreciation

| Year | Revenue Requirement | | | Economic Carrying Charge Rate Progression Stream |
	Return	Depreciation	Total	
Example 1				
1	0.1100	0.1000	0.2100	0.1462
2	0.0990	0.1000	0.1990	0.1521
3	0.0880	0.1000	0.1880	0.1582
4	0.0770	0.1000	0.1770	0.1645
5	0.0660	0.1000	0.1660	0.1711
6	0.0550	0.1000	0.1550	0.1779
7	0.0440	0.1000	0.1440	0.1850
8	0.0330	0.1000	0.1330	0.1924
9	0.0220	0.1000	0.1220	0.2001
10	0.0110	0.1000	0.1110	0.2081
	Present Value		1.00000	1.00000
Example 2				
1	0.1100	0.0500	0.1600	0.0961
2	0.1045	0.0500	0.1545	0.1000
3	0.0990	0.0500	0.1490	0.1040
4	0.0935	0.0500	0.1435	0.1081
5	0.0880	0.0500	0.1380	0.1125
6	0.0825	0.0500	0.1325	0.1170
7	0.0770	0.0500	0.1270	0.1216
8	0.0715	0.0500	0.1215	0.1265
9	0.0660	0.0500	0.1160	0.1316
10	0.0605	0.0500	0.1105	0.1368
11	0.0550	0.0500	0.1050	0.1423
12	0.0495	0.0500	0.0995	0.1480
13	0.0440	0.0500	0.0940	0.1539
14	0.0385	0.0500	0.0885	0.1601
15	0.0330	0.0500	0.0830	0.1665
16	0.0275	0.0500	0.0775	0.1731
17	0.0220	0.0500	0.0720	0.1800
18	0.0165	0.0500	0.0665	0.1872
19	0.0110	0.0500	0.0610	0.1947
20	0.0220	0.0500	0.0720	0.1800
	Present Value		1.0000	1.0000

$$\text{Year 1 value} = (r-i)\left[1-\left[\frac{1+i}{1+r}\right]^{N}\right]^{-1}$$

the new resource in making this comparison. The ECCR
method provides a procedure for assessing more concretely
the optimal timing of resource additions. We can use the
economic carrying charge rate as part of a single-year test that
approximates the multi-year optimality test presented in the
previous chapter, in which we compared the present value of
the stream of fixed charges with the present value of the
operating savings and of the reliability gains. The fixed costs

of a resource addition in its first year of operation can be compared to its estimated production cost savings. If the production cost savings equal the fixed costs as measured with ECCR, then it is cost-effective to add the new resource at once. The California PUC has adopted this approach to developing long-run price offers for private producers (CPUC, 1986).

This approach is still an approximation to a detailed multi-year optimization. Passing the first year cost-effectiveness test using ECCR will result in life-cycle cost savings if the cost of fuels increases faster than the rate of inflation. Under these fuel price conditions, it would actually be economic to install the new resource before it passed the first-year test. It is also possible that load growth alone would cause production cost savings to increase over time as the added resource displaces an increasing quantity of costly fuels. In these cases the problem of finding the best time to add new resources can only be tackled with a complex optimization program.

It is increasingly common to avoid such programs and separate the analysis of the fixed costs and production economies of new resources into discrete stages. This separation makes it easier to focus on the two sides of the analysis without worrying about whether a particular computer program is treating both sides of the issue adequately. There are sufficiently many problems involved in estimating production cost to have inspired a proliferation of models and calculation techniques. Production cost simulations are now being used to estimate marginal costs in both the short and long run and to calculate avoided costs for PURPA producers. Given the increasing importance of this kind of modelling, it is useful to develop some perspective on these models and the use made of them. In the next section we survey this field.

5.3 Production Cost Models

In Section 4.2 we gave a brief glimpse of how marginal energy costs can be developed from a production simulation model using the load duration curve technique. It is useful to put this approach in a larger perspective by characterizing the modelling process more completely, including its inherent lim-

itations and the methodological choices available to practitioners. The discussion will be organized in three parts. First, in
Section 5.3.1 we review the features available in various
models and evaluate their strengths and weaknesses. Second,
in Section 5.3.2 we address the critical issue of simplified
versus detailed models. It is always possible to increase the
complexity of simulation in the hope of achieving greater realism. The cost of this is an often substantial increase in the
pragmatic difficulty of using the model. This trade-off is ubiquitous, and must be faced explicitly by model users. Finally,
in Section 5.3.3 we address the use of modelling techniques to
analyze different problems of interest to planners and regulators.

5.3.1 Review of Features and Their Evaluation

The modern period of power system simulation modelling
began with an explicit treatment of the random nature of generator performance. The goal of the simulation was to
account for forced outages of generating units and to calculate
an expected value of production cost and performance. Thus
the simulations were inherently probabilistic. This makes
them difficult, in principle, to test against reality, since in the
real world events represent a discrete set of particular outcomes of a random process, while the models calculate an
average or expected outcome. To cope with the desire for
assurance of realism, modellers steadily increased the complexity of their representations. In this section we describe
the tension between the desirability of added representational
complexity and the need for computational economy.

Monte Carlo Chronological Models vs. Equivalent Load.
The earliest technique of probabilistic simulation was the
Monte Carlo Chronological Model. Computationally very
intensive, it involves a large number of deterministic simulations which reproduce the dispatch of utility resources under
assumed conditions on the outage status of individual generating units. To account for all possible outages and produce
an expected value, a large number of "draws," sometimes as
many as a thousand individual cases, are required. The computational burden of Monte Carlo makes it difficult to vary
too extensively the resource mix examined. This lack of flexi-

bility inspired the introduction of the equivalent load technique.

The equivalent load technique is based on a non-chronological load representation. By rearranging hourly loads for a given period in a monotonically declining order, the demand for power can be interpreted using probabilities instead of chronological scenarios. This places demand on the same conceptual basis as the randomly available supply, and allows a computationally efficient procedure for dispatching generation against load. The equivalent load is the load requirement facing a given unit after considering the dispatch of all previous units against load requirements and the "outage loads" created by the random failure of those previous units. This technique was introduced by Balerieux and associates in Belgium and Booth in Australia in the late 1960s and early 1970s (Balerieux et al., 1967 and Booth, 1971). It quickly won acceptance among utility practitioners. The great advantage was that computational efficiency allowed evaluation of multiple resource scenarios.

The equivalent load approach has dominated production simulation until quite recently. Constant improvements in computational efficiency and power, however, have eroded the pragmatic justification for the equivalent load procedure. Concerns about the chronological constraints on power system operation have brought attention back to the hourly framework. Among the models which adopt the chronological framework are EPRI's BENCHMARK, TVA'S POWRSYM, General Electric's MAPPS, and Decision Focus' LMSTM.

One of the unique aspects of LMSTM is its "smart" approach to Monte Carlo simulation. Instead of relying on a large number of random draws to produce the outage distribution, it selects a small number of cases based on an intelligent sampling from the outage distribution. The outage distribution is represented analytically, in a manner discussed below, and this representation allows accurate characterization of the outage states with only a small number of direct simulations (Stremel and Bubb, 1985). An alternative approach used by other chronological models is to drop Monte Carlo entirely and treat the outages in each hour as independent events. This simplifies computation, but loses the interdependence of chronological events that these models are designed to capture, such as the probable length of generator outages or the length of time between the deposit and withdrawal of energy in a pumped storage facility.

Analytic Approximation Techniques. A major part of the probabilistic aspect of production simulation involves characterizing the outage distribution. The brute force approach involves the explicit enumeration of all possible outage states and their probabilities. The equivalent load procedure makes this enumeration implicitly and iteratively, accounting for a good part of its efficiency. An alternative approach can be found by appealing to the more sophisticated elements of probability theory. Because the outage distribution is the sum of random variables, in the limit it approaches the normal Gaussian distribution. In most practical cases, however, the naive normal approximation is inadequate because the systems are too small and the individual outage distributions are too skewed. There are several techniques which correct for these problems. A more complete treatment of these approximation techniques is found in Levy and Kahn, 1982; Caramanis, Stremel, Fleck and Daniel, 1983; Mazumdar and Wang, 1985; and Pacific Gas and Electric, 1985.

Short-Run Marginal Cost. Production simulations generate enough information internally to report on short-run marginal costs (SRMC) as well as total production cost. Until quite recently it was not considered important to calculate SRMC explicitly and report it in model outputs. Literature on the definition of marginal cost concepts in production simulation has been sparse, but as attention has begun to focus on marginal cost, the technical literature has expanded somewhat. In this section we will review the various definitions of marginal cost that are used in the models. We begin by focusing on the equivalent load context.

One approach to the definition of marginal cost is to focus on a particular load point and characterize the probability that different units represent the marginal resource at that load. The probabilistic nature of the simulation means that there is no certainty that any one unit is the marginal producer at a given load. If the probabilities that all resources were marginal at a particular load were known, then marginal cost at that point would be easily computed: it is the weighted average of the operating cost of each unit, where the weights are the marginal probabilities. Computing these probabilities requires that we consider the dispatch order up to the load point in question and see how much the dispatch of an additional unit would reduce the probability that load cannot be served at that point. The probability that a unit i is marginal at a load x is equal to the LOLP at x considering all units dispatched before i, minus the LOLP at x when unit i is dispatched.

$$\text{Prob (Unit}_i \text{ marginal at } x) =$$

$$LOLP(x \mid u_1 \cdots u_{i-1}) - LOLP(x \mid u_1 \cdots u_i) \quad . \quad (5\text{-}1)$$

We find the short-run marginal cost by averaging the marginal cost of each unit, weighted by the probability that that unit is on the margin, formally,

$$MC(x) = \sum_i [\text{Prob } (U_i \text{ is marginal at } x) \cdot \text{Cost of Unit } i] . \quad (5\text{-}2)$$

Bloom (1984) published the first derivation of this definition in the technical literature, although it appears to have been in use informally a few years prior to this publication. Among the commercial modeling programs which use this definition are PROMOD and UPLAN.

It is useful to illustrate the meaning of the "LOLP" definition of marginal cost by considering some limiting examples. Suppose we are examining a load of 900 MW and we have already dispatched units with a cumulative capacity of 850MW. Because we have dispatched less capacity than the load, even if these units were perfectly reliable (i.e., had no forced outages) the LOLP would be 1: it is certain we cannot meet the load. Now let us imagine that the next unit we dispatch, call it Unit J, has capacity of 1000 MW and no forced outage rate at all. The LOLP at 900 MW of load with this new unit must be zero. By adding 1000 MW of perfectly reliable capacity, we are completely certain that 900 MW of load can be met, regardless of what outage rate we assume for the 850 MW of capacity previously dispatched. Thus, in this extreme example, we have found that Unit J has probabil-

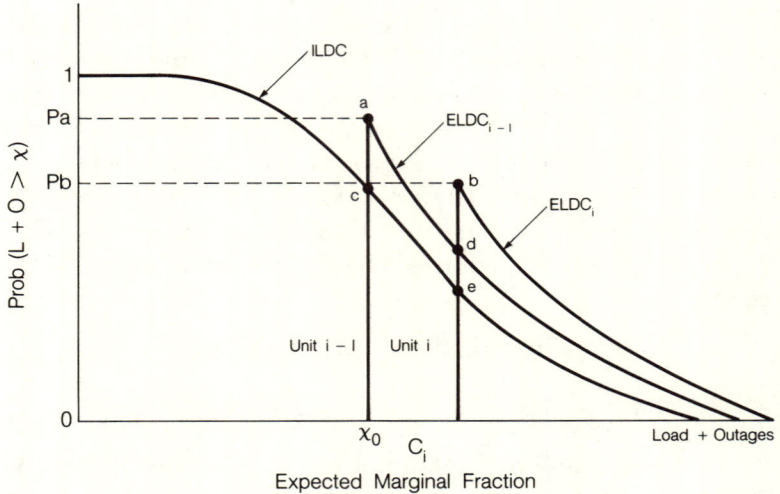

Figure 5-3. Expected marginal fraction computed from equivalent load duration curves (L = load, O = outage, ELDC = equivalent load duration curve, and ILDC = inverted load duration curve).

ity 1 of being the marginal unit at 900 MW. The LOLP without Unit J is 1 and with Unit J is 0, therefore the difference is 1. This means that the marginal cost at this load is precisely the operating cost of Unit J. For less extreme cases the LOLP without a given unit would be less than 1, and with that unit, it still would be greater than zero. Therefore in the general case the total marginal probability at a given load will be spread out over several units.

There is an equivalent definition of LOLP which focuses on the expected fraction of marginal cost attributable to a given unit. This "expected marginal fraction" is the average probability that a unit is marginal when all of the loads in a period are considered. While this definition is merely a notational variant of the LOLP definition discussed above, it is computationally less demanding and conceptually more valuable to the model user. Figure 5-3 illustrates the expected marginal fraction definition. This is a substantially enhanced variation on Figure 4-1. The inverted load duration curve is given a probability interpretation on the vertical axis, and the horizontal axis represents both loads and the outages of previously dispatched units. Equivalent load refers to the combination of load and expected outages from the units then on line. As long as the total power of the units on line exceeds this quantity, all loads can be served. Each curve in Figure 5-3 reflects the conditions for a particular combination of units on line: the righthand curve for *i* units, the middle curve for *i-1* units; and the lefthand curve for *i-2* units. Figure 5-3 has the appearance of a sawtooth, as each subsequent equivalent load duration curve includes a spike representing the outage of the unit previously dispatched. The expected marginal fraction of a given unit is the projection onto the probability axis of the spikes corresponding to the outages of the previously dispatched unit and the unit in question. In Figure 5-3 for Unit *i* this corresponds to the points *a* and *b*.

The expected marginal fraction definition is computationally simpler than the LOLP definition, especially if, as would be expected, the number of loads were greater than the number of units. More important, however, are the conceptual differences. It is useful to understand the structure of SRMC by decomposing it into contributions from different resource types. This is especially helpful if the resource mix is varied with corresponding variations in cost. Aggregating the unit average marginal probabilities by fuel type provides a convenient representation of the dispatch and cost structure. This procedure has been implemented in the Environmental Defense Fund's Electric-Financial (ELFIN) model among others.

Chronological models also can be modified to produce estimates of marginal cost. As in the equivalent load case, the estimation depends upon how random outages are modelled. The Monte Carlo approach depends upon multiple deterministic simulations of particular outage states. In any one state there will be a particular unit which is marginal for a given load in a given hour. The marginal cost for that load will be the average over all the simulations of the costs of the marginal units. This calculation is tedious in the brute force Monte Carlo approach, but straightforward. In the "smart" Monte Carlo approach, each outage state will be weighted by the probability of that state which is estimated analytically. Marginal cost for a given load is then the probability-weighted average of the deterministic results for given states.

An alternative technique involves applying the LOLP definition of marginal cost in the chronological domain. This approach is used in chronological simulation models where outages are modelled as independent events in each hour, rather than as deterministic outage states across many hours, as in the Monte Carlo method. The independence of the hourly outages method is a less computationally intensive approach to chronological simulation than Monte Carlo. It has been implemented in TVA's POWRSYM model and its commercial variants. The independence assumption can lead to anomalous results such as a unit being out in one hour, available the next hour, and out in the hour after that. Such results are undesirable in a modelling framework that is meant to incorporate the representation of chronological constraints such as minimum down-times for generating units. The use of approximations such as the independence of hourly outages illustrates the degree to which computational constraints still limit the accuracy of simulation.

Unit Commitment and Non-Economic Constraints. We have only made brief reference to the rules used in simulation models to produce a dispatch order for generating units. This is a source of substantial variation among models. Although all models aim at performing a minimum-cost dispatch of resources, there are many engineering and contractual constraints on the use of resources which limit the ability of system operators to achieve a theoretical cost minimum. We discuss two of the more important of these constraints and describe how they are implemented in particular production simulation models. These are the unit commitment requirements for "slow-start" units and the related phenomenon of "must-run" resources.

The unit commitment problem is associated with the need to meet peak load requirements and the inability to turn units off and on quickly. Consequently if a unit is required to meet peak loads in a given week, it may not be possible to turn it off in low-load periods. This means it may have to operate at some minimum level even at times when less expensive

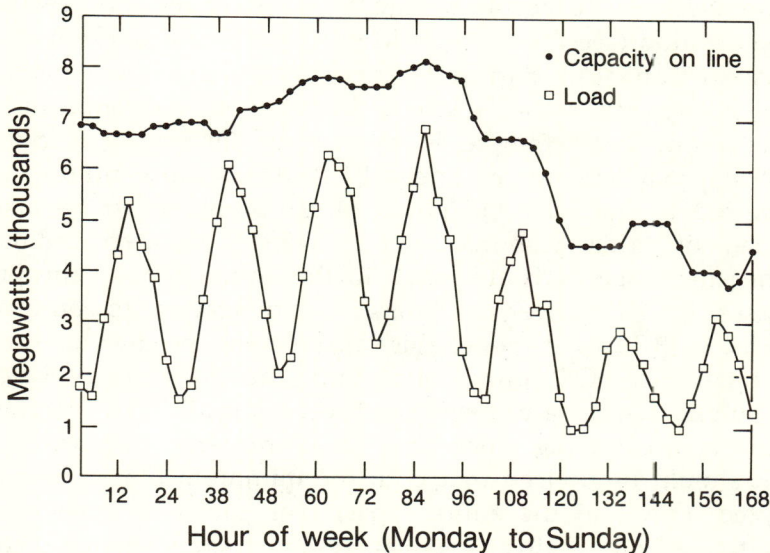

Figure 5-4. Oil- and gas-fired capacity on line, August 1984.

energy is available. Figure 5-4 illustrates this phenomenon for the Southern California Edison system. The upper line shows the amount of oil and gas capacity on line in a particular week. The lower curve shows the load requirement for that capacity. Only when peak loads decline on the weekend can some of this capacity be shut down.

The standard representation of slow start units is the specification of a minimum-capacity block with high operating cost (owing to the cost of fuel to keep the units on line at a minimum level of operation) and one or more larger-capacity blocks with lower operating costs. A production simulation model which attempts to represent the commitment problem identifies the number of such slow start units required to meet peak loads in a given period, and dispatches all of their minimum blocks in the "base load." The remaining capacity blocks of these units are dispatched in economic order. There are alternative procedures for representing the commitment process. In general the simulation models rely on rules of thumb to solve this problem rather than explicit optimization procedures. The technical literature describes the detailed optimization (see for example Merlin and Sandrin, 1983).

Apart from slow start units, there are other circumstances in which capacity must be dispatched out of economic order. One prominent example is the set of Qualifying Facilities (QF's) producing power under PURPA. Because utilities are required to purchase QF power, their output must be taken ahead of other resources. If it were not, then ordinary economic dispatch could result in the curtailment of the purchases of QF power, violating the obligation to purchase under PURPA. To model this requirement, production simulations force QF production into the base load before resources which are dispatched economically. A common term for this forcing procedure is the "must-run" feature.

It should be noticed that both the minimum blocks of committed units and the entire capacity of "must-run" resources are treated identically. This can result in some semantic confusion since it is possible to refer to the minimum blocks of committed units as must-run blocks. Indeed in production simulation models which have the must-run feature, but not the commitment feature, there can be no distinction between the two phenomena. Among the models in this category are ELFIN Version 1.30 and EGEAS Version 3.0. In models of this type, the user can approximate commitment by an appropriate choice of must-run blocks from among the set of slow-start units (Kahn, 1985a and Kahn, 1986).

It is possible that power systems can operate in situations which are so constrained that the set of units which must be dispatched uneconomically is large relative to load. One reason for this may be the contractual terms of purchase contracts such as "take or pay" clauses. In heavily constrained situations it becomes necessary for the simulation model to employ devices which order the dispatch sequence among must-run resources. One common device for this purpose is the use of "dispatch penalty factors." These act like shadow prices in the sense that they tell the model which resources are more or less valuable within the must-run class.

The importance of these details can be seen in their impact on SRMC. The presence of must-run capacity has the effect of lowering marginal cost compared to the case in which there are no such constraints. By forcing large amounts of relatively expensive energy into the base load, these constraints also force lower-cost resources up the loading order and "onto the margin." Detailed examples involving Pacific Gas and Electric Company can be found elsewhere (Kahn, 1985a and Kahn, 1986).

Endogenous Pricing. Not all resources have exogenously determined prices (prices that are independent of the supply/demand balance) which can be input to a production simulation model. Examples of those with endogenous prices are QF's, "split-savings" purchases, and special contracts such as the Geysers steam price formula used by PG&E. In each case the pricing formula differs. What they have in common is that the production simulation model must perform some calculation either before or after the simulation to determine the price of the resource. We summarize the different types of calculation involved in each case.

The simplest case of endogenous pricing involves preprocessing before a particular simulation. Split-savings purchases based on an average of known fuel costs is one such case. The PG&E Geysers steam price formula is essentially also of this kind with the added complexity that the price in a given year depends on the dispatch results from the previous year. This price could be calculated by successive model runs and an exogenous calculation, or it could be done internally by the model as long as the simulation period started one year ahead of the period of interest. The only model which currently calculates the price endogenously is ELFIN Version 1.30.

More complex endogenous pricing requires that the results of a given simulation be fed back into the same simulation. A simple example of this kind is SRMC pricing of QF's. All that must be done in this case is that the marginal cost for a given period be assigned to a non-marginal resource. There is nothing about the simulation that can be affected by the price assigned. The more difficult cases involve multiple model runs to determine price. This will be necessary if QF's are assigned an avoided-cost price that is based on the difference in total production cost with and without the QF's in the supply mix. In this case it is necessary to perform two simulations, but at least the outcome does not affect dispatch results (for examples see Weisenmiller and Yardas, 1986 and Jabbour, 1986). An alternative QF pricing method known as the "zero-intercept" method also requires multiple simulations (see sec. 5.4.1 below).

Probably the most complex endogenous pricing is associated with fully integrated power pools. Such pools commonly use a split savings formula for pricing which requires simulation of both the pool as a whole and the individual company on an isolated basis. These simulations can get quite complex when different rules are used to dispatch resources in each context. Details of these issues including the necessity of a chronological approach for this problem are given in Bloom (1984b).

5.3.2 Simplicity Versus Complexity

The inherent difficulty of testing probabilistic models "against reality" has made the tendency toward complexity pronounced in electricity production simulation modelling, exacerbating the irresistible tendency for simulation models in general to grow increasingly complex. Only by incorporating more features in a model can its designers claim that it is superior to its competitors. There are, however, pragmatic limits on the degree of complexity that is tolerable. Complex models can be difficult to debug, require substantial computing time and have too many independent parameters to yield uniform results. Very often the results produced by complex models cannot easily be tied to causes, and hence appear arbitrary and mysterious. The tool becomes a "black box." For this reason a case can be made for some degree of simplicity. Models should be usable, flexible and understandable. They are often needed to help probe uncertain or unknown conditions rather than to produce estimates that are precise to seven digits.

A principal concern associated with the use of simple models, however, is the extent to which their results are consistent with the more complex models. The simplest adjustment required in going from a complex to a simpler representation is the aggregation of inputs. This is usually not too damaging a step unless some important qualitative feature is

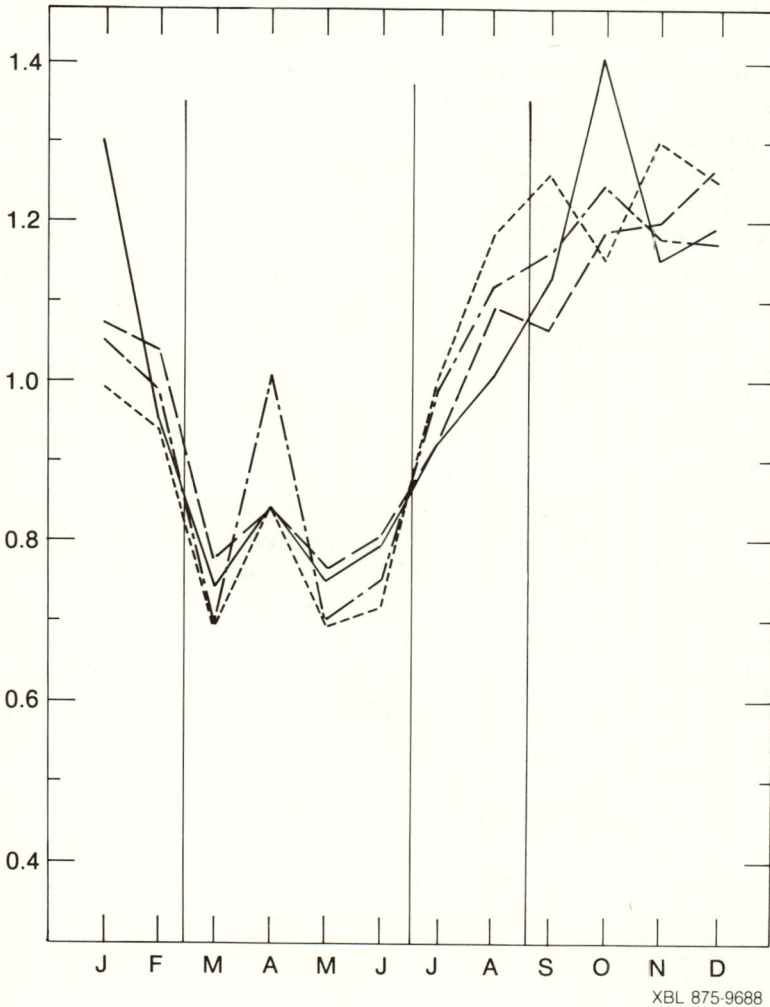

XBL 875-9688

Figure 5-5. Monthly short-run marginal cost curve (SRMC) for Pacific Gas & Electric. (Relative to an annual average value of 1.0.)

suppressed by the averaging process that is inherent in aggregation. Figure 5-5 shows a particularly acute version of the aggregation problem for representing monthly variations in

SRMC on the Pacific Gas and Electric system (PG&E, 1985b and 1986). This figure plots the range of monthly SRMC for different demand scenarios in an average hydro year relative to the average annual value. The range of variation over the months is primarily related to the hydrologic cycle. Low marginal costs in the spring and early summer are due to the run-off caused by the melting of the Sierra snowpack. By fall and early winter, the streamflow in Northern California is relatively low, and seasonal maintenance requirements for large nuclear units make energy relatively scarce and expensive during this period. A model which simplified the demand representation to only four seasons would have some difficulty capturing the full range of variation in Figure 5-5. We show one possible partitioning of the months into seasons in this figure. If the demand representation was reduced to an annual load duration curve, all of the variation would be suppressed.

More than aggregation problems, it is usually feature differences that make calibration of models difficult. Simple models tend to suppress constraints that limit the flexibility of real power systems in optimizing operations. In a situation where the complex model represents such constraints and the simple model does not, it is common to attempt some feature approximation that is achieved by manipulation of input variables. Two examples illustrate this approach: maintenance scheduling and unit commitment.

The most detailed approach to maintenance seeks to construct a unit-by-unit maintenance schedule. The problem is constrained by manpower limits, geographical constraints, economic and reliability considerations among others. The full problem can be formulated in the dynamic programming framework where the objective is to levelize and minimize system risk as measured by LOLP (Wu and Gross, 1977). At the opposite extreme is the simple procedure known as "distributed maintenance" (Stremel and Jenkins, 1981). In this approach all units are de-rated in such a way as to levelize reserve margins from period to period.

For unit commitment, production simulation models use rules of thumb to provide approximate, rather than optimal, solutions. Simple models may omit such rules, or use very crude versions of them. For example, ELFIN Version 1.30 has no commitment logic. The user must rely on a careful choice of must-run oil and gas units for an approximation. Even so, the model does not provide for much seasonal or monthly variation in this choice, although in reality commitment shows a noticeable amount of such variation. The UPLAN model uses a simply specified "commitment target" which allows for a monthly calculation of the units which need to be committed. While UPLAN modellers can fine-tune their choices by manipulation of this target, they cannot capture the weekday/weekend distinction which Figure 5-4 indicates is important. This distinction requires a load model that makes such a differentiation. LMSTM, for example, has this load distinction and therefore can represent this aspect of the commitment problem. The user can specify minimum down-time constraints in such a way that units are effectively "must-run" on weekdays and shut down on weekends (Stremel, 1985 and Kahn et al., 1987). While such a feature is a virtue in the design of LMSTM, the program's seasonal time-frame (as opposed to the representation of individual months of the year) requires the kind of aggregation indicated in Figure 5-5.

This short list of feature distinctions shows the substantial range of variation among models. Choosing the appropriate model in a particular set of circumstances requires a complicated set of trade-offs involving the nature of the problem, the capabilities of various models, and pragmatic considerations.

Models differ in their ease of use and the understandability of their results. Use of a particular model may be required to maintain methodological uniformity with earlier work because someone else has chosen it first and uniformity is important. The preemptive choice can be made by competitors, joint-venturers or regulators. Sometimes the choice is made to prevent understandability or the potential to duplicate and verify calculations, though these concerns are seldom discussed with candor. Considerations of this kind are commonly more significant contributors to the choice of model than purely technical issues concerning features or appropriateness to the particular problem. Even if technical issues alone were the dominant concern, no organization can support a proliferation of models just because one may be slightly preferable to another for a given situation. It can therefore be taken as given that model users will always be working in a less-than-ideal situation, and may often have to rely on approximations that they would prefer to avoid.

Some guidance to these dilemmas can be given in the situation where the modeller is required to use a simpler simulation tool than would be ideal because of the inconvenience or inflexibility of the more sophisticated model. This situation is common where strategic planning questions are concerned, or analysis of uncertainty is important. These applications require analysis of many scenarios which differ substantially. The large, complex models are not well adapted to examining broad ranges of variation. To provide decision makers with confidence in results produced under these circumstances, the modeller will first calibrate the simple model to the complex model in an analogous manner to calibrating a laboratory instrument. Common sense suggests that perfect calibration and certainty is not achievable. To address this concern we describe procedures that are used to assure consistency; a process that is called calibration by analogy with the tuning of a laboratory instrument. As any experienced modeller knows, there are always procedures available to make the results of one model appear consistent with those of another. The calibration exercise consists of defining the extent of legitimate procedures and characterizing the deviations in results. The following tests provide reasonable guidance.

In the most common situation, the simple model has been selected, in all likelihood on some of the pragmatic grounds cited above, and a "base case" simulation is available for the detailed model. Input specifications must be made for the simpler model to deal with aggregation issues and feature approximation. Usually there will be more than one way to approximate features, so some testing of alternatives is useful. The criteria for choosing a best approximation should be the best fit to the modelled annual production by fuel type and marginal cost. These criteria require some discussion.

All production simulation models report annual energy production aggregated to some level or other. It is unreasonable and unnecessary to expect that models replicate results at the level of individual units or even small groups of units. The crucial results for costing purposes are production at the level of fuel types. Models cannot be said to be calibrated if results are wildly divergent at this level. Broadly speaking there are two kinds of fuel types, those which are base loaded and those which are marginal. While this distinction is not iron-clad, it is usually identifiable. Acceptable results match the base-loaded resources within 1 to 2% over the year. Marginal resources are harder to replicate because feature differences come more strongly into play. Deviations of more than 10% in annual production by fuel type for marginal resources mean that calibration is not particularly good.

Most models calculate or can be used to approximate marginal cost. The usual approximation provides a set of variations around the base case simulation and a definition of marginal cost that measures the change in cost divided by the change in energy produced (see Kahn, 1985b). For calibration purposes we are interested in both the level of marginal cost and its structure. A reasonable target for replication of marginal cost averaged over the simulated year is a 5–10% deviation from the detailed model. It is important to investigate seasonal and diurnal variations in marginal cost because this will help provide insight into what causes the deviations between the simple and the detailed models. A good calibration captures the broad pattern of these variations. The closer the match at the seasonal and diurnal level, the more confidence one can have in the robustness of results with respect to variations in the resource mix from the base case configuration. Because we usually cannot explore the fit of the simple model to the detailed model as the resource mix changes, we must rely on the marginal cost results to provide indications of what can be expected as the supply/demand balance changes over the seasons of the year and over times of day.

A useful calibration examines the fit of annual production by fuel type and marginal cost for a number of years in the simulation period. The years selected should differ as much as possible with respect to the supply/demand balance. Because a number of "tunable parameters" are available for which exogenous choices must be made, it is prudent to search for the best fit over a range of these choices. Such tests will provide guidance in defining the nature and extent of mismatches between the models.

The generic calibration exercise which we have defined does not address the most difficult question, the choice of the optimal simple model. In some basic sense this problem is indeterminate. A "good" simplification is good only relative to some particular question. We address this question by surveying the kinds of resource planning problems for which long range production simulation modelling is needed.

5.3.3 The Right Tool for the Job

The discussion of production simulation features in Sec. 5.3.1 can be readily translated into a characterization of modelling tasks and the appropriate choice of tools. Thus a problem that had a characteristically chronological aspect would not be properly modelled using a load duration curve approach. In practice, however, models are sometimes in an intermediate position between these two approaches. PROMOD, for example, relies upon a load representation that divides each typical week into a Weekday, a Weeknight, and a Weekend load duration curve. For many applications this degree of time-differentiation is sufficient. One example is the representation of economy energy markets. In many cases there is a significant difference in how much energy is available for sale in the bulk power market at non-firm, or economy, prices depending on whether the demand is during the day or at night. A PROMOD-style representation is a satisfactory way to characterize a time-varying resource of this kind.

A useful distinction between chronological phenomena that require a chronological model and those which do not is the property of dispatchability. Some time-varying phenomena are not under the control of utility dispatchers. Solar energy and wind-turbine output are examples of this kind. Certain firm-purchase power contracts are also essentially non-dispatchable in the sense that they will be utilized regardless of other conditions on the system. Non-dispatchable, time-varying resources can often be accomodated in load duration curve models by "shaving" a chronological load characterization before it is transformed into the load duration curve domain. This technique is called load modification. Many conservation programs — which reduce the load that must be served by generators, and are therefore comparable in their effect on the system to additional generating units — also are non-dispatchable in nature and can therefore be represented using the load modification approach.

Dispatchable phenomena require some kind of chronological representation. These include load management programs that are actively controlled by the utility, the analysis of time-varying resources such as new transmission lines designed to increase the availability of off-peak economy energy, or dispatchable capacity contracts that are designed for variable on-peak delivery. Even these phenomena can be treated with partially chronological representations — that is, equivalent load duration curves for different kinds of days. In addition to the PROMOD approach, the UPLAN model uses load modification to accommodate some of these phenomena. UPLAN uses a "two-pass" dispatch. Time-of-day or season-dependent resources are accounted for in the first iteration, then the results are used in a second iteration to shave load and re-dispatch remaining resources in the load duration curve domain (Lotus Consulting Group, 1986). The limitation on this approach is the treatment of outages in the first pass. To make this phase computationally tractable, UPLAN simplifies by de-rating the capacity of resources by their forced outage rates. This is an acceptable approximation for resources that are just outside the realm of baseload, such as economy energy. However, it is increasingly unrealistic for resources that are to be dispatched nearer the peak. This means that dispatchable load management and on-peak capacity contracts will be less realistically modeled than economy energy transactions by using UPLAN.

Before leaving the chronological issue, it is worth noting that aggregation differences of a considerable nature arise among the various models of this kind. At one extreme is the hour-by-hour approach adopted by POWRSYM and its derivatives; at the opposite extreme is LMSTM with its 16 typical days. The LMSTM user is free to specify the assignment of days to "day-types," although it is common to reserve one day-type per season for weekends because of

phenomena such as that illustrated by Figure 5-4. This convention leaves 12 day-types to be allocated to about 260 days,
or about 22 days per day-type. This is a lot of aggregation
especially considering that one day-type per season would
typically be set aside to represent a handful of extreme days
during that season, leaving only eight day-types to cover
some 240 days. There are, of course, some intermediate positions. General Electric's MAPPS uses two-hour intervals
instead of single hours, but this model is designed to analyze
multi-area problems with transmission constraints, so that the
load model economy is more than wiped out by expanded
supply capability. MAPPS is clearly in the class of detailed
models. The LMSTM vendor has released a more disaggre-
gated version of the smart Monte Carlo method that is based
on chronological weeks, rather than 16 typical day-types.

A further consideration in the model choice domain is the
extent to which an integrated package with financial capability
is desirable. We argued in Sec. 5.2 against the usefulness of
optimization models that explicitly traded fixed costs against
production economies. One reason the optimization approach
is difficult is the problem of representing constraints on both
production simulation and financial capability — production
constraints were discussed in Sec. 5.3. On the financial side
utilities are also constrained. The state-of-the-art optimization
model, EPRI's EGEAS, does not have an explicit procedure for
treating limitations on the ability of utilities to finance new
capital-intensive projects. Fixed costs are represented using
the busbar techniques outlined in Chapter 2, rather than corporate balance sheets, income statements and other standard
financial reports. This technique makes it impossible to
represent financial constraints in their normal form, i.e., that
of the corporate income statement. As usual these constraints
can be represented in a derivative or proxy manner by the
user. This is achieved by artificially limiting the amount of
capacity available from capital-intensive resources.

Even without resorting to optimization, pragmatic considerations often dominate the decision about how to model
the fixed costs associated with various alternative resources.
Although an integrated software package may be desirable in
theory, the decentralized organization of large utilities may

dictate that production costing and financial analysis be done separately. This separation is rationalized on the ground that production simulation and financial accounting are such technically distinct areas of expertise that it is not practical to unite these functions in one operation. The cost of such separation is a diminished ability to iterate analysis and examine a large range of alternatives.

There is no "correct" model choice. In some organizational settings an integrated analysis capability can be constructed, particularly if the participants are accustomed to working in an interdisciplinary fashion. Each component of the analysis may be somewhat simplified, but strategic and/or sensitivity analysis becomes more feasible. In this kind of setting the results of analysis often require a "credibility check" by the technical specialists in production simulation and financial modelling. This need for verification can reduce the efficiency of integrated modelling. These constraints serve to underline the irreducible tension between simplicity and complexity. Any organization faced with these problems must find its own unique solution.

5.4 From Marginal to Avoided Cost

Although the term "avoided cost" was coined in the legislative arena, in one sense at least it corresponds to the notion of "fuel savings" commonly used by utility planners in the 1970s. "Fuel savings" are the operational economies associated with a resource addition that are independent of its reliability or capacity value. If we interpret the schematic representation of Figure 5-1 as illustrating only capital and energy costs (and not shortage or reliability costs), then it is fuel savings that are responsible for the downward shift in marginal and average costs when a new resource is added to the system. The term "avoided cost" would not have been necessary, however, if it were not for the different context in which it was introduced, namely the pricing of power purchases under PURPA.

The distinction between short-run and long-run value has been transferred from the marginal cost context to the avoided cost context. Many of the same ambiguities about large versus small changes that arise in the marginal cost context also occur when avoided costs are at issue. The original and best-defined meaning of marginal cost involves a small (perhaps infinitesimal) change in demand with a fixed supply configuration. Because of the characteristically large nature of central station supply additions, when long-run marginal cost is considered, the infinitesimal change notion disappears. The transition from the short-run perspective to the long-run perspective must involve a change in the demand increment considered. There is no clear guidance in the economic literature about this transition. In the practice of utility resource planning there has evolved a tradition of cost-effectiveness analysis, summarized in Sec. 5.2 which addresses the onset of the long-run perspective. This utility planning tradition provides some limited (but incomplete) guidance for addressing the PURPA pricing problem.

In the implementation of PURPA to date, there has evolved a tradition of separating short-run from long-run pricing that has analogies with the marginal cost concepts. Long-run pricing is commonly based on costing methods derived from the busbar cost approach outlined in Chapter 2 and adapted to PURPA-type purposes in Sec. 5.2. The Texas Public Utilities Commission has accepted this approach as the basis of pricing long-term contracts for purchases from cogenerators. In California there is also a consensus that long-term avoided cost ought to be computed in this way. From the perspective of the Qualifying Facility (QF), however, long-run pricing needs only to be fixed in nature, regardless of what method is used to arrive at the estimate. The need for fixed prices by the QF stems from financing constraints that will be discussed at some length in Chapter 6. The most popular long-run offer made under PURPA was California's Interim Standard Offer No. 4 which was fixed in nature, but based more on projection of future short-run marginal cost than anything else.

5.4.1 Short-Run Avoided Cost

The short-run pricing alternative which has been more prominent in PURPA implementation is a revisable tariff that is subject to change as economic conditions vary. In many jurisdictions the short-run price is identified with short-run marginal cost. This identity is generally reasonable as long as the amount of QF power is effectively very small. As the size of the QF contribution grows, its presence in the resource mix begins to effect the determination of SRMC. Again Figure 5-1 illustrates the role of a large block of QF output on SRMC. If we imagine that the quantity $Q_C - Q_A$ were QF output, then adding this block of power to the resource mix instantaneously would cause a sharply downward adjustment in SRMC. The correct interpretation of the avoided cost concept then involves calculating the fuel savings associated with the entire block of QF output being priced by short-run methods. This calculation has come to be known as the "QF In/Out" method. The name refers to the procedure of performing two production simulations, one with QFs in the resource mix and one without. The avoided cost price is the total cost difference between these simulations divided by the QF output. This approach is also known as the "but for" technique — how much extra would have been spent on energy, but for the contribution of QF's.

Jabbour (1986) offers an interesting study of the short run pricing problem. The model used in this study abstracts from the representation of outages, but does include an explicit treatment of start-up and shut-down costs. Figure 5-6, which is adapted from this study, shows the relationship between avoided cost (calculated using the QF In/Out method) and SRMC over a wide range of QF output. At 2500 MW, the largest value shown in this figure, QFs represent about half of the peak demand in the system modelled. The simulation results show avoided cost below SRMC at very low levels of QF supply and substantially above it as the QF penetration becomes large.

Short-run or variable avoided cost pricing involves many potential subtleties and complications. One of the more obvious involves the question of which QFs should be removed from the supply mix in the "QF Out" simulation. The usual answer is to remove only those QFs subject to variable pricing and not those which are priced under fixed or long-term pricing rules (Weisenmiller and Yardas, 1986). Other questions surrounding the specification of the "QF Out" simulation include the issue of insuring adequate system reliability for

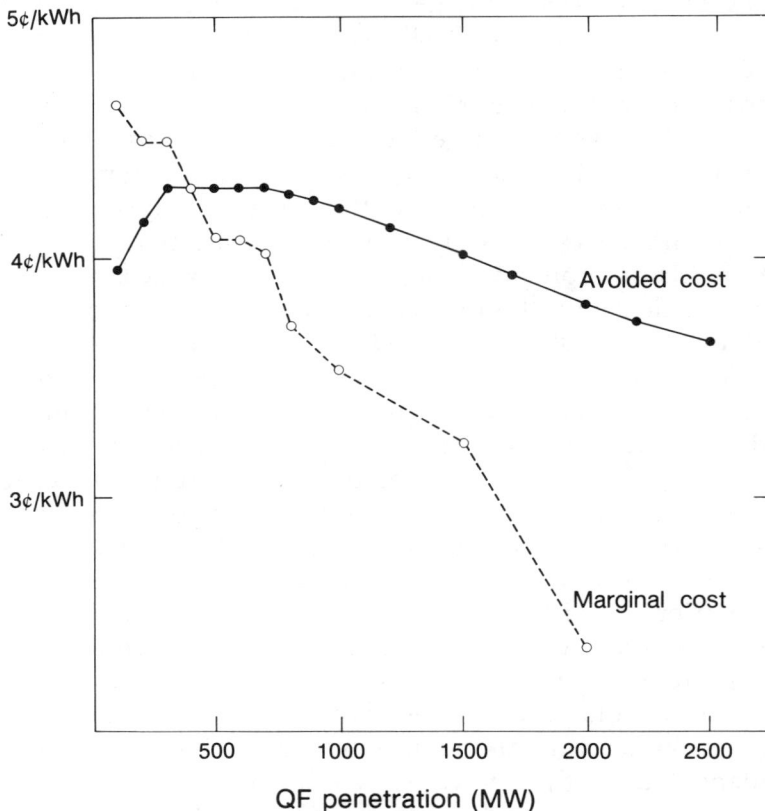

XBL 875-9689

Figure 5-6. QF penetration (MW)

this scenario and correcting for the fact that QF pricing
depends on the supply/demand balance that will be calculated by the model. The reliability issue involves the potential for eccentric results if the simulated system cannot meet
reliability targets. This problem only arises when variable-
priced QFs are a large part of the supply mix. In this case
their removal might cause the system to take unrealistically
high-priced emergency power or to use pumped storage
resources in unrealistic ways. A common technique to handle
the reliability problem is to substitute an equal quantity of
combustion turbine capacity for the QFs removed from the
system. This effectively places a fairly reasonable upper

bound on the cost in this case.

Another potential correction involved in the QF Out simulation is the secondary impact of this change on any endogenous prices associated with other resources. In the case of Pacific Gas and Electric, there is an interaction with the price paid for geothermal steam. Removing QFs from the resource mix has the effect of increasing this price. The California PUC has decided that QFs should receive the benefit of this secondary price effect as part of the avoided cost payment, at least for short-run payments. The secondary impact on endogenous prices could also play a role in other contexts such as fully integrated power pools, or even spot markets. In these cases the calculations could become rather complex.

Short-run methods also seek to capture some time differentiation in avoided cost. SRMC can express some of this quality if the production simulation has enough disaggregation. Where avoided cost diverges from SRMC, other methods must be used. One approach that lies somewhere between SRMC and QF In/Out is a method known as the "zero-intercept" calculation. The idea here is to capture some of the time interdependency in costs associated with unit commitment and minimum downtime constraints. These situations tend to involve costs that are incurred during off-peak hours, but are in some basic sense due to on-peak demands. The calculation technique involves adding and subtracting a load increment during the on-peak hours. The total cost change between the increment case and the decrement case divided by the quantity difference between those cases is assigned as a "marginal cost" during the peak period. Cost calculated in this way definitely captures some of the discontinuities and indivisibilities that are excluded from more conventional approaches to SRMC.

There is a difference of opinion whether the "zero-intercept" method is a substitute for QF In/Out avoided cost or a supplement to it. It is difficult to argue that the zero-intercept method can completely substitute for QF In/Out avoided cost because the method as usually implemented has no direct linkage to the amount of QF power in the supply mix. On the other hand, it would be double counting to just add to the QF In/Out avoided cost the excess of the zero-intercept cost over the SRMC with all QFs in the supply mix. The QF In/Out simulations should capture at least part of the indivisibilities represented by the zero-intercept calculation. One way to resolve this conflict is to use the zero-intercept results as ratios that would allocate different portions of the average avoided cost value calculated by QF In/Out methods to the on-peak and off-peak hours. This approach would preserve the total avoided cost difference, but provide a way to capture its time differentiation.

Clearly there are unresolved issues in short-run QF pricing, many of which are traceable to modelling problems. Others involve economic questions about the appropriate pricing rules. However difficult these questions are, they are inherently simpler than the long-run pricing problem, where the differences between long-run avoided cost and long-run marginal cost become quite complicated.

5.4.2 Long-Run Avoided Cost

The simplest case involving long-run avoided costs is the one in which QF's completely displace an identifiable resource planned for the future whose costs are known. In this case all the procedures described in Sec. 5.2 can be used to translate busbar cost data into long-run avoided costs for capacity and energy. This simple case does not really address the fundamental difficulty of estimating long-run avoided cost, which involves the forecast uncertainties associated with future demand and QF supply.

The capacity expansion modelling framework rests on the assumption that demand forecasts are reliable, and that the only uncertain information is the timing and type of new capacity additions. In fact, it is the demand environment which is now one of the principal uncertainties. This is true not simply because forecasting energy requirements is difficult, but also because of independent energy development. In Chapter 6 we examine the economics of power project development under avoided cost pricing. In addition to privately owned power for sale to the utility, the appearance of bypass projects also makes the demand for new power facilities uncertain. Bypass projects are generating plants operated to supply the loads of large utility customers; their construction is motivated primarily by retail rate considerations, not avoided cost prices. But because the demands of these customers are large, their leaving the system will have an impact on the need for new capacity.

Any method designed to estimate long-run avoided costs must grapple with the jointly determined equilibrium among prices, service demand and the development of independent generation. There is no definitive way to make this determination with great confidence. The typical approach involves independent, consistent estimates of each factor. It is best to bear in mind that a forecast of long-run avoided cost is typically done for a specific purpose. This may be to propose long-term contract prices for new producers, or to evaluate the impact of demand-side programs. We will discuss these two applications in Chapters 6 and 7 respectively.

As a practical matter there are really only two ways to procede with a long-run avoided cost estimate. Either one makes some adaptation of the busbar costing framework for particular projects, or one relies on the uses of production simulation modelling to calculate the value of a designated block of power. As our previous discussion of resource cost-effectiveness indicate, these two methods are really just different sides of the same coin. The differences have more to do with how one structures the analysis than any methodological superiority of one approach over another.

The most general approach to adapting the busbar cost point of departure is to consider the deferral of planned resources, rather than their complete avoidance. Suppose the utility resource plan consisted of the rule of thumb that 300 MW of baseload capacity were to be added every four years. If the planner, or the regulator, wanted to estimate the long-run avoided cost value of 150 MW of capacity, they might conclude that it could be measured by deferring all resources in the supply plan by two years. The difference in present-value revenue requirements between the deferral case and the base case resource plan would represent the long-run avoided cost.

The production simulation approach to this problem involves calculating the reliability and energy value of a capacity block by removing it from the projected future supply plan or deferring it for a number of years. Nominally this method requires more information than the busbar approach because a complete characterization of supply and demand is required for the entire simulation period. The only data not required are the capital and financing costs of the deferred or avoided resource. The choice of method is usually determined by which data the user feels more comfortable with.

The utility industry will continue struggling to find better ways to identify and analyze its marginal costs. It is unlikely that any new conceptual breakthrough will make this job suddenly easy and mechanical. Instead, there will probably be steady improvement in simulation methods and increasing effort directed to refining the data used in these models. As competitive forces begin to play a role in the utility industry, it is likely that the short-run marginal cost approach based on simulation methods will become more dominant. While this method is no perfect substitute for better data on busbar plant costs, it is fundamentally more flexible and more adaptable to different marginal cost problems. Progress on marginal cost estimation therefore will largely come through improvements in simulation models.

Chapter 6

Independent Power Production

6.1 Introduction

We have had several occasions to mention cogeneration, a small-scale power generation technology (see Sections 3.7 and 4.5), and the related broader issue of avoided cost rates (Section 4.6 and 5.4). In this chapter we will expand on these ideas by discussing independent power production in a more systematic manner. To understand this phenomenon we will briefly discuss the history of technologies currently being used to produce independent power and the emergence of the federal law encouraging their development. To illustrate the range of characteristics exhibited by these technologies, we explore two examples of their engineering economics, wind turbines and cogeneration. The first is highly capital-intensive, with very limited operating costs, characteristics it shares with small hydro and solar electric conversion. Cogeneration on the other hand, has significant operating, i.e., fuel, costs, while being less capital-intensive. Geothermal and solid waste combustion may also be of this type depending on the ownership structure of the resource. The examples we develop are aimed at demonstrating the requirements for financing independent power projects.

The passage of PURPA in 1978 marks the re-emergence of small-scale, independent electricity production after half a century or more of decline. The growth of electric utilities had been founded on a scale economy strategy which succeeded because small technologies could not compete economically. Scale economies led to a consolidation of firms and the demise of independent production. The transition to an increasing cost structure reversed this relationship. Many of the cost factors discussed in Chapter 3 became diseconomies of scale, favoring smaller-scale technologies. More important in the short run was the political upheaval in state utility regulation. Utility management came under scrutiny, review and attack over the prudence of its planning methods. This political expression of concern about rate increases and their causes created a new kind of regulatory proceeding, the "Need-for-Power" Review (see American Bar Association, 1981). In hearings of this kind, the political critics of utility management documented the declining productivity of large-scale electric generation (particularly nuclear power), creating an atmosphere conducive to policy initiatives favoring increased competition in electricity generation.

PURPA may be seen as an element in the broader social trend toward deregulation. It is a very limited step in that direction, and more procedural than substantive, but part of the same drama. In essence the basic thesis of deregulation policies is that competition (where feasible) will minimize consumer costs in the long run. Efficiency gains result from competition. In the case of electric utilities, for instance, capital cost escalation for new plants was perceived as a symptom of weak management, so to control these costs, society made a political choice to introduce competition in a limited way. PURPA requires utilities to purchase power from Qualifying Facilities (QFs), using "obligation to purchase" as the means of introducing and limiting competition. Facilities achieve QF status by falling under a certain size limitation (80 MW); cogenerators could be of any size, as long as they met minimum efficiency criteria. Furthermore, principal ownership of QFs was intended to be limited to non-utility entities, so that competition would come from independent sources. No utility could own more than 49% interest in any QF.

Requiring utilities to purchase output from QFs created a new definition of the rights of utility competitors. Before this requirement, a potential energy producer would have no guarantee that a utility would purchase the power it produced.

Furthermore, since PURPA exempts QFs from state utility regulation, there is no limit on their profits. We will see that returns can sometimes be very high for QFs. While lack of regulation has an effect, the primary determinant of QF profits is the price they receive for their production. This is determined within the avoided-cost framework introduced in Sections 4.6 and 5.4. The basic requirement of the legislation is that utilities offer avoided-cost prices in the form of a tariff. Since this means that the prices are subject to change and revision like any other tariff, this structure has substantial negative consequences for the financing of QF projects. To secure long-term financing, QFs need long-term contracts with some assurance about prices. Unlike other industries (such as lumber or primary metals) subject to widely fluctuating prices, power producers cannot look for distant markets for their products. Power transmission is still controlled by utilities who are under no obligation to transmit for QFs. Although PURPA explicitly allows for long-term contract prices, it does not require them. Our examples illustrate different ways in which QFs might obtain price assurance.

There have been substantial policy debates about implementing PURPA. For instance, Section 5.4 has shown that avoided cost is an ambiguous notion subject to different interpretations. QFs have argued that they should be treated symmetrically with utilities and get the kind of revenue stream associated with new power plants. But if the intention of PURPA is to introduce competition, shouldn't a different standard apply? If so, how different? These policy issues go straight to the heart of regulation. Is independent power being encouraged because there is no longer a natural monopoly on electricity generation? There cannot be any need to completely eliminate regulation, however, because the QFs want special regulatory treatment to be viable — or at least the guarantee of some symmetries with conventional utility-owned plants. We will return to these issues in Chapters 8 and 9 where the whole notion of natural monopoly and the role of regulation will be examined.

In this chapter we focus on concrete examples of QF operation and its relationship to regulatory structure. We begin by defining project financing and its application to independent power projects in Section 6.2. A representative wind energy project, illustrated in Section 6.3, shows how financial constraints determine the economic viability of a project and illustrates the crucial role of tax credits for this technology in the early 1980s. The economics of cogeneration are discussed in Section 6.4. In both examples the crucial role played by estimates of long-run avoided cost becomes apparent. Finally, in Section 6.5 we discuss the bypass phenomenon and introduce the auction mechanism as an alternative procedure for determining avoided cost and encouraging competition.

6.2 Project Financing

To understand the economic structure of independent power projects, we must take account of the methods through which they are financed. In most cases this is different from the corporate finance used by utilities and other large corporations. The typical independent power project is based upon a project finance structure. Project financing means simply that revenues associated with a project must be sufficient to meet all costs without outside infusion of funds after the initial capitalization. Although this definition may sound similar to what we have been used to in the corporate context, there are important differences. A project undertaken by a corporation need not be immediately profitable in order to be a sound, viable investment. Indeed most projects with large start-up costs or substantial R&D requirements will not achieve immediate positive cash flow. The continuing losses of such projects must be financed by corporate capital until cash flow becomes positive in the hope that returns in the later years will more than offset the early losses. At least, such are the expectations when corporations approve such projects.

Corporate finance requires that there be a decision rule which relates the firm's overall cost of capital to the rate of return on potential projects. This decision rule is typically some multi-year summary statistic such as Net Present Value (NPV) or Internal Rate of Return (IRR) which may or may not involve a cash-flow constraint. Project finance, on the other hand, is constrained by both rate-of-return and cash flow. Not only must equity investors receive their required return, but they will only contribute to capitalization once. Therefore, revenues must be adequate to meet the project's debt service and cash operating costs from the start.

Why is project finance popular if it is more constrained than corporate finance? Why do corporations themselves set up project-financed ventures? Some answers to these questions are offered by Wynant (1980). We will first consider project finance from the viewpoint of leverage. Projects which can generate immediate positive cash flow typically will be able to bear more debt (i.e., have a higher debt fraction in total capitalization) than projects which cannot, since there will be more cash available with which to make loan payments in the short run. Although it also increases the financial risk, equity investors prefer leverage (i.e., more debt) because it magnifies the potential return if the project succeeds. A small power project can generate substantial cash flow because a market for its output is guaranteed by PURPA. Furthermore, if avoided-cost payments are likely to be high, then cash flow prospects will look even better.

The second reason for favoring the project finance structure involves taxation. Small power projects can produce substantial tax benefit from investment credits and accelerated depreciation. Before the tax reform legislation of 1986, this was a very substantial consideration, particularly because renewable resource projects benefitted substantially from special tax credits enacted at the same time as PURPA. Corporate shareholders often cannot make use of incremental tax benefits since effective corporate tax rates are already low. A project finance structure, however, can pass these tax benefits along to investors who can make use of them, typically high-income individuals seeking tax shelters. The sale of limited partnerships in project-financed small power facilities has become a popular method of creating tax shelters, effectively providing a new source of capital investment in the utilities industry.

6.3 Wind Energy Example

We examine both aspects of project financing in the context of a particular project based on wind energy conversion. This example represents conditions of the early 1980s when the wind power industry was just beginning its development in

California. California, a state with good wind energy resources, offered developers and investors a state income tax credit in addition to the federally available credits. Table 6-1 is a spreadsheet representation of this project which we will discuss in detail. Spreadsheets are the ideal vehicle for studying small power projects because the requirements for financial viability are easily examined. The project analyzed in Table 6-1 (labeled Floor Price for reasons that will become apparent) is a 75kW wind generator to be sold to an individual limited partner in a California windfarm. The expected output for the site and technology in question is 223,380 kWh per year (34% capacity factor). It is anticipated that this output would be sold to Southern California Edison whose 1983 total avoided cost would be 6.4/kWh for this project (about 5.2 energy and 1.2 capacity). The expected avoided cost trajectory to the year 2000 is given on line 6 of Table 6-1. Analysis of this project using this avoided cost trajectory and the capitalization and expense structure given in Table 6-1 will reveal that the project is not feasible. This will be shown in Table 6-2. For our purposes now, we will show how the project succeeds (on paper at least) at a levelized "Floor Price" of 8.5/kWh. It will be useful to summarize the basic assumptions underlying the analysis with respect to capitalization, expenses and taxation. These are collected in Table 6-3. These conditions reflect expectations of the early 1980s including relatively high capital costs, interest rates, output expectations and avoided costs. We will now explain the structure of Table 6-1.

Table 6-1 combines in a "bare-bones" manner the functions of an income statement, sources and uses of funds statement, and investor's return projection. We assume a constant revenue stream (line 10) based upon the levelized price and expected production. The standard income statement expenses are listed (lines 14–18) and subtracted from payments to yield Pretax Income (line 19). The actual cash-flow will differ for several reasons. First, depreciation is only an accounting item, not a cash flow (it is added back in on line 23). Second, debt repayment of principal is a cash flow requirement but not an income statement expense (it is listed on line 31). Finally, capital funds are added to sources of funds (lines 24 and 25) and equipment cost is the primary Year 1 use of funds. The net of sources and uses is Funds Available for Dividends (line 34). This line represents the cash flow constraint on project financing. It must be positive, because if it were negative, the project could not meet expenses and a further cash infusion would be necessary, which would amount to changing the project. If equity funds were increased to cover the shortfall, for example, the investor's rate of return would go down because the same ultimate returns would be allocated among a larger total equity investment.

To calculate the return on equity, we must consider tax effects because so much of the value to investors comes as tax benefits. Line 37 is identical to line 19. The assumed tax rate is 50% reflecting the marginal tax rate of a hypothetical high-income investor at this time. By convention, we assume that "negative taxes" are the tax savings accruing to investors from the net operating losses generated by the project. Notice that it is the substantial depreciation deductions which generate the net operating loss: the depreciation is large in the early years because it is based on a five-year write-off of the capital cost. Line 40, Tax Savings (Liabilities), is the negative of the sum of line 38 and the Year 1 Tax Credits. Line 41 is the After Tax Net Equity Cash Flow. This is calculated as follows:

$$\begin{matrix} \text{After} \\ \text{Tax} \\ \text{Net} \end{matrix} = \begin{matrix} \text{Funds} \\ \text{Available} \\ \text{for} \\ \text{Dividends} \end{matrix} + \begin{matrix} \text{Equity} \\ \text{Cash} \\ \text{Flow} \end{matrix} + \begin{matrix} \text{Tax} \\ \text{Saving} \end{matrix} - \begin{matrix} \text{Equity} \\ \text{Funds} \end{matrix} \quad (6\text{-}1)$$

Lines 42 and 43 represent the Net Present Value of the line 41 stream discounted at 15% and 30%, respectively. Since the NPV > 0 at 30%, the investor's rate-of-return requirement of 30% is being met.

Careful examination of line 41 reveals a troublesome feature of this project. Investor returns are negative in Years 6–10. This occurs because there is no longer any depreciation expense to shelter project cash flow from taxes, and this cash is needed for debt repayment. During these years the investor would owe taxes but get no cash. This is just the opposite of years 1–5, when there is both cash and tax savings.

Table 6-1

Spreadsheet representation of wind power project "Floor Price."

		1983	1984	1985	1986	1987	1988	1989	1990	1991
1	Floor Price									
2	Year	1983	1984	1985	1986	1987	1988	1989	1990	1991
3	**Assumptions**									
4	KWh/yr	223,380	223,380	223,380	223,380	223,380	223,380	223,380	223,380	223,380
5										
6	Avoided Cost (¢/kwh)	6.40	6.60	6.80	7.00	7.40	7.90	8.50	9.00	9.70
7										
8	**Income Statement**									
9	Floor Price (¢/kwh)	8.50	8.50	8.50	8.50	8.50	8.50	8.50	8.50	8.50
10	Total Payments	18,987	18,987	18,987	18,987	18,987	18,987	18,987	18,987	18,987
11										
12										
13	**Expenses**									
14	O & M	1,429	1,474	1,518	1,563	1,653	1,764	1,898	2,010	2,166
15	Land Rent	714	737	759	781	826	882	949	1,005	1,083
16	Depreciation	18,412	27,005	25,777	25,777	25,777				
17	Interest	10,885	10,322	9,680	8,949	8,115	7,164	6,080	4,844	3,436
18	Total Expenses	31,441	39,538	37,735	37,071	36,372	9,811	8,928	7,859	6,686
19	Pre-Tax Income	-12,454	-20,551	-18,748	-18,084	-17,384	9,176	10,059	11,127	12,301
20										
21	**Pre-Tax Cash Flow**									
22	Sources of Funds									
23	Pre-Tax Income + Depreciation	5,957	6,453	7,028	7,692	8,392	9,176	10,059	11,127	12,301
24	Debt Funds	77,750								
25	Equity Funds	45,000								
26	Total Sources	128,707	6,453	7,028	7,692	8,392	9,176	10,059	11,127	12,301
27										
28	**Uses of Funds**									
29	Capital Equipment	122,750								
30	Interest During Construction									
31	Debt Repayment	4,020	4,584	5,225	5,957	6,790	7,742	8,825	10,060	11,469
32	Total Fixed Uses	126,770	4,584	5,225	5,957	6,790	7,742	8,825	10,060	11,469
33										
34	Funds Available for Dividends	1,937	1,869	1,803	1,735	1,602	1,434	1,234	1,067	832
35										
36	**Tax Effect**									
37	Pre-Tax Income — Equity	-12,454	-20,551	-18,748	-18,084	-17,384	9,176	10,059	11,127	12,301

#		1992	1993	1994	1995	1996	1997	1998	1999	2000
38	Income Taxes	-6,227	-10,275	-9,374	-9,042	-8,692	4,588	5,029	5,563	6,150
39	Income Tax Credit	31,250								
40	Tax Savings (Liability)	37,477	10,275	9,374	9,042	8,692	-4,588	-5,029	-5,563	-6,150
41	After Tax Net Equity Cash Flow	-5,584	12,145	11,178	10,778	10,295	-3,153	-3,795	-4,496	-5,318
42	Present Value	31,195								
43	PV2	13,296								
44										
45										
46										
47										
1	Floor Price									
2	Year	1992	1993	1994	1995	1996	1997	1998	1999	2000
3	**Assumptions**									
4	KWh/yr	223,380	223,380	223,380	223,380	223,380	223,380	223,380	223,380	223,380
5										
6	Avoided Cost (¢/kwh)	10.40	11.20	12.10	13.00	14.00	15.00	16.50	18.15	19.97
7										
8	**Income Statement**									
9	Floor Price (¢/kwh)	8.50	8.50	8.50	8.50	8.50	8.50	8.50	8.50	8.50
10	Total Payments	18,987	18,987	18,987	18,987	18,987	18,987	18,987	18,987	18,987
11										
12										
13	**Expenses**									
14	O & M	2,323	2,501	2,702	2,903	3,127	3,350	3,685	4,054	4,459
15	Land Rent	1,161	1,250	1,351	1,451	1,563	1,675	1,842	2,027	2,229
16	Depreciation									
17	Interest	1,830								
18	Total Expenses	5,314	3,752	4,054	4,355	4,690	5,026	5,528	6,081	6,689
19	Pre-Tax Income	13,672	15,234	14,932	14,631	14,296	13,961	13,458	12,905	12,297
20										
21	**Pre-Tax Cash Flow**									
22	Sources of Funds									
23	Pre-Tax Income + Depreciation	13,672	15,234	14,932	14,631	14,296	13,961	13,458	12,905	12,297
24	Debt Funds									
25	Equity Funds									
26	Total Sources	13,672	15,234	14,932	14,631	14,296	13,961	13,458	12,905	12,297
27										
28	**Uses of Funds**									
29	Capital Equipment									
30	Interest During Construction									

Table 6-1 (continued)

31	Debt Repayment	13,075	0	0	0	0	0	0	0	0
32	Total Fixed Uses	13,075								
33										
34	Funds Available for Dividends	597	15,234	14,932	14,631	14,296	13,961	13,458	12,905	12,297
35										
36	**Tax Effect**									
37	Pre-Tax Income — Equity	13,672	15,234	14,932	14,631	14,296	13,961	13,458	12,905	12,297
38	Income Taxes	6,836	7,617	7,466	7,315	7,148	6,980	6,729	6,452	6,148
39	Income Tax Credit									
40	Tax Savings (Liability)	−6,836	−7,617	−7,466	−7,315	−7,148	−6,980	−6,729	−6,452	−6,148
41	After Tax Net Equity Cash Flow	−6,238	7,617	7,466	7,315	7,148	6,980	6,729	6,452	6,148
42	Present Value									
43	PV2									
44										
45										
46										
47										

Table 6-2

Analysis of wind power project using the Avoided Cost trajectory

		1983	1984	1985	1986	1987	1988	1989	1990	1991
1	SCE Avoided Cost Path									
2	Year	1983	1984	1985	1986	1987	1988	1989	1990	1991
3	**Assumptions**									
4	KWh/yr	223,380	223,380	223,380	223,380	223,380	223,380	223,380	223,380	223,380
5										
6	Avoided Cost (¢/kwh)	6.40	6.60	6.80	7.00	7.40	7.90	8.50	9.00	9.70
7										
8	**Income Statement**									
9										
10	Floor Price (¢/kwh)	8.50	8.50	8.50	8.50	8.50	8.50	8.50	8.50	8.50
11	Total Payments	18,987	18,987	18,987	18,987	18,987	18,987	18,987	18,987	18,987
12	Revenues — Avoided Costs	14,296	14,743	15,189	15,636	16,530	17,647	18,987	20,104	21,667
13	Tracking Account									
14	Discount Factor	0.97	0.97	0.97	0.97	0.97	0.97	0.97	0.97	0.97
15	Discount Revenue	13,867	14,300	14,734	15,167	16,034	17,117	18,417	19,501	21,017
16	Annual Payment — PTA	−5,119	−4,686	−4,253	−3,819	−2,953	−1,869	−569	513	2,030
17										
18	**Expenses**									
19	O & M	1,429	1,474	1,518	1,563	1,653	1,764	1,898	2,010	2,166
20	Land Rent	714	737	759	781	826	882	949	1,005	1,083
21	Depreciation	18,412	27,005	25,777	25,777	25,777				
22	Interest	10,885	10,322	9,680	8,949	8,115	7,164	6,080	4,844	3,436

	1992	1993	1994	1995	1996	1997	1998	1999	2000
23 Total Expenses	31,441	39,538	37,735	37,071	36,372	9,811	8,928	7,859	6,686
24									
25 Pre-Tax Income	−17,145	−24,795	−22,546	−21,435	−19,841	7,835	10,059	12,244	14,981
26									
27 **Pre-Tax Cash Flow**									
28 Sources of Funds									
29 Pre-Tax Income + Depreciation	1,266	2,209	3,231	4,342	5,935	7,835	10,059	12,244	14,981
30 Debt Funds	77,750								
31 Equity Funds	45,000								
32 Total Sources	124,016	2,209	3,231	4,342	5,935	7,835	10,059	12,244	14,981
33									
34 **Uses of Funds**									
35 Capital Equipment	122,750								
36 Interest During Construction									
37 Debt Repayment	4,020	4,584	5,225	5,957	6,790	7,742	8,825	10,060	11,469
38 Total Fixed Uses	126,770	4,584	5,225	5,957	6,790	7,742	8,825	10,060	11,469
39									
40 Funds Available for Dividends	−2,753	−2,374	−1,993	−1,614	−854	93	1,234	2,184	3,512
41									
42 **Tax Effect**									
43 Pre-Tax Income — Equity	−17,145	−24,795	−22,546	−21,435	−19,841	7,835	10,059	12,244	14,981
44 Income Taxes	−8,572	−12,397	−11,273	−10,717	−9,920	3,917	5,029	6,122	7,490
45 Income Tax Credit	31,250								
46 Tax Savings (Liability)	39,822	12,397	11,273	10,717	9,920	−3,917	−5,029	−6,122	−7,490
47									
48 After Tax Net Equity	−7,930	10,023	9,279	9,102	9,066	−3,824	−3,795	−3,937	−3,978
49 Present Value	24,854								
50 PV2	9,842								
51									

	1992	1993	1994	1995	1996	1997	1998	1999	2000
1 SCE Avoided Cost Path									
2 Year									
3 **Assumptions**									
4 KWh/yr	223,380	223,380	223,380	223,380	223,380	223,380	223,380	223,380	223,380
5									
6 Avoided Cost (¢/kwh)	10.40	11.20	12.10	13.00	14.00	15.00	16.50	18.15	19.97
7									
8 **Income Statement**									
9									
10 Floor Price (¢/kwh)	8.50	8.50	8.50	8.50	8.50	8.50	8.50	8.50	8.50
11 Total Payments	18,987	18,987	18,987	18,987	18,987	18,987	18,987	18,987	18,987
12 Revenues — Avoided Costs	23,231	25,018	27,028	29,039	31,273	33,507	36,857	40,543	44,597
13 Tracking Account									

Table 6-2 (continued)

14	Discount Factor	0.97	0.97	0.97	0.97	0.97	0.97	0.97	0.97	0.97
15	Discount Revenue	22,534	24,268	26,218	28,168	30,335	32,501	35,751	39,327	43,259
16	Annual Payment — PTA	3,547	5,280	7,230	9,180	11,347	13,514	16,764	20,339	24,272
17										
18	**Expenses**									
19	O & M	2,323	2,501	2,702	2,903	3,127	3,350	3,685	4,054	4,459
20	Land Rent	1,161	1,250	1,351	1,451	1,563	1,675	1,842	2,027	2,229
21	Depreciation									
22	Interest	1,830								
23	Total Expenses	5,314	3,752	4,054	4,355	4,690	5,026	5,528	6,081	6,689
24										
25	Pre-Tax Income	17,916	21,265	22,974	24,683	26,582	28,480	31,329	34,461	37,908
26										
27	**Pre-Tax Cash Flow**									
28	Sources of Funds									
29	Pre-Tax Income + Depreciation	17,916	21,265	22,974	24,683	26,582	28,480	31,329	34,461	37,908
30	Debt Funds									
31	Equity Funds									
32	Total Sources	17,916	21,265	22,974	24,683	26,582	28,480	31,329	34,461	37,908
33										
34	**Uses of Funds**									
35	Capital Equipment	13,075								
36	Interest During Construction									
37	Debt Repayment	13,075								
38	Total Fixed Uses		0	0	0	0	0	0	0	0
39										
40	Funds Available for Dividends	4,841	21,265	22,974	24,683	26,582	28,480	31,329	34,461	37,908
41										
42	**Tax Effect**									
43	Pre-Tax Income — Equity	17,916	21,265	22,974	24,683	26,582	28,480	31,329	34,461	37,908
44	Income Taxes	8,958	10,632	11,487	12,341	13,291	14,240	15,664	17,230	18,954
45	Income Tax Credit									
46	Tax Savings (Liability)	-8,958	-10,632	-11,487	-12,341	-13,291	-14,240	-15,664	-17,230	-18,954
47										
48	After Tax Net Equity	-8,958	10,632	11,487	12,341	13,291	14,240	15,664	17,230	18,954
49	Present Value									
50	PV2									
51										

Table 6-3

Wind project analysis assumptions

1. Capitilization
   Debt: 63.3% of Capital
       10 Year Amortization, 14% Interest
   Equity: 36.7% of Capital
       Expected Return (after taxes) = 30%

2. Expenses
   O & M/year = 10% of avoided Cost Revenues
   Rent/year = 5% of avoided Cost Revenues

3. Taxation (Federal only)
   Depreciation = 5 year ACRS
   Tax Credit = 25%
   Tax Rate = 50%

Are the negative investor earnings in years 6-10 a threat to the economic feasibility of this project? The answer is probably not. While the negative earnings clearly encourage the investor to sell the project in Year 6, a more prudent approach would be to set aside some of the earnings from years 1–5 to cover the deficits in order to benefit from long-term profits. A third alternative would be to abandon the project in year 6, but this alternative would not really provide the investor with any escape. In year 6 there would still be approximately $51,000 of unamortized debt, and in all likelihood, in order to be eligible for the 25% tax credit in year 1, the investor would have accepted personal liability for this debt. The IRS has generally required that investors be "at-risk" for those sums upon which they take credits. In this case both the debt and equity would ultimately be the responsibility of the investor, this type of debt is technically known as being of a "recourse nature"; i.e., the lender has recourse to the investor's personal assets to recover his funds. Project finance is more often set up with "non-recourse" debt. In this case lenders must be satisfied that project assets will secure the debt or that it is guaranteed by some outside party (such as a government agency). This usually results in a smaller fraction of debt in project capitalization. The "at-risk" rule also means that the non-recourse debt fraction of investment does not qualify for tax credits. Project developers must choose a financial structure which optimizes the debt, risk and return preferences of their investors. The project characterized by Tables 6-1 and 6-3 is relatively high risk and high-leverage. Other windpower projects have been structured in a more conservative manner, with correspondingly lower expected returns.

To understand the features of the Floor Price version of our example wind power project, it is useful to examine some variations on the cash flows of Table 6-1. We will concentrate attention on three features: (1) Revenues at avoided cost, (2) Longer Term (15 yrs.) Debt, and (3) Ratepayer Repayment for Levelized Floor Prices. These first two features are examined in Tables 6-2 and 6-4.

Let us begin with Table 6-2, where project revenues are calculated at the anticipated trajectory of SCE's avoided cost, and not at the Floor Price. On this basis the project is not feasible because the cash flow constraint is violated: the requirement of positive values for Funds Available for Dividends is not met. Year One revenues at the avoided cost are about $4,700 less than at the Floor Price of 8.5 cents/kWh. This turns a $1,938 surplus of cash into a $2,753 deficit. These cash deficits diminish as avoided cost increases — only by year 6 (1988) does cash flow become positive, while in the meantime, a $9,590 cash deficit has been accumulated. For the project to be feasible, there must be additional capital to finance this six-year projected deficit. This capital must be raised at the start of the project, thereby increasing its initial cost and reducing investor returns. Notice that if the entire projected deficit were raised with equity funds and there were no tax credits for these funds, the present value of equity returns for the year 2000 at 30% would be negligible ($9843 − 9590 = $253). Thus even additional capitalization may diminish returns so much that investors would not be able to earn the cost of capital.

Let us compare this situation to that illustrated in Table 6-4, in which the project obtains 15-year debt instead of 10-year debt. The difference in annual payments at 14% interest, is $2,247, almost enough to eliminate the year 1 cash deficit, which appears in Table 6-4 as $506. The total cash deficit is only $632 and ends in Year 3. Financing an additional $632 out of equity funds would not cause any major change in equity returns. The present value of the equity returns at 30% to the Year 2000 would go down to $15,983 ($16,615 − 632). This is still substantially better than the Floor Price value of $13,297. It is clear that with 15-year debt and avoided cost, the project is both feasible and more attractive than a Floor Price version with 10-year debt. Why then not do it this way?

There are several answers to this question. The most important reason is that lenders will not loan to such projects for 15 years, a phenomenon that is not unique to wind power or other small energy projects. It represents part of a restructuring of the debt markets in general away from long-term fixed-interest securities and toward variable rates or much shorter debt maturities. One major effect of prolonged and unanticipated inflation is an erosion of the value of long-term fixed rate-debt, a condition from which borrowers gain and creditors lose. To protect themselves against such losses, which were very substantial in the late 1970s, lenders reduce their risk by limiting the term of loans, indexing interest rates or both. The shortening of debt maturities makes investment in long-lived assets less attractive because the financing of such assets does not match their economic lifetimes. In the case of variable rate debt the investor's problem is that costs are not predictable.

Even if longer-term debt were available in principle, it is not clear that small power projects could obtain financing under revisable avoided-cost tariffs. There is still a predictability problem for future avoided cost. Even if today's avoided cost were enough to meet debt service, what is to say that it won't go down in the future? Indeed the forecast of SCE avoided cost in this example turned out to be substantially incorrect by the mid 1980s when the world price of oil (on which this forecast was implicitly based) went down by a factor of two instead of increasing steadily as expected. Lenders need assurances about project revenues over the

Table 6-4

Southern California Edison Avoided Cost path (15-year debt)

	1983	1984	1985	1986	1987	1988	1989	1990	1991
1 SCE Avoided Cost Path (15 Year Debt)									
2 Year									
3 **Assumptions**									
4 KWh/yr	223,380	223,380	223,380	223,380	223,380	223,380	223,380	223,380	223,380
5									
6 Avoided Cost (¢/kwh)	6.40	6.60	6.80	7.00	7.40	7.90	8.50	9.00	9.70
7									
8 **Income Statement**									
9									
10 Floor Price (¢/kwh)	8.50	8.50	8.50	8.50	8.50	8.50	8.50	8.50	8.50
11 Total Payments	18,987	18,987	18,987	18,987	18,987	18,987	18,987	18,987	18,987
12 Revenues — Avoided Costs	14,296	14,743	15,189	15,636	16,530	17,647	18,987	20,104	21,667
13 Tracking Account									
14 Discount Factor	0.97	0.97	0.97	0.97	0.97	0.97	0.97	0.97	0.97
15 Discount Revenue	13,867	14,300	14,734	15,167	16,034	17,117	18,417	19,501	21,017
16 Annual Payment — PTA	-5,119	-4,686	-4,253	-3,819	-2,953	-1,869	-569	513	2,030
17									
18 **Expenses**									
19 O & M	1,429	1,474	1,518	1,563	1,653	1,764	1,898	2,010	2,166
20 Land Rent	714	737	759	781	826	882	949	1,005	1,083
21 Depreciation	18,412	27,005	25,777	25,777	25,777				
22 Interest	10,885	10,637	10,353	10,031	9,663	9,243	8,766	8,221	7,600
23 Total Expenses	31,441	39,853	38,408	38,153	37,920	11,890	11,614	11,236	10,850
24									
25 Pre-Tax Income	-17,145	-25,110	-23,219	-22,517	-21,389	5,756	7,373	8,867	10,817
26									
27 **Pre-Tax Cash Flow**									
28 Sources of Funds									
29 Pre-Tax Income + Depreciation	1,266	1,894	2,558	3,260	4,387	5,756	7,373	8,867	10,817
30 Debt Funds	77,750								
31 Equity Funds	45,000								
32 Total Sources	124,016	1,894	2,558	3,260	4,387	5,756	7,373	8,867	10,817
33									
34 **Uses of Funds**									
35 Capital Equipment	122,750								
36 Interest During Construction									

		1992	1993	1994	1995	1996	1997	1998	1999	2000
37	Debt Repayment	1,773	2,021	2,305	2,627	2,995	3,414	3,892	4,438	5,059
38	Total Fixed Uses	124,523	2,021	2,305	2,627	2,995	3,414	3,892	4,438	5,059
39										
40	Funds Available for Dividends	−506	−126	253	633	1,392	2,342	3,481	4,429	5,758
41										
42	**Tax Effect**									
43	Pre-Tax Income — Equity	−17,145	−25,110	−23,219	−22,517	−21,389	5,756	7,373	8,867	10,817
44	Income Taxes	−8,572	−12,555	−11,609	−11,258	−10,694	2,878	3,686	4,433	5,408
45	Income Tax Credit	31,250								
46	Tax Savings (Liability)	39,822	12,555	11,609	11,258	10,694	−2,878	−3,686	−4,433	−5,408
47										
48	After Tax Net Equity	−5,683	12,428	11,862	11,891	12,087	−535	−205	−4	349
49	Present Value	31,175								
50	PV2	16,615								
51										

		1992	1993	1994	1995	1996	1997	1998	1999	2000
1	SCE Avoided Cost Path (15 Year Debt)									
2	Year	1992	1993	1994	1995	1996	1997	1998	1999	2000
3	**Assumptions**									
4	KWh/yr	223,380	223,380	223,380	223,380	223,380	223,380	223,380	223,380	223,380
5										
6	Avoided Cost (¢/kwh)	10.40	11.20	12.16	13.00	14.00	15.00	16.50	18.15	19.97
7										
8	**Income Statement**									
9										
10	Floor Price (¢/kwh)	8.50	8.50	8.50	8.50	8.50	8.50	8.50	8.50	8.50
11	Total Payments	18,987	18,987	18,987	18,987	18,987	18,987	18,987	18,987	18,987
12	Revenues — Avoided Costs	23,231	25,018	27,028	29,039	31,273	33,507	36,857	40,543	44,597
13	Tracking Account									
14	Discount Factor	0.97	0.97	0.97	0.97	0.97	0.97	0.97	0.97	0.97
15	Discount Revenue	22,534	24,268	26,218	28,168	30,335	32,501	35,751	39,327	43,259
16	Annual Payment — PIA	3,547	5,280	7,230	9,180	11,347	13,514	16,764	20,339	24,272
17										
18	**Expenses**									
19	O & M	2,323	2,501	2,702	2,903	3,127	3,350	3,685	4,054	4,459
20	Land Rent	1,161	1,250	1,351	1,451	1,563	1,675	1,842	2,027	2,229
21	Depreciation									
22	Interest	6,891	6,084	5,164	4,114	2,918	1,555			
23	Total Expenses	10,375	9,836	9,218	8,469	7,608	6,581	5,528	6,081	6,689
24										

Table 6-4 (continued)

25	Pre-Tax Income	12,855	15,181	17,810	20,569	23,664	26,925	31,329	34,461	37,908
26										
27	**Pre-Tax Cash Flow**									
28	Sources of Funds									
29	Pre-Tax Income + Depreciation	12,855	15,181	17,810	20,569	23,664	26,925	31,329	34,461	37,908
30	Debt Funds									
31	Equity Funds									
32	Total Sources	12,855	15,181	17,810	20,569	23,664	26,925	31,329	34,461	37,908
33										
34	**Uses of Funds**									
35	Capital Equipment									
36	Interest During Construction									
37	Debt Repayment	5,767	6,574	7,495	8,544	9,740	11,103	0	0	0
38	Total Fixed Uses	5,767	6,574	7,495	8,544	9,740	11,103	0	0	0
39										
40	Funds Available for Dividends	7,088	8,607	10,315	12,025	13,924	15,822	31,329	34,461	37,908
41										
42	**Tax Effect**									
43	Pre-Tax Income — Equity	12,855	15,181	17,810	20,569	23,664	26,925	31,329	34,461	37,908
44	Income Taxes	6,427	7,590	8,905	10,284	11,832	13,462	15,664	17,230	18,954
45	Income Tax Credit									
46	Tax Savings (Liability)	-6,427	-7,590	-8,905	-10,284	-11,832	-13,462	-15,664	-17,230	-18,954
47										
48	After Tax Net Equity	660	1,016	1,410	1,740	2,092	2,359	15,664	17,230	18,954
49	Present Value									
50	PV2									
51										

whole term of the loan. Where avoided cost is based upon oil and gas prices, there is no guarantee that these will not decrease.

There is also another series of influences on avoided cost apart from fuel prices which affect the efficiency of electricity production. Recall that the energy portion of avoided cost is calculated as follows

$$\begin{matrix} \text{Avoided} \\ \text{Energy} \\ \text{Cost} \end{matrix} = \frac{\text{Fuel Cost}}{(\$/\text{Btu})} \times \frac{\text{Heat Rate}}{(\text{Btu}/\text{Kwh})} \qquad (6\text{-}2)$$

Several factors can cause the efficiency to improve (i.e., the Heat Rate to go down). These include increased hydroelectric generation and baseload generation additions. Both such changes cause increasingly efficient units to become the marginal producer of electricity. PG&E, for example, experienced at least a 10% decline in the marginal heat rate when the Diablo Canyon units came into full operation. Imported power from the Pacific Northwest in large quantities can reduce the marginal heat rate still further. Even where 10-year debt is concerned, lenders do not want to take these risks. Therefore QFs seek some kind of assurance in long-term levelized energy contracts that the price will not go below a certain value. Thus some kind of price floor is an essential feature of energy contacts for QFs, and involves some regulatory complexity.

The basic problem with levelized Floor Price contracts is that premature project termination may result in ratepayer losses. The QF gets paid above avoided cost with a levelized Floor Price for some period of time. In return, the QF accepts a price below avoided cost to pay back the overpayment. Figure 6-1 illustrates this process. From t = 0 to t = t*, the QF is overpaid. After t*, the ratepayer benefits by paying less than avoided cost. If the project terminates before t*, the ratepayer clearly loses. Even if the QF produces after t*, the amount of time required to pay back the excess payments made before t* may be long. Project termination before repayment is another ratepayer risk. The problem for regula-

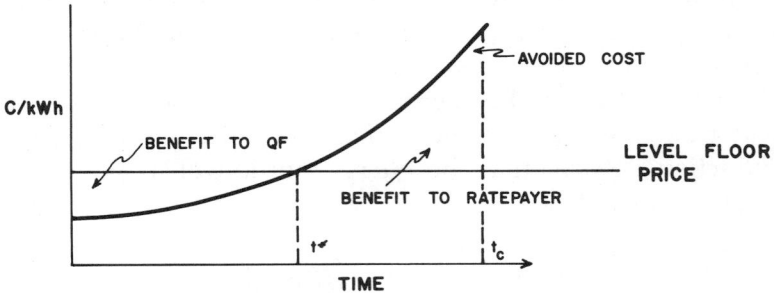

XBL 842-682

Figure 6-1. QF accepts price below avoided cost to "pay back" the overpayment.

tors is to balance these risks and find suitable pricing formulas.

The difficulty of the task is substantial. To begin with, "paying back" must be defined more precisely. Operationally we are looking for a time (t_e) when the levelizing period ends such that the present value of overpayments equals the present value of underpayments. Formally

$$\sum_{i=1}^{t^*} \frac{\left(P_F - AC_i \right)}{(1+r)^i} = \sum_{i=t^*}^{t_e} \frac{\left(AC_i - P_F \right)}{(1+r)^i} \quad (6\text{-}3)$$

where

P_F = the Floor Price per kWh,
AC_i = the avoided cost per KWh in year i, and
r = the discount rate.

We cannot specify t^* and t_e in advance because we do not know what the avoided cost trajectory will be. Of course we can make a forecast of the future avoided cost, but it cannot be estimated with accuracy.

Even if we find a rule that will satisfy Eq. (6-3) under most outcomes, there is an additional issue. In agreeing to level Floor Price contracts, ratepayers undertook risk. Shouldn't there be some continuing benefit as compensation for this risk? The typical proposal for such compensation involves formulas for discount on avoided cost. That is, in the long run, the ratepayer does not pay full avoided cost to QFs seeking levelized Floor Price contracts. There are a variety of ways in which avoided cost discounts can be structured in proportion to the terms of levelized Floor Price contracts. In Tables 6-2 and 6-4 we indicate one such device known as the Payment Tracking Account (PTA).

Some record must be kept of over- and under-payments (line 11 minus line 15 in Table 6-2), and a rule developed for determining when repayment has occurred. The issues involved in fixing such a rule include whether avoided cost should be discounted, by how much, and whether interest should be paid on the unamortized PTA balance. All of these factors will affect the size of the PTA and the time it takes to zero out. There are a number of possible variations on this theme. Perhaps the most difficult issue is determining the size of avoided cost discount which should be specified for a given Floor Price. The example in Tables 6-2 and 6-4 is an instance of the "10 to 1" rule, which has been suggested by small power producers (Weisenmiller, 1983). The idea is to discount avoided cost by 1% for every 10% that the levelized price is above the Year-One avoided cost. In this case, the 8.5 price is about 33% above the 6.4 avoided cost in 1983; thus the discount is set at 3%. In fact, the "10 to 1" rule has not been widely accepted, but then neither has any other formula.

The PTA mechanism involves another substantial uncertainty that limits its applicability. PG&E has said that the tax status of the PTA is not clear. It may not be construed by the IRS as a deductible business expense, and instead may be characterized as a loan to the QF. In some ways, of course, it is a loan. Therefore, PG&E demanded that QFs receiving new PTA contracts assume PG&E's tax liability attributable to the PTA, and agree to pay any extra taxes PG&E incurred. Understandably, QFs were reluctant to do this, and later agreements did not include a PTA.

The example discussed so far neglects consideration of the potential for wind turbine technology to mature, and become more economic. The most obvious form of improvement would be a reduction in capital costs due to the economies of increased production. There is evidence that such cost economies were achieved by the mid 1980s (Cox, Blumstein and Gilbert, 1986). Unfortunately such savings were effectively cancelled by a performance record substantially poorer than the assumed 34% capacity factor in our example. Many of the machines installed in California in the early 1980s were of very poor quality — in many cases they failed to achieve capacity factors greater than 10%. Even the best performers were only able to achieve a capacity factor of about 25%. The net effect of relatively low capital costs but poor operations was that by the time the energy tax credits were due to expire, the net productivity of wind turbines had not improved over the case represented by our example.

Expiration of federal tax credits has drastically slowed the growth of the wind energy industry. Even before tax reform, the special 15% energy tax credit which was so important for investor returns was scheduled to expire. For a project similar to our example, investor returns would fall to a rate very nearly the same as the assumed cost of debt; i.e., around 14%. Tax reforms that eliminated other credits, reduced depreciation allowances and lowered the marginal tax rates further eroded the tax shelter value of wind projects (Kahn and Goldman, 1987). For such meager returns the risks of investing in wind projects are no longer worthwhile.

By contrast, cogeneration has increasingly emerged as the most economically viable small-power technology under PURPA. It does not depend on tax benefits to produce its return. Yet many of the same financing problems that face wind turbine investors are present in this case as well. It is useful to examine the economics of this technology, and to see how revenue stability can be provided in this case without as many of the attendant risks to ratepayers.

6.4 Cogeneration

There are other methods for providing long-term price assurance to QFs that do not depend on the levelized Floor Price idea. The principal approach designed specifically for cogeneration projects is not a price floor but a heat rate floor, based on prices indexed to the utility's price of gas, in a fixed relationship that helps to stabilize prices to QF. To see why this would help cogenerators, we will follow the discussion of Joskow and Jones (1982) to examine the economics of such projects in some detail.

Cogeneration is a joint production process, in which fuel is burned to produce both heat and power. To characterize the efficiency of electricity production by cogenerators, it is convenient to define a concept that measures the net electrical heat rate N. This is a measure of the efficiency of power production after accounting for the joint use of steam. It can be derived from a fuel use identity such as:

$$T_c = T_b + EN \qquad (6-4)$$

where

T_c = total heat rate of the cogenerator (Btu fuel/Btu usable heat),
T_b = total heat rate of the conventional boiler alternative,
     = (Btu fuel/Btu usable heat),
E = electricity production rate (kWh/Btu),
N = net electrical heat rate (Btu/kWh).

In Eq. (6-4) the total fuel consumption of the cogenerator is split into the boiler-only equivalent usage rate T_b and a residual term allocated to electricity production at rate E. Eq.(6-4) can be re-written to give a definition of N as follows:

$$N = \frac{T_c - T_b}{E} . \qquad (6-5)$$

Eq. (6-5) implicitly assumes a constant rate of operation (by assuming E, T_c and T_b to be constant). Therefore the values of N given in Joskow and Jones (4,000 − 7,000 Btu/kWh) represent upper bounds on the efficiency of various cogeneration technologies and therefore lower bounds on the heat rate. When load variations and operating strategies are considered, the net electric heat rates are higher (i.e., efficiency is lower). Merrill's characterization is more representative of actual average values for N, ranging from 6,000 to 8,800 Btu/kWh. By comparison, the average heat rate for utility thermal power is around 10,000 Btu/kWh.

The viability of any particular cogeneration project depends upon the trade-off between the variable cost savings S, and the incremental capital costs K. It is the savings term S

which requires the most analysis. This may be expressed as follows:

$$S = V_b - V_c + V_e \tag{6-6}$$

where

V_b = operating cost of conventional boiler ($ per Btu usable heat),

V_c = cogeneration operating cost ($ per Btu usable heat),

and

V_e = $P_e E$ where P_e = value of electricity ($ per kWh).

Since $V_c > V_b$, it is the electricity credit V_e which determines the size of S. We can rewrite Eq. (6-6) in terms of heat rates and fuel prices in the form:

$$S = P_{fb} T_b - P_{fc} T_c + P_e E \tag{6-7}$$

where

P_{fb} = price of boiler fuel ($/Btu),
P_{fc} = price of cogeneration fuel ($/Btu).

Using Eqs. (6-5) and (6-7) we can write:

$$S = E\left[P_e - NP_{fc} + T_b \left(P_{fb} - P_{fc} \right) \right]. \tag{6-8}$$

The last term in Eq. (6-8) only contributes to S if the cogeneration system uses a different fuel than the conventional boiler. This term will be negative if the cogeneration fuel is more expensive than the conventional boiler fuel (say, gas vs. coal). In some cases, the cogeneration fuel may be less expensive than the conventional boiler fuel (if it were biomass, for example). In this case the last term is positive. Typically the fuels will be the same, so savings are all due to the electricity term. Let us expand P_e in Eq. (6-8) using Eq. (6-2) for avoided cost and assume $P_{fb} = P_{fc}$. Then we can write, with a suitable change of units:

$$S = E\left[HR_u\, P_{fu} - NP_{fc} \right], \tag{6-9}$$

where

HR_u = utility's average incremental heat rate(Btu/kWh), and
P_{fu} = price of utility fuel.

Equation (6-9) illustrates that, in the case where $P_{fu} = P_{fc}$ S depends only on E and $(HR_u - N)$. It is unlikely that P_{fc} will be greater than by any large amount — if the cogenerator used much more expensive fuel than the utility, an enormous efficiency differential $(HR_u - N)$ would be needed to compensate. On the other hand, P_{fc} less than P_{fu} is more plausible. Examples would be coal or biomass cogeneration where the utility burns oil and gas. By far the most typical case will be $P_{fu} = P_{fc}$. In this case Eq.(6-9) becomes

$$S = EP_f \left(HR_u - N \right) . \qquad (6\text{-}10)$$

Equation (6-10) illustrates that cogeneration projects depend critically on their heat rate advantage over utility generation. The difficulty with the relation given in this equation is that none of the quantities involved are constants. We have seen that HR_u depends upon the supply mix of the utility and the balance between supply and demand, and obviously the fuel price P_f can fluctuate. The problem of designing a cogeneration system is choosing a technology and capacity level which optimizes savings compared to capital costs. For a given choice of technology and capacity, there will be fixed values of E and N. The subtle dependencies involve capital cost scale economies and the variations of heat demand. The optimal sizing trade-off can be analyzed by a representation of the heat load variation in the form of a load duration curve.

Figure 6-2 plots steam load versus load duration. Denoting steam load by C and number of hours by Y, then $Y = L(C)$ is the number of hours per year that steam load is at or above the level C. The total steam supplied (TSS) by a cogeneration system of capacity C_i then is given by:

$$TSS = \int_0^{C_i} L(s) \, ds . \qquad (6\text{-}11)$$

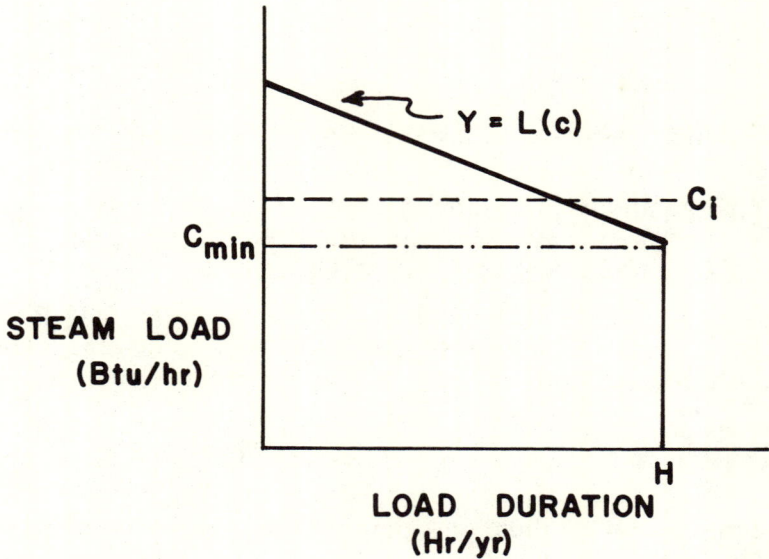

XBL 842-683

Figure 6-2. Steam load versus load duration.

It is usually economic to size cogeneration systems at some level above the minimum load C_{min}. In this case, the total steam supply is less than $C_i H$ and the difference is rejected, that is, dissipated into the environment. To account for this difference in the definition of net heat rate N (Eq. [6-5]), we write the expressions for total heat rates T_b and T_c in terms of TSS, i.e.,

$$T_c = \frac{\text{Fuel Input}_c}{TSS} \quad , \tag{6-12}$$

and

$$T_b = \frac{\text{Fuel Input}_b}{TSS} \quad .$$

Then Eq. (6-5) becomes

$$N = \frac{\Delta F}{TSS \cdot E} \tag{6-13}$$

where

$$\Delta F = \text{Fuel Input}_c - \text{Fuel Input}_b \quad .$$

Compared to Eq. (6-5), the net heat rate defined in Eq. (6-13) for $C_i > C_{min}$ will always be greater than the value for $C_i < C_{min}$. This follows because some fuel is wasted if steam is not supplied, reflected mathematically as $TSS < C_i H$.

We can use Eq.(6-13) in Eq.(6-8) to express the savings term with variable steam loads. Again neglecting the second term of Eq. (6-8) we get

$$S = P_e E - \frac{\Delta F}{TSS} P_f \quad . \tag{6-14}$$

The choice of C_i affects both terms of Eq.(6-14). A larger C_i will increase E, the electricity output. It will also increase ΔF without a proportional increase in TSS, thereby increasing the second term. This creates an operating revenue trade-off; electric revenues go up, but they are counter-balanced by an increase in net fuel costs. The optimum sizing decision requires balancing these revenue effects against the scale economies for capital costs.

You will recall our discussion of scale economies for central station power plants. Eq. (3-11), for example, indicated one specification of such cost curves in which total costs increase less than linearly with capacity. This relation is

$$TC(x) = Kx^{1-a} \quad , \tag{6-15}$$

where

$TC(x)$ = total cost of capacity of size x,
K = constant,

and

a = constant < 1.

In a situation such as this, the incremental cost of capacity diminishes with increasing capacity, i.e.,

$$\frac{dTC(x)}{dx} = \left(1 - a\right) Kx^{-a} \quad . \tag{6-16}$$

Therefore the sizing decision comes down to a trade-off

between the diminishing costs (Eq. [6-16]) and diminishing benefits (Eq.[6-14]) of larger systems.

The last remaining complexity is that capacity is "lumpy"; it is not available in the continuously varying range of sizes implied by Eqs.(6-15) and (6-16). Even though scale economies still persist, the range of actual sizes is not infinite, or even very large. Perhaps the most popular prime mover for cogeneration systems under development in California is the General Electric LM-2500 gas turbine engine. This unit produces 25 MW of electricity at a full-load gross heat rate of 12,500 Btu/kWh. To be economic, such units must serve a fairly large steam or heat load. Only then will the net electric heat rate N be competitive with the utility's incremental heat rate HR_u.

In many cogeneration projects currently under development, the economic trade-offs dictate large electricity production to be sold at avoided cost. The benefits to project developers come primarily from the heat rate difference between N and HRu. To finance projects of this kind, lenders will be secure if the regulator can guarantee a heat rate floor below which the utility's avoided cost payment will not go. This does not eliminate price risk, but mitigates it to a substantial degree, so long as the cogenerator and the utility use the same fuel and the avoided cost price is based on this situation. Then the only exogenous uncertainty is the fuel price (see Eq. [6-10]). These arrangements are most common where the fuel in question is natural gas. While the price may go down, so do the cogenerator's costs, and the lender faces little practical risk. For QFs the problem reduces to determining whether "heat rate floors" offered by utilities yield required returns. If they do not, the projects are not feasible.

There remains the regulatory question concerning whether utility forecasts of "heat rate floors" are reasonable. The magnitude of ratepayer exposure here is considerably less than in the case of Floor Price contracts for wind turbine projects. In the latter case some California producers obtained contracts at $0.09/kWh in the early 1980s. By the mid-1980s the avoided energy price was below $0.03/kWh due to declining natural gas prices. The change in heat rates over this period was considerably smaller—the utility heat rate dropped perhaps 30%. Because of the inherent long-term uncertainty, it is difficult to have confidence in any forecast of heat rates, although they are more reliable than price forecasts. The basic decision facing regulators under these circumstances is to trade off the desirability of obtaining long-term supply against the uncertainty over price.

California's experience with long-term heat rate contracts is mixed. Such contracts were offered in the summer of 1983, under a procedure known as Interim Standard Offer No. 4 (ISO4). The immediate response by QFs was not particularly strong. As perceptions grew that oil prices were declining and any revision in ISO4 terms would be less favorable, a "gold rush" mentality developed and very large numbers of these contracts were signed. By 1985 the CPUC suspended ISO4. By this time contracts representing over 17,000 MW of capacity were outstanding, although very real uncertainty existed about how many of these projects would reach operational status. Since the cost to developers of signing these contracts was low and the potential benefits were great, developer behavior was rational. A considerable planning problem was created by the ISO4 gold rush, because no one knew what the future QF supplies would really be.

Several lessons emerged from this experience. First, it became clear that very substantial amounts of capacity could be obtained in principle from long-term heat rate contracts. Second, a major failure of ISO4 was its open-ended nature. There were no quantity limits associated with the prices offered, so no supply and demand feedback was reflected in the pricing terms. Third, the whole notion of avoided cost becomes very difficult to define if the principal supply alternatives are actually QF projects and not utility costs.

While the California experience was unique because state regulators required the utilities to offer long-term contracts (only Texas, New Jersey and Maine showed similar substantial out pourings of QF projects), the lessons of ISO4 had a significant effect on the evolution of PURPA. First, interest began to increase in adapting to the large potential QF supply (mostly cogeneration) by instituting a competitive bidding procedure to allocate long-term QF contracts. Secondly, a shift in QF sizing strategy emerged that began to center on bypass projects that only met industrial on-site electrical demands and did not depend on avoided cost sales. These two trends require independent analysis.

6.5 Bypass and Bidding

Several of the principal assumptions implicit in the original PURPA legislation were shown to be wrong during its first decade of implementation. The avoided cost notion on which QF pricing was based was usually interpreted as being identical with SRMC, although states that sought to encourage QF development included payment for the long-run capacity benefits as well. As the discussion in Sec. 5.4 indicates, avoided cost and SRMC diverge when QF supplies are large. In QF glut environments, it can be increasingly argued that the true avoided cost is no longer determined by the utility cost, but by the costs of the QFs themselves. It is this argument which led to the interest in bidding and auction systems for QF contracts. The inaccuracy of the implicit PURPA assumption that QF supply was small led not only to auctions, but also to "bypass" — energy consumers producing their own power, bypassing the utility companies.

The original estimates of PURPA impact (FERC, 1980) recognized the possibility of bypass in certain limited markets. The basic motivation for a bypass project is that retail rates for such customers are higher than the cost of independent supply. The potential for this happening was first thought to be limited to the very high-cost commercial building sector in New York City, where retail utility rates are at the highest level in the country. Actually PURPA experience has shown that more bypass projects have been initiated by the industrial sector, because industrial plants are more likely to attain the minimum economic scale for cogeneration than other facilities in other sectors. Interest in independent supply has been spread around many regions, largely as a response of industrial customers to the rise in utility rates caused by the phase-in of expensive new power plants. In California, bypass also has been motivated by the large PURPA-related costs associated with QF developments, and industrial electricity rates that subsidized other customer classes.

The utility cost structure during the formulation and early implementation of PURPA was characterized by SRMC at higher levels than retail rates. As Eq. (6-14) shows, the value of a cogeneration project depends critically on the price of the displaced electricity. If avoided cost prices are greater than retail rates, cogenerators will choose larger-capacity plants to capture the extra value. By the mid-1980s, the relationship between SRMC and retail rates had effectively reversed (recall Figure 1-4). With retail rates at substantially higher levels than SRMC, the incremental value of cogeneration capacity for sale to the utility is low. This has led to the bypass sizing strategy.

At some point in the 1990s it is possible that avoided cost will again approach and perhaps exceed retail rates. As demand continues to grow and supplies remain relatively stable, higher-cost sources of electricity must be used more often, and the value of electricity on the margin increases. There is likely to be wide regional variation in this process depending on the balance between regional economic growth, the amount of bypass from large customers, previous QF development and other factors. When the need for new capacity emerges, there will be efforts to modify the PURPA implementation process. The modification which appears most promising is the auctioning of long-term contracts to QF bidders.

The auction mechanism has already been implemented in Maine, and there is similar activity in Massachusetts. California and other states are considering the adoption of this approach as well. The New England region, however, has experienced the greatest need for new power in the mid-1980s, and therefore has had to face the PURPA implementation lessons soonest. The three principles which are common to the auction proposals are: (1) recognition of the need for long-term contracts, (2) limitation of contract offers to pre-specified amounts of capacity, and (3) the desirability of competition among QF bidders. These principles do not define the form of a PURPA auction with any precision. There are many choices involving format, design, bid evaluation and acceptance rules, and the role of negotiation. Many of these issues have been reviewed by Rothkopf, et al. (1987). We will summarize the issues and choices involved in achieving the desirable properties of the auction mechanism.

The first issue which arises in the design of auctions is the choice of format. There are two principal choices of format; bids can either be oral (i.e., open for observation by all) or they can be sealed. Winning bidders can either be paid the price of their bid ("first price") or the price of the first losing bidder ("second price," or in the case of multiple items, a "non-discriminatory" price). Given the magnitude of the projects and their complexity, it is unlikely that oral formats can be used. Although there are theoretical arguments in favor of the non-discriminatory procedure, these are not robust, and this format is rare in actual practice. It is therefore likely that PURPA contract auctions will be of the familiar "discriminatory" (lowest bids win), sealed-bid type.

The role of non-price factors in the evaluation of bids involves a trade-off between simplicity and complexity. The approaches taken by the two large utilities in Massachusetts illustrate this contrast. Western Massachusetts Electric uses a highly complex scoring mechanism to rank proposals on criteria including the financial risk they impose on utility ratepayers, dispatchability (ability and willingness to follow load fluctuation to some degree or another), the bidder's operational profile, experience, and credit rating. Boston Edison, by contrast, considers some of these factors, but much less elaborately. Rules proposed for future California auctions neglect all non-price features.

Many difficulties can arise from the imposition of a quantity limit on the amount of capacity that can be purchased. Because QF projects come in discrete chunks, it is unlikely that the sum of capacity offered by the "best" bidders will equal the quantity desired. Rothkopf calls this the "lumpiness" problem. There are a number of procedures that can be used to mitigate lumpiness. First, a reasonable tolerance can be defined around the desired quantity. Second, the marginal bidder can be given an opportunity to downsize the quantity offered if it is too big to be acceptable given the other lower bids. Third, in the event the quantity offered by the marginal bidder is too large, the utility can value the excess power at some appropriate avoided cost to determine if it is acceptable. Using all of these remedies will require a rather detailed protocol for determining in what order these measures are applied. The last available measure is directed at the form of bids. Lumpiness can be reduced if bidders are encouraged to offer multiple bids for incremental quantities, a form of institutionalized downsizing which forces the bidder to offer some approximation to its own cost curve.

Very little experience with the auction mechanism for PURPA contracts exists. The information available suggests that the process is feasible, and can have a beneficial effect on consumer costs. Whether this experience will generalize and become the standard form of PURPA implementation is unclear. In addition to the practical design issues just outlined, there may be issues of legal interpretation as well. If successful on a broad scale, the auction mechanism may offer a means of reducing the role of regulation in the determination of bulk power prices. Whether this may lead to deregulation remains to be seen.

Chapter 7

Demand-Side Utility Programs

7.1 Introduction

The traditional demand-side activity of utilities had been marketing new loads by promoting appliances, all-electric homes, or electric industrial processes. With the cost increases of the 1970s, a new interest in conservation emerged in the utility industry. This did not occur uniformly or very quickly. Although the basic economics of increasing-cost conditions favored conservation activities as broadly beneficial to society, it was not clear what role utilities should take in promoting it. The minimalist view suggested that utilities should limit their activities to informational programs — for a variety of reasons, the utility was seen as uninterested or unsuited to promote activities that would reduce its market. A more activist view favored direct intervention that would include financial incentives for conservation. In this chapter we will explore the activist view. While this strategy has meant different things in different places, fundamentally the active promotion of conservation programs represents a radical departure from the traditional role of electric utilities. The key distinction involves the capital-intensive nature of efficiency improvements. Even if it is socially efficient to reduce energy consumption, financing the necessary investments is a major undertaking. Consumers will typically under-invest due to imperfect capital markets, regulated energy prices below long-run marginal cost and insufficient information. If the utility were to promote conservation as a demand-side intervention in a serious manner, it would have to participate in financing efficiency improvements.

233

Various political forces emerged advocating that utilities finance conservation investments. Some utilities voluntarily initiated such programs, but in many cases outside pressure was fundamental. Intervenors appeared before state regulators arguing that utility resources should be shifted away from central station plants and directed to conservation and small power projects. David Roe of the Environmental Defense Fund represented this perspective in an address at a symposium on this subject in 1980.

> After all, it's the ratepayers' money; its our money. And very frequently the least-cost approach is going to turn out to be conservation and other alternatives.

> The pressure to perform this kind of work, and the pressure to look seriously at alternatives in time to get utilities to invest in them, rather than in large central station plants, is going to be felt ..... I suggest to you that that pressure, directly applied on the utilities, is what will make the difference, what will get utility dollars squarely into conservation and alternatives on a massive scale. This will start to turn all the familiar talk about the virtues of conservation into reality.

> (California Public Utilities Commission, 1980)

Even among intervenors, however, there was no uniformity of opinion. In California the consumer group TURN (Toward Utility Rate Normalization) which had been instrumental in promoting lifeline rates, opposed utility financing of customer conservation. TURN's position was that allowing utilities to finance conservation was just extending their monopoly, and that this was unwise social policy. TURN's opposition did not prevail, however, and was explicitly rejected by the California Public Utilities Commission in approving the major conservation financing program proposed by Pacific Gas and Electric Company (CPUC, 1981). The decision in this case was remarkable for the broad range of issues discussed other than the questions of monopoly and competition. Among the most delicate of all these issues were the questions of equity and fairness.

Fairness questions have dominated many discussions of utility conservation programs. The underlying concern is that some customers will benefit directly from these programs and others will only get indirect benefits, at best. Therefore conservation can amount to cross-subsidization, which regulation should prevent. In this chapter, we will review the evolution of the regulatory perspective on utility conservation programs. The economic framework which was developed to analyze conservation programs addresses such cross-subsidization issues directly. In Section 7.2 this framework will be reviewed in some detail. Later in the chapter, we will see how regulators began to adopt an approach known as a "rate impact" analysis, which was more symmetric in its evaluation of conservation and expansion of supply.

Despite the logic of the concerns for equity, it is reasonable to ask why so much is made about fairness in this context. Leonard Ross, the California PUC Commissioner who led the majority implementing lifeline rates, made this case succinctly at the 1980 symposium mentioned earlier:

> Anyone who starts from the assumption that existing utility rates reflect 2,500 years of Western concern for equity and justice and the only deviation is how you finance a .... conservation program is living in a world of dreams or bias.

While it is certainly true that traditional rate-making is not a model of equity and justice, conservation programs do tend to increase the ways in which costs could be distributed unequally. The basic problem is that not all customers will have the opportunity to participate in these programs. Low-income customers in particular may not benefit directly. Even if existing utility rates also have regressive effects, that should not be reason enough to reject concerns that conservation can make matters worse. It is also possible that the unprecedented change in role for the utility induces the perception that something must have previously been wrong or unfair. Many consumers and their political representatives find it hard to believe that utilities, which formerly promoted consumption, would actually want to reduce their own sales. We will see in Section 7.3 that the nature of regulation does induce some bias into the structure of utility conservation programs. A major ambiguity associated with conservation programs involves their scale. If these programs are essentially small in nature, then the rules of economic analysis are simpler, but the potential for inequities may be greater. If the programs are large enough to alter the supply plans of the utility, then economic analysis becomes more difficult, but issues concerning unequal participation may diminish. In section 7.4 we investigate the scale issue.

Finally, Section 7.5 provides a discussion of current research issues. The utility role in conservation is still not well understood. There are many unsettled planning, evaluation and regulatory aspects to these programs. Among these are questions involving the balancing of short-term against longer-term considerations. With the re-appearance of excess capacity and low short-run marginal costs in the mid-1980s, does the rationale for conservation programs disappear? Under these conditions, the case for marketing re-emerges as the best demand-side intervention.

In this chapter we will focus attention on the conservation strategy. This focus assumes that excess capacity is a short-term phenomenon. The existence of low marginal costs in the near-term and the expectation of high costs in the long-term creates a serious planning problem. For conceptual clarity we begin with an account of the economic conditions favoring utility conservation programs.

7.2 Basic Framework of Analysis

Economic analysis of utility conservation programs is unusually complicated. Useful expositions of the relevant factors are given by White (1981) and Fiske, *et al.* (1981). It is convenient to begin our discussion of the elements involved in economic evaluation by focusing on the generic case of increasing marginal cost conditions under embedded cost regulation.

In an unregulated industry, equilibrium output would not be expanded if marginal cost could not be recovered with marginal revenue. If costs were increasing, prices would be raised correspondingly. If consumers did not want to purchase the commodities at these higher prices, they would not. The cost, price and demand interaction would result in a market-determined equilibrium. For regulated electric utilities, it is typically the case that marginal costs are not reflected in rates. It is unprofitable to increase output when marginal cost is greater than marginal revenue, since the cost of capital cannot be earned and in most states, no provisions exist for the utility to recoup that shortfall through the following year's rates. Because the utility still has the obligation to provide service in this situation, it cannot simply curtail delivery when it would not be profitable. The social allocation of resources under these conditions is also unsatisfactory because there is excessive consumption compared to the cost of resources. Consumption will continue to grow even when the marginal benefit is less than the marginal cost. One way to illustrate the ambiguous nature of conservation under price regulation and high marginal costs is to examine how its benefits are distributed when avoidable marginal costs exceed marginal revenues. White gives a useful discussion of this, starting first from the social perspective.

Society benefits from conservation when the resource costs of increased user efficiency are less than the cost of new utility supply. Formally we may write

$$\begin{matrix} \text{Net} \\ \text{Social} \\ \text{Benefit} \end{matrix} = \begin{matrix} \text{Marginal} \\ \text{Cost} \end{matrix} - \begin{matrix} \text{Conservation} \\ \text{Cost} \end{matrix} \quad . \qquad (7\text{-}1)$$

As long as consumer prices are less than the long-run marginal cost of supply, the consumer benefit of conservation will be less than the net social benefit. In this situation, the utility ratepayer gets that part of the avoided cost benefit of conservation which does not go to the conserving consumer. This can be expressed as

$$\begin{matrix} \text{Net} \\ \text{Ratepayer} \\ \text{Benefit} \end{matrix} = \begin{matrix} \text{Marginal} \\ \text{Cost} \end{matrix} - \begin{matrix} \text{Avoided} \\ \text{Retail} \\ \text{Rates} \end{matrix} \quad , \qquad (7\text{-}2)$$

and

$$\begin{matrix} \text{Net Conserving} \\ \text{Customer Benefit} \end{matrix} = \begin{matrix} \text{Avoided} \\ \text{Retail Rates} \end{matrix} - \begin{matrix} \text{Conservation} \\ \text{Cost} \end{matrix} \quad . \ (7\text{-}3)$$

Together Eqs. (7-2) and (7-3) can be substituted into Eq. (7-1) to show how the social value of conservation is distributed, i.e.,

$$\begin{matrix} \text{Net Social} \\ \text{Benefit} \end{matrix} = \begin{matrix} \text{Net Ratepayer} \\ \text{Benefit} \end{matrix} + \begin{matrix} \text{Net Consuming} \\ \text{Consumer Benefit} \end{matrix} \quad . \ (7\text{-}4)$$

One way utilities might encourage the consumer to invest more in conservation than would be justified by the benefits under average cost pricing [Eq. (7-3)] is by providing incentives that would return some of the social benefits to consumers.

Indeed, the essence of the utility's intervention in the consumer's conservation investment decision is the provision of a financial incentive, as justified by the previous argument. The logic of this argument suggests that Eq. (7-2), the net ratepayer benefit, defines an upper bound on the size of the incentive the utility should offer. While this is certainly true from a distributional point of view, it is not necessarily true from a resource allocation or societal point of view — it is possible to have a situation in which utilities offer such large incentives that some ratepayers are injured by conservation because ratepayers provide the revenues which fund these incentives. Therefore where incentives are provided we must re-write Eqs. (7-2) and (7-3) as follows:

$$\begin{matrix} \text{Net} \\ \text{Ratepayer} \\ \text{Benefit}_{ucp} \end{matrix} = \begin{matrix} \text{Marginal} \\ \text{Cost} \end{matrix} - \begin{matrix} \text{Avoided} \\ \text{Retail Rates} \end{matrix} - \begin{matrix} \text{Conservation} \\ \text{Incentive} \end{matrix} \cdot (7\text{-}5)$$

$$\begin{matrix} \text{Net Conserving} \\ \text{Customer Benefit}_{ucp} \end{matrix} = \qquad\qquad\qquad (7\text{-}6)$$

$$\begin{matrix} \text{Avoided} \\ \text{Retail Rates} \end{matrix} - \begin{matrix} \text{Conservation} \\ \text{Cost} \end{matrix} + \begin{matrix} \text{Conservation} \\ \text{Incentive} \end{matrix}$$

We use the subscript *ucp* to denote the case of a utility conservation program involving incentives. The net social benefit is still the sum of ratepayer and consumer benefits as is unchanged by the conservation incentive, which is simply a transfer payment from ratepayers to conserving customers. Even if Eq. (7-5) < 0 (i.e., ratepayers are injured), the social benefit may be positive. The evaluation question centers on whether we require only positive social benefits, i.e., Eq. (7-4) > 0, or positive ratepayer benefits as well, i.e., Eq. (7-5) > 0.

Utilities which first initiated conservation incentives required both positive social benefits and ratepayer benefits.

This is essentially a strict Pareto optimality rule, as defined in Chapter 3. The rationale for this is equity-related. Equation (7-5) is often referred to as a non-participant cost-effectiveness or a "no losers" test. The ratepayer who does not invest in conservation is discriminated against if Eq. (7-5) < 0. There has been substantial debate over this issue. Some have argued that if the ratepayer loss from conservation is small, then their interest is not unduly damaged. This is like Merrill's concept of strong Pareto optimality where small differences are suppressed.

Another critique of the non-participant test is the demographic or sociological analysis of discrimination in utility conservation programs. Conservation incentives typically involve cost sharing between the utility and the participant consumer. This may be in the form of favorable financing, cash rebates or rate discounts. In all cases the participant consumer must come up with the cash or the credit to finance the major part of the efficient appliance or weatherization installation. Low-income consumers and renters commonly lack either the resources or the incentive to make these investments. Why should a tenant improve the landlord's property? How can low-income consumers benefit from a loan subsidy, if they cannot qualify for credit? These segments of the population will be systematically discriminated against even by a utility conservation program which passed the non-participant test. Such programs can amount to middle class subsidies that will be funded disproportionately by the poor, and represent regressive taxation in the pursuit of economic efficiency.

These arguments have often found a sympathetic ear among regulators reviewing utility conservation programs. One response has been the targeting of low-income consumers for special direct action programs in which the utility installs weatherization or other conservation devices and bears the total cost. Since these efforts will almost certainly fail the non-participant test when considered alone, they may either be limited by the size of the program, or offset by other, less costly incentives. We will consider other examples of such cross-subsidization in the utility's conservation portfolio when we examine the case of Southern California Edison.

In practice, the regulator will often settle for a "not too large" net ratepayer loss from utility conservation programs. It is difficult to specify what the toleration level for this should be. It does highlight, however, the importance of measurement for both costs and benefits. To examine these issues it will be useful to refer in detail to a paper published by White and one by Fiske, *et al.* White speaks from the perspective of a company in which coal-fired generation represents the marginal cost, and the goal of conservation is primarily to reduce energy consumption. Fiske focuses on capacity savings through load management, with a fuel base of oil and gas. Let us begin with White.

Table 7-1 represents estimates made in 1980 of avoided cost components associated with the long-run costs of a coal plant. It also includes a projection of lost revenues over this period. The accounting is done using a mixture of levelized and escalating cost streams. The coal plant capital cost of 27.31 mills/kWh is based on the assumption of a 75% capacity factor (equal to 6570 hr./year) and implies annual fixed costs of $179/kW (levelized). White used a pre-tax cost of capital of 17.1%, which implies a total capital cost of the plant equal to $1,049 per kW. This estimate is somewhat lower than might be expected for a plant ordered in 1980 because it reflects projects under construction at that time. The capacity factor estimated may be somewhat high compared to most operating experience. At a 60% capacity factor, the levelized cost would be 34 mills/kWh. Transmission and distribution costs would be avoided somewhat later than the initial reduction of demand, since it would have taken some length of time for the capacity of the existing system to be reached. Here that lag is assumed by very rough estimates to be four years, thereby reducing the present value of the avoided T&D costs. The category called Dry-Hole Risk represents the avoided risk of investing in supply projects that may never materialize — recall Table 3-1 in which the national totals for cancelled power plants are given. Even if the ratepayers do not bear those costs directly, they will arguably shoulder them through higher capital costs that the utility will incur to compensate investors for the higher risk level. The value chosen for this cost is also an estimate, and a very imprecise one at that. To

Table 7-1

Components of avoided costs immediate long-run marginal cost savings
(Nominal Mills/kWh)

Year	Coal Power Capital	Coal Plant Operating	Peaking	Wheeling	Transmission & Distribution	Dry Hole Risk	Losses	Total Avoided Costs	Lost Revenue
1981	27.31	21.40	1.97	.75		2.73	5.07	59.23	42.4
1982	27.31	23.22	2.12	.81		2.73	5.26	61.45	48.2
1983	27.31	24.99	2.26	.87		2.73	5.46	63.62	49.6
1984	27.31	26.88	2.42	.92		2.73	5.66	65.92	52.1
1985	27.31	28.81	2.57	.98	5.81	2.73	5.87	74.08	56.8
1986	27.31	30.79	2.74	1.05	5.81	2.73	6.08	76.51	60.5
1987	27.31	32.78	2.90	1.11	5.81	2.73	6.30	78.94	62.7
1988	27.31	34.83	3.07	1.18	5.81	2.73	6.52	81.45	65.9
1989	27.31	36.92	3.24	1.24	5.81	2.73	6.75	84.00	71.9
1990	27.31	39.07	3.42	1.31	5.81	2.73	6.98	86.83	77.8
1991	27.31	41.42	3.61	1.38	5.81	2.73	7.23	89.49	80.2
1992	27.31	43.91	3.82	1.46	5.81	2.73	7.50	92.55	81.5
1993	27.31	46.56	4.03	1.54	5.81	2.73	7.79	95.77	82.4
1994	27.31	49.32	4.25	1.63	5.81	2.73	8.09	99.14	89.4
1995	27.31	52.23	4.49	1.72	5.81	2.73	8.40	102.69	96.9
1996	27.31	55.26	4.73	1.81	5.81	2.73	8.73	106.38	99.1
1997	27.31	58.42	4.98	1.90	5.81	2.73	9.07	110.22	107.6
1998	27.31	61.78	5.24	2.00	5.81	2.73	9.43	114.30	115.8
1999	27.31	65.23	5.51	2.11	5.81	2.73	9.80	118.50	199.5
2000	27.31	68.78	5.79	2.22	5.81	2.73	10.19	122.83	125.5
2001	27.31	72.50	6.08	2.32	5.81	2.73	10.59	127.35	131.8
2002	27.31	76.43	6.39	2.44	5.81	2.73	11.01	132.12	138.4
2003	27.31	80.57	6.71	2.57	5.81	2.73	11.46	137.16	145.3
2004	27.31	84.94	7.04	2.69	5.81	2.73	11.93	142.45	152.6
2005	27.31	89.55	7.40	2.83	5.81	2.73	12.43	148.08	160.2
2006	27.31	94.41	7.77	2.97	5.81	2.73	12.95	153.95	168.3
2007	27.31	100.31	8.15	3.12	5.81	2.73	13.50	160.14	176.7
2008	27.31	104.91	8.56	3.28	5.81	2.73	14.08	166.68	185.6
2009	27.31	110.60	8.99	3.44	5.81	2.73	14.69	173.58	194.9
2010	27.31	116.60	9.43	3.61	5.81	2.73	15.33	180.82	204.6
Present Value								760.5	670.6

these three level cost items, White adds operating costs at escalating nominal values. It is interesting to note that White's peaking category, which corresponds to part of the conservation capacity savings, is very low-valued. This suggests that load management will not be particularly interesting to this utility.

To measure the balance between Total Avoided Cost and Lost Revenue, White adds the annual cost components and then finds the present value of the 30-year cost-and-revenue stream. This is legitimate as long as the levelized cost components were levelized using the same discount rate used to "present value" the sum. The present value in Table 7-1 is the same if we add up the rows first and then present value the columns, compared to present valuing the columns first and then adding.

This calculation technique assumes that the utility immediately begins saving the long-run marginal cost (with the exception noted above for T&D). It is as if all the long-run cost is to be incurred in a lump the following year and can be avoided in a lump at will. White also examines the effect of various supply adjustment lags and other arrangements on avoided cost. The point of these calculations is that unless the utility can find a market for the power from its next power plant, conservation will cause an under-recovery of the plant's capital costs because the plant will be under-utilized. Avoided cost will be lower in these cases than in the under-utilized immediate adjustment scenario of Table 7-1. Thus avoided cost benefits depend critically on timing and measure the balance of supply and demand to a large degree. If the conservation programs have a small total impact, then it will be easier to dispose of the avoided capacity than if they were large-scale — unless they were of large enough scale to defer the construction of a power plant, a case that we will treat in Section 7.4.

Avoided cost is far from the only uncertain quantity in the measurement of quantities in Eqs. (7-1) to (7-6). Perhaps the most crucial quantity in the entire exercise is the load impact of a particular conservation measure or program. Here the Fiske *et al.* paper shows considerably more sophistication than the White paper. Instead of relying upon engineering estimates, Fiske reports on actual field measurements PG&E has taken of the load response to air-conditioner cycling. Air-conditioner cycling means that the utility, using direct control devices, turns off the appliance for some fraction of each hour to reduce aggregate power demand. The measurement issue is determining the size of the aggregate load reduction. This is essential for load management programs, where timing and magnitude are critical. The benefits of load management are concentrated into a small number of peak hours of the year. It is useful to examine the PG&E estimation carefully to see what factors are involved.

PG&E develops regression equations to describe the consumption of air-conditioning customers during the cycling period as well as before and after it. The customers are not end-use-metered, but rather their total consumption is broken into 2- or 6-hour periods. Each period's consumption (kWh) is regressed against temperature and dummy variables for cycling and time of day. The sample includes both households with and without cycling devices. The coefficient of the dummy variable for cycling customers, divided by the number of hours per period, gives the kW load impact of the program. Fiske estimates both kW reductions during cycling (-1 kW/customer) and increases during the post-cycling period (+0.45 kW/customer). Because the value of the former outweighs the cost of the latter, the program is productive.

PG&E's cost-effectiveness analysis follows the general lines indicated in Eqs. (7-1) to (7-6). The main interesting features are empirical or judgmental in nature. When PG&E assesses the avoided costs associated with load management, they appear to include avoided T&D. This is certainly clear in our Table 4-2 which is designed to assess the cost-effectiveness of programs such as this one. Fiske's exposition is unclear on this point. If White's assumption is correct, however, that T&D costs are avoided only with a lag, then PG&E is overestimating benefits. A more careful analysis of this issue has shown that the nature of this benefit depends critically on the local demands on the T&D system (Rosenbloom and Eto, 1986). A reduction in benefits would primarily affect the rate-payer or non-participant interest. Indeed, the 1982 assessment of PG&E was that the costs of cycling (incentives to participants and the cost of the switching equipment) exceeded its benefits for ratepayers (Testimony of L. Baldwin, PG&E CPUC Appl. No. 82-12-48, Ex. PG&E-14, Table 1). Nonetheless PG&E recommended such programs on the grounds of their cost-effectiveness to society as a whole.

A further area of ambiguity or uncertainty associated with utility conservation programs involves the size of incentives. These can be difficult to calculate if they are interest rate subsidies, because they depend on the terms of the loan repayment. Many of the original homeowner incentive programs proposed by utilities were zero-interest, delayed repayment loans which only came due when the original owner sold the house. These were both very costly to utilities and uncertain in liquidity since it was not known when such sales would occur. White, for example, assumes a 7.5-year period on average, while in other cases it was decided to eliminate the uncertainty by specifying a 4- or 5-year amortization. This alternative was chosen in the PG&E weatherization financing plan (CPUC, 1981). In some cases, utilities have shown a preference for fixed rebates over loan subsidies because low-interest loans lead suppliers to inflate prices. A well-known incident of this kind involved solar water heating in Southern California.

7.3 Portfolio Considerations

A more difficult problem with incentives is to know how much is enough to induce the desired level of participation. Determining the desired level of participation is itself a complex problem, which typically begins at the level of end-use disaggregation of electricity demand. This kind of detail is commonly used in forecasting models (McMahon, 1987), where statistics on ownership, efficiency and utilization characterize each end-use. These properties of energy consumption are then compared to data on the cost and performance of more efficient devices. The difference between current and projected patterns compared to cost-minimizing alternatives is then calculated. This difference is often referred to as the technical potential. Practical programs only aim at some fraction of the technical potential. It is not uncommon to use some rule of thumb to determine the goal (i.e., the fraction of technical potential) of a particular conservation program. This is not a well-defined problem, but there is a certain amount of evidence suggesting a large range of variation.

To illustrate this concretely, it is useful to examine in some detail the conservation program of the Southern California Edison Company (SCE). One can compare the conservation benefits to the size of the incentives by looking only at the change in utility revenue requirements associated with the various programs. This set of accounting rules is sometimes called the utility perspective. It is related to the social costs in the following way:

$$\frac{\text{Net}}{\text{Social Cost}} = \frac{\text{Net}}{\text{Utility Cost}} + \frac{\text{Net}}{\text{Participant Cost}} \quad (7\text{-}7)$$

where the change in total revenue requirement is defined as the utility cost, and the net participant cost is the cost of the conservation measure, less the incentive from the utility, less the energy savings. Notice that for a mandatory load management program without special rate incentives, there is no difference between the utility cost and the social cost, since the participant pays nothing. Where the participant shares the cost, net social and utility costs will differ. Table 7-2 shows the different relationships between utility cost and benefit of some of the conservation programs proposed by SCE in 1981 and 1982.

The programs listed in this table come from two separate applications by SCE to the CPUC. Although the program as adopted did not include all of the detail presented here, the data are representative of the experiences of SCE and others. Inspection of the program elements aggregated to this level shows an order of magnitude difference in the benefit/cost ratios. The most productive programs from the utility's standpoint are characterized by the relatively small size of the utility incentive compared to customer investment in conservation. The Commercial and Industrial Audit Program typically underwrites about 10% of the customer costs. When these consumer costs are added in, the social benefit/cost ratio is only about 2.5 to 1 instead of 25 to 1 from the utility perspective. Similarly the efficient refrigerator incentive program underwrites about 15% of consumer cost, so that the total social benefit/cost ratio in this case is also about 2.5 to 1. By comparison, all the load management programs have about a 2.2 to 1 benefit-cost ratio. In this case, since all costs are paid by the utility, there is no difference between this perspective and the social perspective.

Table 7-2

1983 Total SCE proposed program — utility perspective
(Millions of 1983 Dollars)

	Cost	Benefit	Benefit/ Cost
1. Commercial and Industrial			
a) Conservation	28	696	
(Audit + Incentives)			
b) Load Management	18	32	
Total	46	728	
2. Residential			
a) Conservation			
1) ZIP/CIP	18	54	
2) Rate Case	17	58 (?)	
b) Load Management	28	68	
Total	63	180	
TOTAL BUDGET COMMITMENT			
Complete Program	109	908	8.3
3. Selected Elements			
a) Total Load Management	46	100	2.2
b) ZIP/CIP Refrigerators	1.5	23	15.3
c) C & I Audits (= 1a)	28	696	24.9
4. Total Program Sensitivity			
a) Without C & I Audits	81	212	2.7
b) Without C & I Audits and	81	154	1.9
Residential Information			
Programs Fail			

The principal problem associated with Table 7-2 is understanding what contributes to the structure of the program as a whole. One way to pose this problem is to ask why SCE allocates such a large fraction of the total budget to load management (42%) when the benefits produced by it are such a small fraction of the total (11%). To answer the question, we will try to account for the uncertainties associated with the Table 7-2 estimates and to consider explicitly the shareholder interest in these programs. These two factors have been largely neglected in the cost-effectiveness accounting framework. Let us begin with the uncertainty issue.

To understand the sources of variability in the benefits estimated for SCE's or any utility conservation program, it is convenient to decompose the benefit term as follows:

$$\text{Conservation Benefit} = \text{Annual Load Impact} \cdot \text{Lifecycle} \cdot \text{Value per Unit} \qquad (7\text{-}8)$$

The value of each term in Eq. (7-8) is uncertain. Even if the load impact were measured, estimates of values needed to calculate the systemwide impact of the measure would have some unavoidable error associated with them. The impact of certain programs, such as information dissemination, is almost impossible to measure. Even if an annual load impact can be determined to within a reasonable tolerance, the persistence or duration of the effect may be uncertain. Eq. (7-8) uses the term "lifecycle" to indicate the number of years the load impact is expected to last. Residential appliances, for instance, have reasonably well-known lifetimes, so the uncertainty with respect to lifecycle may be minimal for appliance efficiency programs. Conservation practices that have a greater dependence on the behavior of consumers can be of very uncertain duration. Even conservation hardware may be removed sooner than had been expected as occupancy or use patterns change.

Finally, there is a substantial difference between uncertainties in the value of energy and that of capacity, particularly in the case of an oil-and-gas fuel-based utility like SCE. Putting quantitative estimates on uncertainties is difficult, but some simple estimates are possible. One way to approach this problem for commodity prices is to examine their variation over time. This variation can be normalized to compare relative variability. We will take up this point of view in some detail in Chapter 8 where measurement issues are explored

Table 7-3

Uncertainty matrix

	Annual Load Impact	Lifecycle	Value per Unit
Information Dissemination	large	large	kWh; $\sigma = 30\%$
Appliance Efficiency	small		kWh; $\sigma = 30\%$
Load Management		moderate	kW; $\sigma = 10\%$

systematically. For present purposes, however, a few simple estimates will suffice. The recent history of oil prices on the world market suggests about a 30% standard deviation of real price from expected values. Gas turbine costs, the typical proxy for capacity value, show only about a 10% standard deviation. This implies that capacity savings are less uncertain per unit of value than oil-and-gas-based fuel savings. The uncertainties in the three terms of Eq. (7-8) are evaluated qualitatively in Table 7-3 for three representative programs.

The Table 7-3 summary suggests that load management benefits are, on the whole, less variable or uncertain than other programs. This greater certainty allows for somewhat lower benefit/cost ratios. A factor perhaps equally important, however, is the recipient of the benefits. Capacity savings associated with load management are essential in the case of SCE to produce net positive ratepayer benefits. One illustration of this is Figure 7-1, which shows the difference between avoided energy costs and lost revenues per conserved kWh estimated by SCE (ZIP/CIP) and by the CPUC staff (Czahar). When a capacity value of roughly 20 mills/kWh is added to these estimates, the value of the benefits to the ratepayer switches from negative (as shown in Figure 7-1) to positive.

Another illustration of the recipient issue is found in Table 7-4. Here SCE's ZIP/CIP program is summarized from three different perspectives. In general, non-participants lose or get

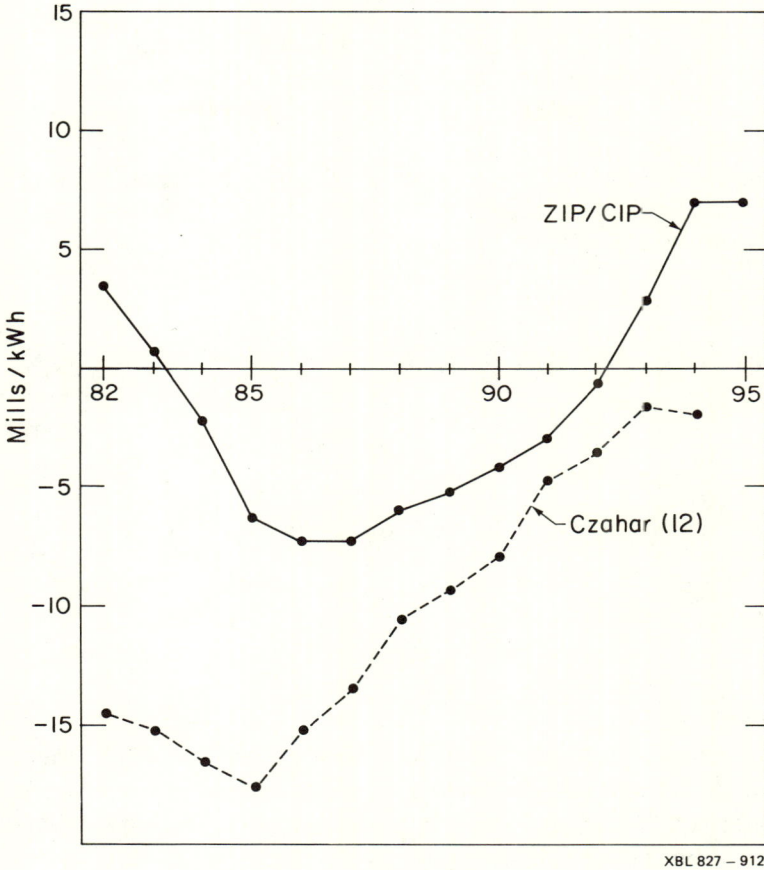

XBL 827 – 912

Figure 7-1. Southern California Edison avoided energy cost — lost revenues.

only a small share of the benefits from each element. When fixed overhead costs of administration are added, the non-participants would always be losers, except for the load management benefits. Only here do the participants receive relatively little, and the non-participants capture a major portion of the benefit.

One less-thoroughly discussed reason why the interests of the ratepayer or nonparticipant get so much attention in the conservation program evaluation literature is that they are

Table 7-4

SCE ZIP/CIP: Distribution of benefits
present value of life-cycle savings
(Thousands of 1983 Dollars)

Measure Type	Utility	Participant	Non-Participant
Building Shell Improvements	1,874	1,502	−4
Appliances			
Heat Pumps	4,048	3,048	−325
Cooling	26,181	19,562	515
Refrigerators	23,125	15,133	1,305
Load Management	2,769	2	2,769
TOTALS	57,997	39,243	4,257
Fixed Costs	−4,201		−4,201
Net Benefit	53,796	39,243	56

substantially identical to those of the shareholder. This can be illustrated in the following manner: suppose there were no conservation. If demand increased one kWh, the fuel cost would be automatically recovered through the utility's fuel adjustment clause. If peak load increased one kW and the utility had to recover the capital investment cost through rate increases, there would be a risk that the full cost of capital would not be earned. Thus the capital minimization strategy of utility investment favors load management expenditures. Recall that Eq. (3-23) says that where the utility's market-to-book-value ratio is less than one, it is in the shareholder's interest to limit investment. A load management program which can be "expensed" (i.e., whose costs can be recovered immediately) instead of capitalized helps achieve this limitation. (For a formal analysis of the capitalizing vs. "expensing" decision, see Linhart, *et al.* (1974), which concludes that where investor returns are less than the cost of capital,

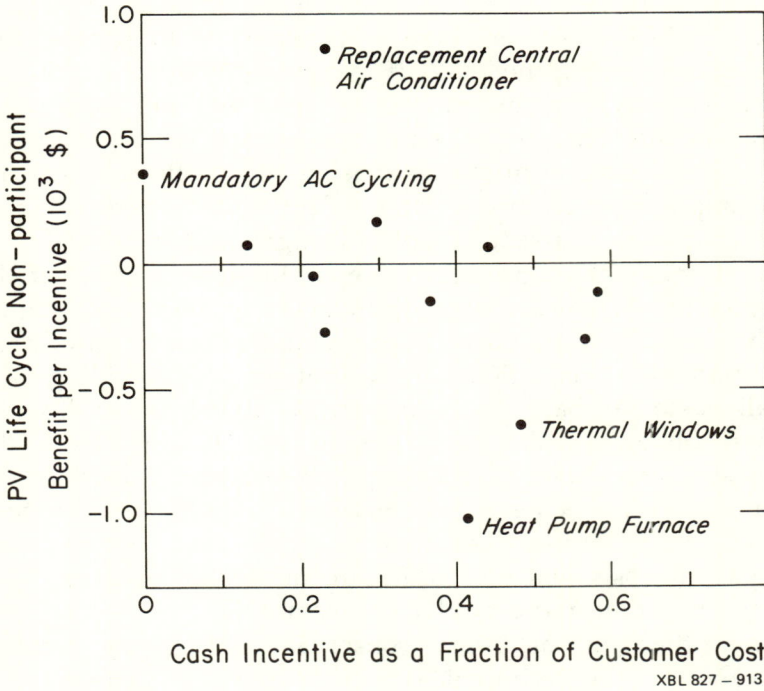

Figure 7-2. **Participant versus non-participant. Southern California Edison ZIP/CIP.**

expensing will be favored by shareholders.)

As a final illustration of the ambiguities that conservation represents to the shareholder's interest, note the use of cross-subsidies in the design of the particular set of programs known as ZIP/CIP. Figure 7-2 shows how the various program elements fall out with respect to incentive size (x axis) and ratepayer benefit (y axis). The mandatory load management program of Table 7-4 is labeled AC Cycling here. Since it is mandatory, the incentive is zero. Now observe the Heat Pump Furnace. Over 40% of the cost of this item has been subsidized, involving a net ratepayer cost of about $1,000 for each unit installed. Then why promote this? Is it really conservation? The answer depends on what the heat pump is displacing. If it displaces electric resistance heating, it can certainly represent conservation, but if it displaces natural gas, it constitutes fuel-switching at best. While it is impossible to give conclusive answers here, it is plausible to suggest that SCE may be using the ZIP/CIP program to hedge against too much conservation by promoting load-building activity as well. In the long run, electric heat pumps represent one of the few available technologies that might significantly increase consumption of electricity by residential customers. Should cost conditions warrant it, utilities might find it profitable to market the heat pump aggressively. In some regions of the country this is already done (principally by coal-fired utilities with a great deal of excess capacity and relatively low short-run marginal costs). SCE can be thought of as building up a small customer base for heat pumps, giving the utility the option of aggressive marketing in the future. Here the interest of shareholders and ratepayers diverge, at least, in the short run. To achieve this market foothold for the heat pump, SCE imposes substantial costs on nonparticipant ratepayers, costs that are hidden in the overall program, subsidized by other, more productive elements.

Thus the role of utility conservation programs remains ambiguous. The economic rationale for this activity rests largely on assumptions about future cost structure that are uncertain — as does the rationale for many new power plants. As an investment or "production" strategy for utilities, conservation is at best novel, and perhaps only a temporary accommodation to unfavorable conditions. It would be a happy coincidence if shareholder interests and customer interests could both be served by conservation as they were once served jointly by load growth. This unity of interest is not necessarily likely in the long run. As analysts gain more experience with conservation programs, they are coming to distinguish among different types of programs. Crash programs have less predictable effects and higher costs, in general, than building or retrofit codes that affect a small fraction of the total building stock each year. They also differentiate between deferrable and non-deferrable conservation opportunities (such as building retrofit and new construction, respectively); they gear the emphasis on deferrable conservation to the utility's current supply/demand balance, while continuing to promote non-deferrable conservation. The cost conditions necessary for a coincidence of shareholder and customer interests might also induce more general structural changes in the organization of the electric utilities. After all, if costs are increasing in the long run, perhaps the entire basis of the natural monopoly has been eroded permanently.

The questions raised by utility conservation programs strike at the core of the principles of public utility regulation. The changes in cost structure over the past decade raise questions about whether the traditions of regulation and the more recent adaptations are compatible. To answer these questions we must examine the theory of natural monopoly more carefully. These theoretical issues are raised in Chapter 8.

7.4 Scale Effects and Resource Planning

The economic analysis framework presented in Sec. 7.2 was based implicitly on the assumption that the aggregate load impact of the conservation programs was small. The impacts observed since these programs were initiated typically have been small, although separating the effects of these programs from price-induced conservation is difficult. As experience with conservation has increased over time, there has been increasing interest in the potential for large-scale efforts, and in some cases, the impact has indeed been large. Many of the political activists promoting conservation have consistently taken the position that these programs should be large in nature. The remarks of David Roe cited earlier are representative of the proposition that conservation ought to substitute for large central station power plants. There has been little discussion, however, of how the economic analysis would change as the scale of the load impact increases. The fundamental problem is how to trade off demand-side changes against supply-side investments.

One way to understand these problems is to focus attention more precisely on the definition of the avoided cost benefit associated with conservation. If the conservation programs are too small to cause the deferral of capacity, the benefit is essentially the sum of the short-run marginal cost of energy as calculated from a production costing model and the capacity value on an as-available basis. The definition of "small" in this context is that the program does not itself alter the marginal costs. Central station power plants are "large" in the sense that their addition to the resource mix makes a significant change in short-run marginal cost. Figure 5-1 is a schematic illustration of the discontinuity in short-run marginal cost caused by the addition of a new central station power plant.

To evaluate large-scale conservation programs, some account must be taken of their effect on the utility's cost structure. Analogies with the valuation methods used for Qualifying Facilities under PURPA suggest themselves. One approach would be to measure the value by a differencing approach, simulating production cost with and without the programs. This method would give a more accurate result than short-run marginal cost, but it does not address the question of how the utility's resource plan would adjust to the presence of the conservation resource. The value calculated by "with and without" simulations still does not capture the trade-off against supply-side resources.

The shift of attention toward big conservation programs has been marked by subtle changes in the economic analysis framework. As indicated above, the nonparticipant or ratepayer perspective has been redefined from a "hard" constraint to a "soft" one. The question is no longer whether rate increases for conservation programs are acceptable, but how much is acceptable. One formulation of this change is the re-definition of Eq. 7-5 into a percentage change in rates. This can then be compared to supply-side alternatives that also may increase consumer rates.

As the economic analysis perspective has broadened, new language has emerged to describe the resource planning process where conservation is an explicit alternative to supply. This paradigm has been called Least Cost Utility Planning, or LCUP for short. This term derives from a study by Roger Sant in 1979, but like most broad generic labels, it has come to mean a variety of things to a variety of audiences. In regions where marginal costs are low due to excess capacity

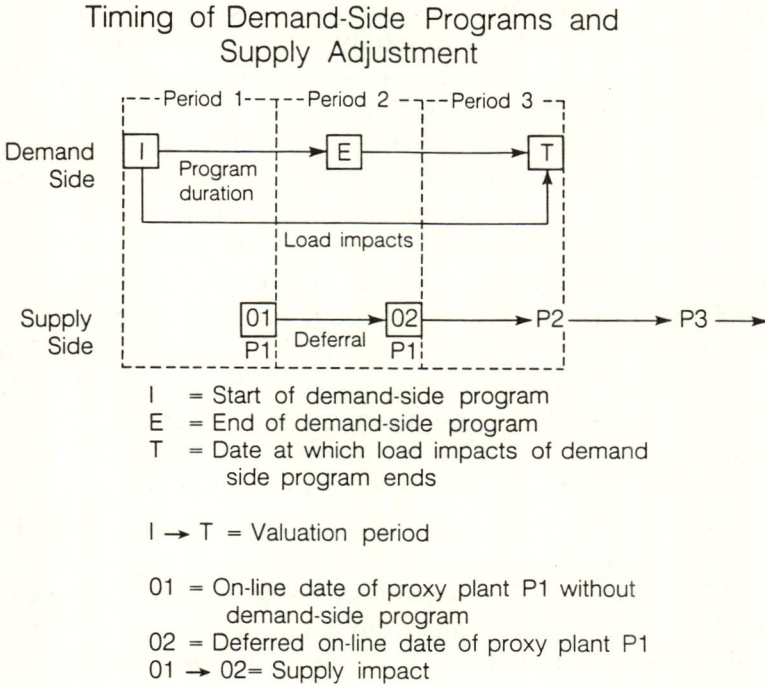

Timing of Demand-Side Programs and Supply Adjustment

```
    ---Period 1--T--Period 2 --T--Period 3 -
Demand   ┌──┐                ┌──┐              ┌──┐
Side     │ I│───────────────▶│E │─────────────▶│T │
         └──┘  Program       └──┘               └──┘
               duration                           ▲
                                                  │
                        Load impacts

Supply        ┌──┐                ┌──┐
Side          │01│───────────────▶│02│──────────▶ P2 ─────────▶ P3 ──▶
              └──┘  Deferral      └──┘
               P1                  P1
```

I = Start of demand-side program
E = End of demand-side program
T = Date at which load impacts of demand side program ends

I → T = Valuation period

01 = On-line date of proxy plant P1 without demand-side program
02 = Deferred on-line date of proxy plant P1
01 → 02 = Supply impact

XEL 864-11053

Figure 7-3. Timing of demand-side programs and supply adjustment.

and/or low fuel prices, marketing programs to increase sales have been promoted as cost-reducing strategies. Thus LCUP can mean both growth and conservation, depending on the circumstances.

A more complete representation of the long-run value of large-scale conservation programs can be formulated by focusing on the utility's supply plan in the absence of such efforts. A large-scale intervention on the demand side means that the need for new resources is deferred. There are complicated timing issues involved in determining the appropriate deferrals due to the lead times on both the supply and demand sides. Figure 7-3 shows how the timing on the two sides interact, and suggests how the program valuation might be constructed in light of these lead times.

Figure 7-3 is based on the assumption that the utility has a resource plan in which a "deferrable unit" can be identified. Loosely speaking, this unit acts as a proxy for the value of the conservation program. We will call it P_1, the proxy plant, to emphasize the connection between the costs of the plant and the value of the demand-side program; we can say that these costs are a proxy for this value. Strictly speaking, the value of the demand-side program is not identical with the costs of P_1 unless its load impacts are great enough to cause P_1 to be deferred for its entire economic lifetime. More typically we would expect the deferral period (from O_1 to O_2) to be less than the lifetime of P_1. Figure 7-3 also indicates that additional deferrals will occur involving plants P_2 and P_3. These deferrals can be included by further delaying O_2. The heart of the problem is finding the appropriate value for O_2.

One of the main planning difficulties involved is that the demand-side program must begin even before O_1. Portions of it will be completed and paid for in some way each year. If it took as long to accomplish the equivalent conservation as it would take to build the power plant, the present value of the revenue requirements would be higher, since the costs of conservation would be paid sooner. The planner must anticipate the impact of a demand-side program to truly defer a plant, rather than simply assuming the sale of an unneeded plant after it is already built or substantially built. The long-run analysis offered by White and summarized in Table 7-1 essentially ignores the deferrability issue by assuming that the proxy plant, or a portion of it, can be sold. This may be true if the conservation programs are small. If these programs are large and ubiquitous, however, there may not be a buyer.

Various methods can be used to calculate the appropriate deferral period for a resource plan adjustment corresponding to the scenario illustrated in Figure 7-3. Simple rules of thumb are of course the easiest approach. If new capacity requirements are driven primarily by growing peak demands, then deferral periods can be estimated by comparing the peak load impacts of demand-side programs with peak-load growth projections in the absence of the programs. More sophisticated measurements would use reliability indices over many high-load and high-risk hours to compute the impact of demand-side changes on supply-side requirements. Between the simplistic peak load impact equivalence and the complex reliability assessment, there are methods for averaging the demand-side impact over the hours of high load and high risk. There should be some adjustment using these averaging methods for line losses and reserve requirements associated with translating demand-side kWs to supply-side kWs. Eq. (7-9) shows the form of this relationship,

$$\frac{\text{(Demand-side kW)}(1 + RM)}{1 - TL} = \text{Supply-side kW} \quad , (7\text{-}9)$$

where

$$TL = \text{transmission loss rate}$$

$$RM = \text{reserve margin} \quad .$$

Typical values for TL and RM might be 0.07 and 0.20 respectively. The more common case would be more complex than the simple use of Eq. (7-9) because the capacity addition in the resource plan would involve fuel-mix optimization effects as well as reliability effects. In this case production simulation is necessary to calculate appropriate deferrals.

Let us assume that the load impacts from the demand-side programs have been estimated by the use of forecasting models. As Figure 7-3 indicates, these impacts are likely to persist beyond the deferral date of the proxy plant. We can calculate a "revenue-neutral" deferral by the following three-stage process. First we simulate the resource plan without the program. Let us call the present value of production costs in this case S_1. Next we simulate the same supply plan but use a load forecast which accounts for the load impacts of the program. We call the present value of production costs from this case S_2. We know that S_2 is less than S_1, since demand is lower in S_2. The revenue-neutral deferral of the proxy plant is found iteratively. We defer the plant and simulate the system using the load forecast reflecting the program. The present value of production costs in these cases, which we will call generically S_3, will be greater than S_2. This follows because we are serving the same loads as in S_2, but with fewer resources, forcing us to use more expensive resources for a higher fraction of the time. At some point, as the proxy plant is deferred further and further, S_3 equals S_1. This is the revenue neutral deferral.

Implementing this approach is time-consuming. Strictly speaking it should be repeated for any change in the load impacts of demand-side programs, but in practice it can be expected that shorthand methods of one kind or another will be used to simplify and expedite the analysis. One approach used by Eto *et al.* (1987) is to calculate a "generic deferral" that is used to value a family of related demand-side programs that are all reasonably similar in scale. The total value of these programs is S_1 (or S_3) less S_2. This value is an aggregate which must be decomposed into capacity and time-differentiated energy components. Methods for implementing this approach are described in Kahn (1986).

Even the "generic deferral" approach is likely to be too tedious for strategic policy analysis of widely differing demand-side programs. A simplified capacity planning capability has been used by Ford and Geinzer (1986) to address this kind of issue. Their study is designed to help the Bonneville Power Administration assess the planning and co-ordination of demand-side programs among the utilities of the entire Northwest region. To gain the flexibility needed to examine a broad range of activities, the Ford and Geinzer approach must rely on a simplified representation of the supply-side. As analysis of the resource planning aspect of utility conservation programs progresses, there will inevitably be a trade-off between the simplified and the more detailed methods. Given the enormous data requirements for conducting such trade-off analyses, the process of finding a least-cost mix of supply and demand resources is formidable.

7.5 Current Areas of Research

Because conservation is both a relatively new subject and a difficult one for planners, there is much which remains to be learned. A useful way to understand the current limits of analysis is to survey the research agenda. This section will illustrate the problems associated with and disagreements about the cost/benefit framework outlined above.

The basic problem for conservation planners is the difficulty of estimating how much demand reduction is possible and economic. The total potential is the sum of many small actions whose cumulative effect is large. The aggregation of individual measures is difficult because there may be technical interactions among measures and complicated economics. One approach to the aggregation problem is the conservation supply curve (Meier, 1983). This formulation converts conservation capital costs into a cost per unit of energy saved by assuming (1) performance per unit, (2) lifetime, and (3) a discount rate to determine a capital recovery factor. Having achieved the transformation to cost per unit, some estimate of total potential market is needed. With such estimates, a total potential supply of conservation can be arranged on an increasing-cost basis as normal supply curves are drawn.

There are many problems with this approach. The transformation of conservation capital costs to a unit basis requires estimating uncertain quantities. The choice of lifetime and discount rate in particular can express either a long-run social perspective or a more short-run consumer perspective. The shape of a given curve will change depending on the choice of perspective. There are also ambiguities surrounding the estimated performance per unit of a conservation measure. Some of these problems are measurement difficulties involving the variability of consumption patterns. Others are evaluation problems. Even if consumption variability can be controlled in the analysis, it is not clear that measured savings in a given situation can be fully attributed to a particular conservation program.

The evaluation issue has been discussed most extensively by Hirst and associates. For many conservation programs the kind of rigorous load impact testing described by Fiske has not been done. Especially in the case of energy impacts, it is important to account for price-induced demand reductions. One must also normalize for climate variations, self-selection of program participants and other factors. But of all these effects, price is the most important and difficult to understand. The problem is difficult here because of the conceptual confusion between the conservation-as-supply framework and the micro-economic perspective that conservation is a demand response induced by price. Hirst tries to solve this by using a gross versus net theory, which can be illustrated by imagining two customer groups, whose levels of consumptions are D_a and D_b, and two time periods 1 and 2; while customers with usage D_a participate in a conservation program, those who consume D_b do not. The gross program impact, GI, is then given by

$$GI = D_{a1} - D_{a2} .$$
                                                            (7-10)

But if price increases during the time interval in question, some part of the reduction in use represented by GI would have happened anyway. This can be found by looking at the suitably normalized consumption changes of D_b. Let us call this MR (for market response); then MR is given by

$$MR = D_{b1} - D_{b2}$$
                                                            (7-11)

and then

$$\text{Net Impact } NI = GI - MR .$$
                                                            (7-12)

The basic problem is that MR is very difficult to measure and its conceptual relation to GI is not clear. MR includes both a substitution effect which is a response to a long-run change in the stock of appliances and therefore comparable to GI, but also an effect due to income changes, which is much harder to relate to GI. Separating the mix of long- and short-run effects in both GI and MR is also difficult. Therefore, calculating NI is quite uncertain. All that can be said in general is that because we expect MR to be greater than zero, we also expect NI to be less than GI. Ford (1983), among others, points out that it is really only effective to subsidize NI. Therefore the subsidies to GI include a redundant element. It would be better then to target subsidies only to the less cost-effective region of the conservation supply curve, conditional on inducing customers to purchase the more cost-effective measures themselves. Southern California Edison's C&I Audit Program has such a feature in it, but it is atypical.

The Hirst paradigm is also difficult to implement because the price elasticity of demand implied or embodied in the estimate of MR is itself quite complex. Again the issue is the substitution versus the income aspects. Standard micro-

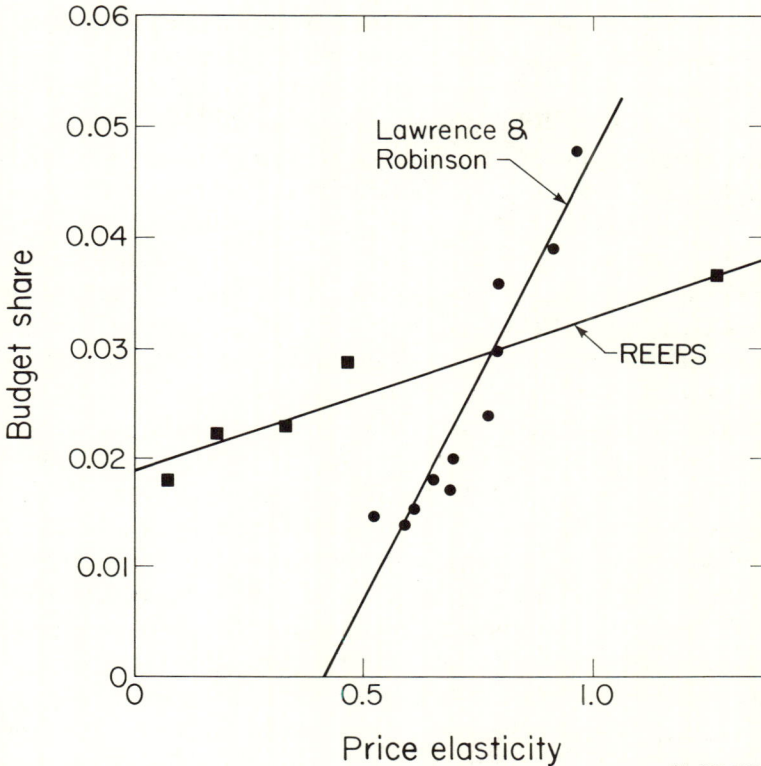

Figure 7-4. Elasticity as a function of consumer budget share of commodity.

economic theory suggests that elasticities are a function of the consumer's budget share for the commodity. Empirical estimates of this relation in the long run are shown in Figure 7-4. The general trend is clear but the estimates differ widely. This figure suggests that distributional issues are fundamental to conservation program evaluation. The budget share of electricity varies with income level, being higher for low-income customers. The demand for conservation, as well as the demand for energy, depend on both the current and future distribution of income. To date most methods of estimating these demands do not incorporate distributional considerations.

The one principal exception to this trend is the Residential End-use Energy Planning System model (REEPS), based on the work of McFadden and associates. This model simulates the household demand for appliances based on surveys of existing holdings and a behavioral model of the purchase decision. The model is primarily designed to forecast electricity demand for residential customers, but it is also useful to assess the impact of certain conservation programs. Because it is structured to represent different income groups explicitly, REEPS is a uniquely valuable tool for assessing distributional issues. Its main drawback is its very substantial data requirements based on a fine level of disaggregation by customer group. Another approach to the distributional aspect of demand and conservation behavior is analysis of sales frequency distribution data such as that discussed in Chapter 4.

Finally there are a number of regulatory issues which are still far from being settled. These include the difference between conservation in a growing versus a no-growth utility. An explicit treatment of this issue is embodied in the Florida Public Service Commission cost-effectiveness reporting format (1982). In the case in which utility load growth persists even with large-scale demand-side programs, there has been criticism of the nonparticipant test defined in Eq. (7-5). The principal issue is the question of "lost revenues." While it is clear that conservation can cause the utility to undercollect revenues in the short run, it is less obvious that this will persist in the long-run. As rates are periodically adjusted, the effect of conservation programs should be accounted for without systematic error. A better measure of the basic issue might be a comparison of rates over time with and without demand-side programs. In this case rate increases in the early years of a program (owing to early investments in conservation) would tend to be balanced by decreases in later years thanks to the power plant not having been built (Ford and Geinzer, 1986).

The question of rate treatment for conservation costs is also a matter of some contention. Utilities have shown a preference for expensing these costs instead of capitalizing them, generally for reasons consistent with Linhart's classic analysis: capital minimization, as discussed in Sec. 3.4. However, counter-examples such as the guaranteed return for PG&E's

ZIP program are not explained by this theory. The choice between capitalizing and expensing program costs will affect the time pattern of rates. In general, expensing will produce a larger total impact, because the costs are passed on sooner and thus will raise the present value of revenue requirements by a larger sum.

It is likely that conservation will remain fraught with problems. Although clearly a demand-side behavior, it substitutes for supply-side activities. Hence, there is a tendency for planners to put the conservation resource into the framework of supply analysis. This transformation is neither unambiguous nor straightforward. Furthermore, as we shall see in Chapter 8, the utility has an ambiguous attitude toward conservation. At some point it will not be in the shareholder's interest to diminish the market by reducing demand. To understand this conflict we need to understand the role of conservation in the overall structural problems of the electric utility industry. This means re-examining the theory of natural monopoly.

Chapter 8

Theoretical Perspective

8.1 Introduction

To explore incentives for different evolutionary paths in the electric utility industry, in this chapter we develop a theoretical perspective on the developments we have surveyed thus far. We first review the theory of natural monopoly, which, in its modern form, indicates that there are cost configurations which are still natural monopolies even though costs generally rise with output. At some point, however, natural monopoly breaks down. The certain test for this breakdown is the entry of other firms into the market. Entry means not just the appearance of other firms, but their long-run viability. Thus in electricity the mere existence of QFs does not mean that the market is not a natural monopoly. Only the long-run survival of QFs means that.

We will consider in this chapter how regulation of electric utilities affects the uncertainty and instability of the industry. The political and economic upheavals of the 1970s clearly destabilized the electric utility industry. Conditions like demand and cost that were once predictable became uncontrollable, uncertain and volatile. Under these circumstances inflexible supply projects such as nuclear and coal power plants exacerbated the difficulties. We will develop a simple example due to Sharkey illustrating these conditions.

The advantage of considering regulation as a stabilizing force is the availability of a theoretical language suited to describe this situation. One of the regulator's services to society is providing stabilization to unstable markets. This is particularly clear in the area of agriculture, where government authorities buffer producers and consumers from price and production fluctuations. We will argue that it is also a useful way to characterize regulation of electricity. Students of administrative processes have observed that stabilization, caused primarily by procedural delays, is the *effect* of regulation, even though it is not its announced intention. Actors in the regulatory process consciously use this feature to achieve policy goals. However, the direction of benefits which flow from this delay-induced stabilization can be ambiguous: the regulatory lag of delayed price adjustment favors producers when cost is declining and favors consumers when cost is increasing.

Most students of regulation focus on the issue of what determines regulatory policy. Critics of regulation often argue that the regulator becomes "captured" by the industry, and that consequently decisions always favor producers. We will suggest a somewhat different theory, that regulators simply serve the interest that benefits most from stabilization actions. To develop this point of view, we adapt some simple characterizations of the value of stability to the electric utility context, and use these tools to distinguish the producer interest from that of the consumer. This framework accounts for the pro-consumer bias of utility regulation during the 1970s and can be used to predict a shift in policy back toward producer interests.

The stabilization framework also allows formulation of strategic alternatives for the electric utility industry. If, while costs are generally increasing, the cost structure is fundamentally unstable, what should the traditional firm do? To answer this question, we estimate for which generic production strategies the producer value of stabilization is greatest. It turns out that "unregulated" producers benefit most from stabilization compared to central-station-regulated producers or utility conservation programs. Benefits to the latter turn out to be ambiguous. If conservation can bring the utility cost structure back into the sustainable monopoly region, then its competitive strategic value will be great because it has the effect of driving small power producers out of the market. The risk of too much conservation is that the utility ends up with excess capacity. It will then have won a battle, but gained little in the process.

The value of stabilization to "unregulated" production, together with the theory of unsustainable natural monopoly, suggests that the structure and number of firms in the electric utility industry will change as a result of regulatory action, but it may be misleading to label these changes deregulation. Although more competition will be introduced in the market for power generation, the traditional firm is unlikely to disappear. Transmission and distribution remain natural monopolies. There are still economies of vertical integration with generation. Instead of old firms disappearing we will more probably see new entrants and new roles for the traditional firm.

We begin the discussion with a review of the theory of natural monopoly in Section 8.2. Sharkey's example of an unstable market is given in Section 8.3. The stabilization theory of regulation is applied in Section 8.4. In Section 8.5 we consider the gap between the lessons of theory and the realities of current institutions.

8.2 The Theory of Natural Monopoly

The standard definition of a monopoly equilibrium is that the monopolist maximizes profit by choosing a price that yields the optimal output. The classical illustration of this process in a single-product market is Figure 8-1. The monopoly output is that which maximizes the difference between revenues and costs. The revenue function can be expressed as the product of the inverse demand function $p(q)$ (the line D) and the quantity q. This may be written

$$\text{Maximize } p(q)q - C(q) \quad , \tag{8-1}$$

where

$p(q)$ is the price when quantity q is produced, and

$C(q)$ is the total cost function.

Since p and q are related through the market demand function, we can just as easily view the process as finding an

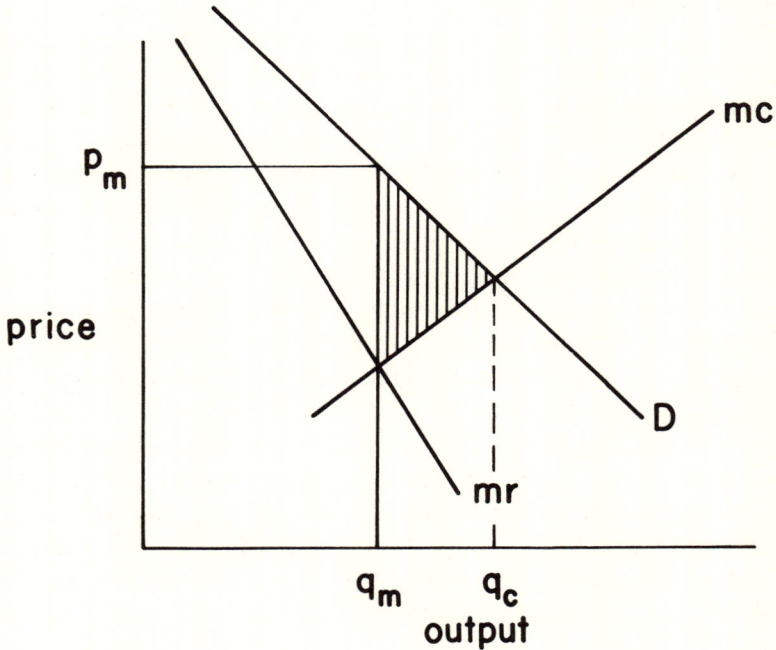

Figure 8-1. Price versus output.

optimal output q_m. Solving the first-order condition leads to the result that when $q = q_m$

$$p(q) + q \,\frac{dp}{dq} \;=\; \frac{dC(q)}{dq} \; . \tag{8-2}$$

The left-hand side of Eq. (8-2) is the marginal revenue MR, and the right hand side is the marginal cost, MC. The shaded area represents the welfare loss of monopoly, because every unit of output between q_m and q_c is valued by consumers at a level higher than the cost of production. Regulation typically forces a lower price, corresponding to the average cost at q_c, thereby expanding output, lowering profit and eliminating the welfare loss.

Figure 8-1 is too simple a representation to account for many of the complexities inherent in an accurate description of market forces on monopolies such as electric power.

Among the difficulties are (1) multiple demand curves (corresponding to customer classes with different price elasticities), (2) multiple outputs (capacity and energy are not the same commodities), (3) uncertainties and non-linear prices, and (4) the public-goods aspect of utility service. All of these factors influence both the definition of a natural monopoly and the empirical issue of whether a particular industry has the properties to so define it.

Many of these issues arise from the existence of scale economies or increasing returns phenomena of other kinds. A large electric power system typically can serve many customers with diverse demands more efficiently than can atomized or totally decentralized producers. The nature of this service, however, entails many constraints that prevent simple pricing or output rules from being formulated. For instance, some commodities such as reliability are produced which cannot be easily priced. While all consumers benefit from reliability, they do so to different degrees. Since reliability is like a public good and cannot be easily decomposed, everyone consumes the same amount of it, at least at the bulk power level. Consumers do not reveal their true preference for this commodity since it is not easy to experiment with the acceptability of various quantities of reliability. Recent theoretical work suggests that "priority pricing" would improve the efficiency of the electric utility industry (Chao and Wilson, 1987). Attempts to implement a differentiation of reliability services are being sponsored by the Electric Power Research Institute.

Even within the realm of more conventional commodities, scale economies are ubiquitous. There are many ways to define this concept, but the modern notion of sub-additivity of the cost function is the most general (Baumol, Panzar and Willig, 1982). This concept is defined formally by the property:

$$C(q_2) < C(q_2 - q_1) + C(q_1) \quad \text{for} \quad q_2 > q_1 > 0 \quad (8\text{-}3)$$

where

$C(q)$ = the total cost function for output q.

Equation (8-3) says that a cost function is sub-additive if the sum of costs for two output levels produced separately is always greater than the cost of producing the sum of the two output levels. This notion includes the case of declining average cost but is broader. This can be illustrated by considering a cost function with global scale economies. A cost function, *C(aq)*, where *a* is some constant and *q* is any output level may be considered to have global scale economies when

$$C(aq) < a\, C(q) \quad \text{for} \quad a > 1, q > 0 \ . \qquad (8\text{-}4)$$

Dividing both sides by *aq* shows that Eq. (8-4) defines average cost as a decreasing function of output. We then get

$$\frac{C(aq)}{aq} < \frac{C(q)}{q} \qquad\qquad (8\text{-}5)$$

which says that unit costs go down on the average with increasing output. Sharkey uses the property defined in Eq. (8-5) to show that global scale economies imply cost subadditivity. For $q > x$ then

$$\frac{C(x)}{x} > \frac{C(q)}{q} \quad \text{and} \quad \frac{C(q-x)}{q-x} > \frac{C(q)}{q} \ .$$

Therefore we can add *C(x)* and *C(q-x)* as follows

$$C(x) + C(q-x) > C(q)\left[\frac{x}{q} + \frac{q-x}{q}\right] = C(q) \ ,$$

which is the definition of sub-additivity.

Cost sub-additivity provides a natural definition for the notion of cross-subsidy which is so important in public utility regulation. The idea is to compare the prices charged to a particular customer or group of customers with the "stand-alone cost." If a group is asked to pay less than the stand-alone cost of providing it service, then there is no subsidy. As long as the cost function is subadditive, then subsidy-free prices can be found. This can be seen by rearranging the terms of Eq. (8-3). Let output $q_3 = q_1 + q_2$. Sub-additivity implies that

$$C(q_1 + q_2) < C(q_1) + C(q_2) \ ,$$

or

$$C(q_1 + q_2) - C(q_2) < C(q_1) \ . \qquad\qquad (8\text{-}6)$$

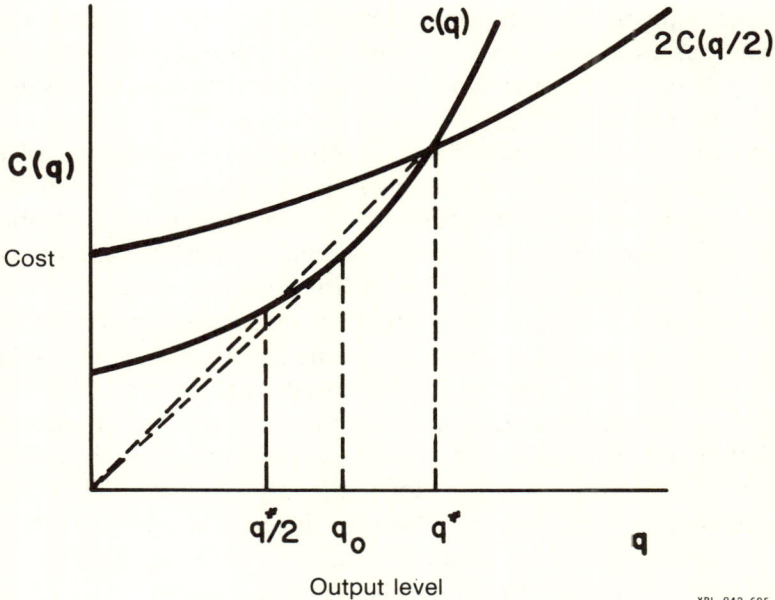

XBL 842-685

Figure 8-2. Costs of production as a function of output.

Equation (8-6) says that the cost of serving any group of customers alone exceeds the incremental cost of service when the group is part of a larger whole.

The importance of the sub-additivity notion is that it extends to situations involving increasing average cost. An example of such a situation is illustrated in Figure 8-2. Here the cost function is sub-additive up to the quantity we have designated q^*. Beyond that there are no increasing returns, i.e., $2C(q/2)$ is less than $C(q)$. The quantity q_0 represents the point at which the cost function $C(q)$ increases in average cost. The slope of the line from $C(q)$ to the origin decreases as q approaches q_0, and then increases as q exceeds q_0. This slope represents average cost, $C(q)/q$. The region between q_0 and q^* is important because it represents a cost structure in which, although costs are increasing, natural monopoly conditions still obtain. While this possibility was not treated explicitly in the literature until recently, it has considerable relevance for the long-run evolution of the electric power industry. The critical question is whether a long-run tendency toward higher costs has proceeded to the point where subsidy-free prices can no longer be constructed, i.e., the cost function ceases to be sub-additive.

In practice, such questions are difficult for a number of reasons. One approach to this issue is the investigation of Ramsey prices, prices which depend on consumers' price elasticity. In the limit, price elasticity becomes complete substitution, i.e., the consumer leaves the utility system and incurs stand-alone costs. Economists favor constructing discriminatory prices using the Ramsey pricing rule because this rule retains the efficiency properties of marginal cost prices. The basic idea is that departures from marginal cost pricing are still efficient if all outputs are in the same proportion as they would have been if pricing were done at marginal cost. This notion is formalized by defining two or more outputs (which also may be construed as customer classes) called q_a and q_b. We can write the demand functions, $D(p)$, as follows:

$$q_a = D_a(P_a) \quad ,$$

$$q_b = D_b(P_b) \quad . \tag{8-7}$$

The Ramsey rule for departing from marginal costs C_a and C_b requires that the following ratio holds:

$$\frac{D_a(P_a)}{D_a(C_a)} = \frac{D_b(P_b)}{D_b(C_b)} \quad . \tag{8-8}$$

Equation (8-8) indicates that P_a may depart more from C_a than P_b does from C_b if the demand for the first good is less elastic. A condition for achieving this result in the case of independent demands is given by

$$\frac{P_i - C_i}{P_i} = \frac{K}{n_i} \quad , \quad i = 1, 2 \tag{8-9}$$

where

n_i = elasticity of demand of good i,
K = constant.

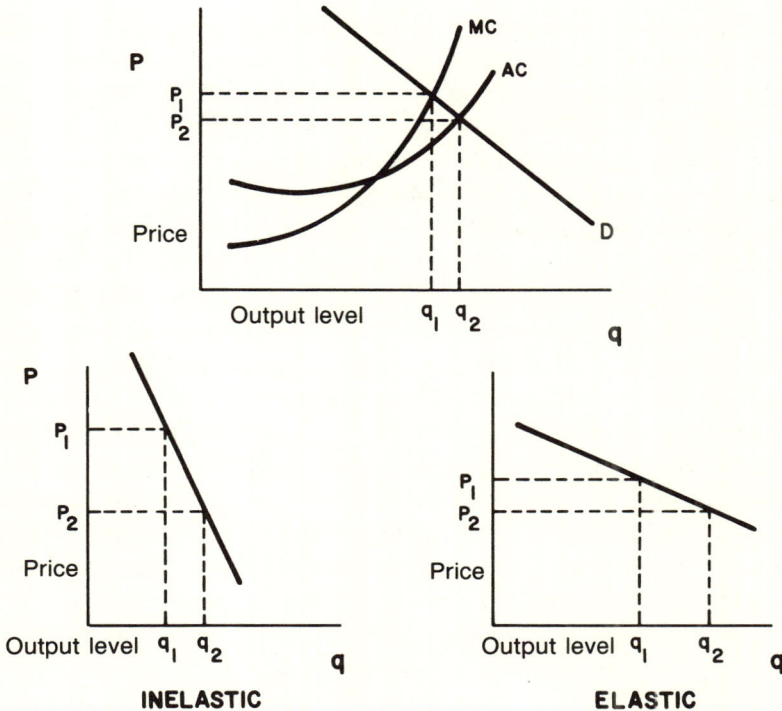

XBL 842-686

Figure 8-3. Price versus elastic and inelastic output levels. (MC = marginal cost, AC = average cost.)

Figure 8-3 illustrates the logic of the Ramsey rule. Curtailing demand from q_2 to q_1 requires a greater increase in price (p_1 compared to p_2) for inelastic markets than for elastic markets. For increasing cost conditions, Ramsey pricing implies that large users (whose willingness to pay is typically more price-sensitive) will get smaller rate increases than small residential users, whose consumption is less elastic. Conversely, when marginal costs are decreasing, large elastic customers ought to get larger rate decreases than smaller, inelastic customers.

Thus Ramsey pricing bridges the gap with the concept of cost sub-additivity because demand elasticity is related to stand-alone cost. If utility prices are very high, a large elastic user can always produce its own power and bypass the utility system; the potential for substitution is complete. Therefore to keep such customers in the system, the utility must discriminate in their favor, although there is a point at which either the price cannot be made sufficiently favorable to retain the elastic customer, or it becomes too expensive for the inelastic consumer to maintain the burden of the elastic class as utility customers. At this point natural monopoly breaks down.

It is difficult to apply much of this theory to real industry situations. The theory is couched in such general terms that it is difficult to translate it into empirical analysis. One development of this approach in the direction of completeness is the extension of the definition of cost sub-additivity from single-product to multi-product markets. Here the issue often turns on whether there are economies of joint production or cost complementarities between the outputs in a multi-product firm. It is possible, of course, that dis-economies could exist as well. An example from academia of a joint production dis-economy is the combined education of lawyers and philosophers. While the latter must be taught to pursue only the truth, this proclivity is not efficient for producing the former.

The main result of the Ramsey pricing theory is that natural monopolies (i.e., cost functions which are sub-additive) would be harder to sustain in multi-product cases because there would be more room for entry into the market by firms producing a subset of the goods sold by the worthwhile monopolist. An unsustainable monopoly (or industry structure) is one in which entry is feasible. The central question posed by this analysis is whether electric power is still characterizable as a natural monopoly, and if so, whether it is sustainable. In all likelihood the answer will turn out to be that even if the cost function were still sub-additive, entry is indeed possible. Therefore, there exists an equilibrium industry structure that will include many firms, or there is no equilibrium at all.

To pose these questions with any specificity requires a more detailed view of the production process than we have seen from the theory so far. Sharkey's example of an unstable market is a good step in this direction.

8.3 Example of Market Instability

Sharkey poses these problems in the language of game theory, using the notion of the "core" of a particular game to define when a natural monopoly is sustainable. Sustainability is established when the natural monopoly firm can deter entry by other firms in its market. As an empirical fact, entry can only be deemed to exist if firms which attempt to enter can actually persist and avoid bankruptcy. Thus the mere existence of small power producers does not mean that the natural monopoly in electricity has been proven unsustainable. It is necessary that these firms survive over time, i.e., recover the cost of their capital investment. For bypass customers the test is whether they abandon their bypass investments and return as customers of the utility system. To test for this in an abstract way, Sharkey defines a certain cooperative game called welfare maximization. The players are all consumers and all possible combinations of consumers. The role of firms is reduced to the passive function of merely representing particular consumer coalitions.

In the language of game theory, solutions correspond to the notion of equilibrium more commonly used in economics. The core of a game is a special kind of solution in which the welfare of players cannot be improved in whole or in part without damaging some individual. Thus the core is essentially the notion of Pareto optimality. The basic result used by Sharkey is that if the coalition of all consumers is a solution to the welfare maximization game in the presence of a natural monopoly cost function, then the core is non-empty and the monopoly is sustainable. These conditions again boil down to the existence of Ramsey prices which can simultaneously satisfy the revenue requirement exactly and still be less than the cost of substitution for any coalition.

These conditions are very special and are rarely met in reality, particularly when the cost function is subadditive but not decreasing. Large, elastic customers or other demand-side constraints can cause the core to be empty when output must cover the whole market (alternatively where the market is large, relative to scale or scope economies). To illustrate this concretely, Sharkey introduces an example of a market with random demand where scale economies are not sufficient to provide for a non-empty core. The cost function consists of a fixed component f and a component that varies with output q by a constant amount cq. In this highly simplified case, the fixed costs do not depend on the number of plants—they represent overhead for the firm as a whole. Further, each plant of capacity q is assumed to have only two cost states: off, producing zero output, and incurring zero operating cost; or on, producing some output less than or equal to q, and incurring cost cq. Formally the cost function can be written as the step function

$$C(q) = f + cq. \tag{8-10}$$

It is assumed that cq can be wholly avoided if the firm chooses to produce no output. Notice that average cost is declining for this function since

$$\frac{C(q)}{q} = \frac{f}{q} + c$$

decreases as q increases.

Sharkey assumes that demand is completely random. It is characterized by a drawing from a uniform probability distribution in which every customer is of the same size and is equally likely to demand one unit of output. Each unit can be sold for a price equal to b, which is greater than the unit cost c. To choose an optimal plant capacity under these conditions, it is useful to examine Figure 8-4. The line bz is the total revenue function for any output z. If we let t equal the number of customers, then t also represents the total demand. It is measured in units identical to q, which is normalized to 1. This convention facilitates a probability interpretation of demand. Let us define output and monopolist's surplus for any realization t of demand.

The demand $t = cq/b$ for a fixed capacity, represents the first point at which operating the plant does not induce a loss. If t is less than this point then revenues are less than avoidable cost, so no production occurs. For any $t > q$ the producer's surplus $S = (b-c)q$ since q is the full capacity of the plant. The total expected surplus is just the shaded area in Figure 8-4 which can be written as

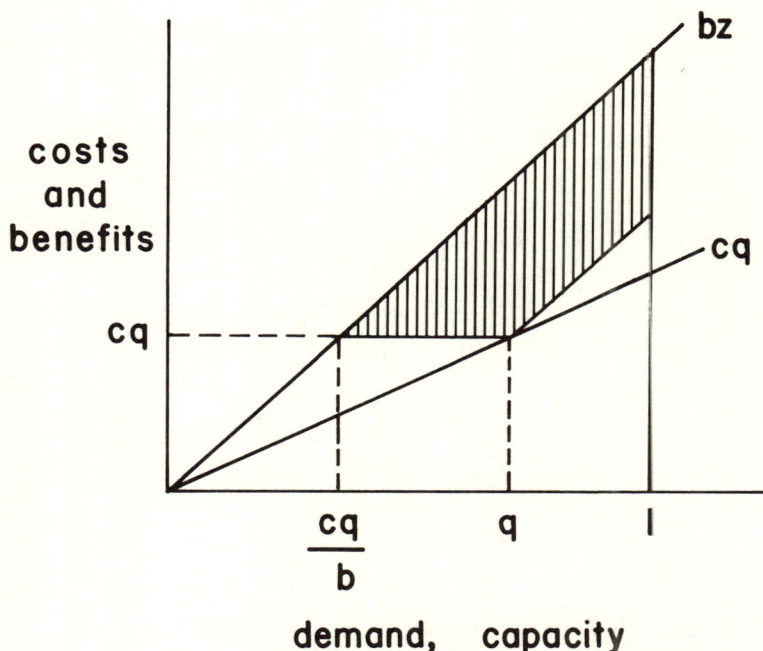

XBL 842-687

Figure 8-4. Costs and benefits versus demand, capacity (single-plant case).

$$S(q) = \int_{cq/b}^{q} (bt - cq)\, dt + (1 - q)(b - c)\, q \quad . \text{(8-11)}$$

The first term is the surplus for $t < q$, weighted by the probability of that demand occurring. The second term is the surplus when $t > q$ times the probability $(1 - q)$ that this demand occurs. The optimal q will maximize Eq. (8-11). Sharkey calculates this optimal size to be equal to $b/(b+c)$, and calls it output level q^*.

Now suppose that the firm decides to operate two plants of outputs q_1 and q_2, whose combined output is equal to q^*, where q_1 is smaller than q_2. The total surplus will increase in the manner shown in Figure 8-5. The increased surplus comes from the added flexibility of being able to serve low

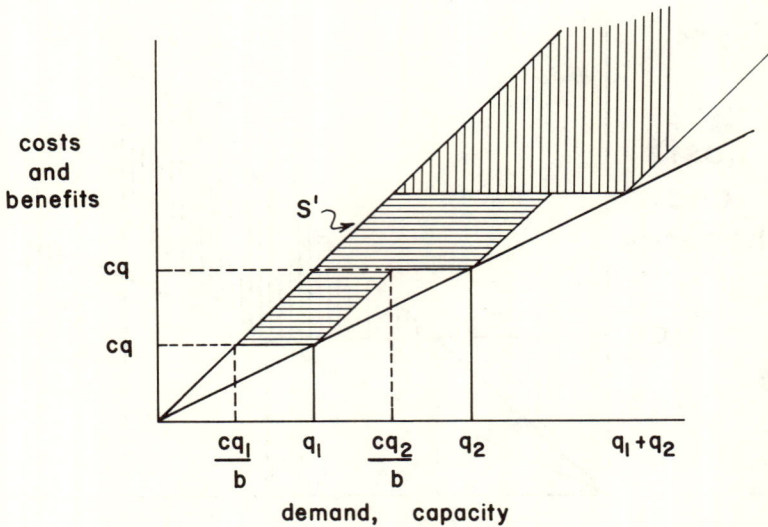

XBL 842-688

Figure 8-5. Costs and benefits versus demand, capacity (two-plant case).

levels of demand that could not be economically served with a single plant.

For t less than q_1, there will be a break-even point at cq_1/b where it becomes economic to operate the plant with output q_1. For t greater than cq_1/b output will be constrained to q_1 until t reaches the break-even point for operating plant q_2. This will occur when t equals q_1. For t greater than this value, only the plant with output q_2 operates until it equals cq_2/b, when both plants operate. When t is greater than the sum of q_1 and q_2, we have the same situation as in Figure 8-4 for t greater than q, and the firm would realize the benefit represented by the vertically shaded area. The economics of multiple-plant operation involve trading off the additional surplus S (the horizontally shaded area) against the added fixed cost, i.e., the scale economy at the plant level. Formally the two-plant case is preferable if

$$(f_1 + f_2) - f^* < S' \qquad (8\text{-}12)$$

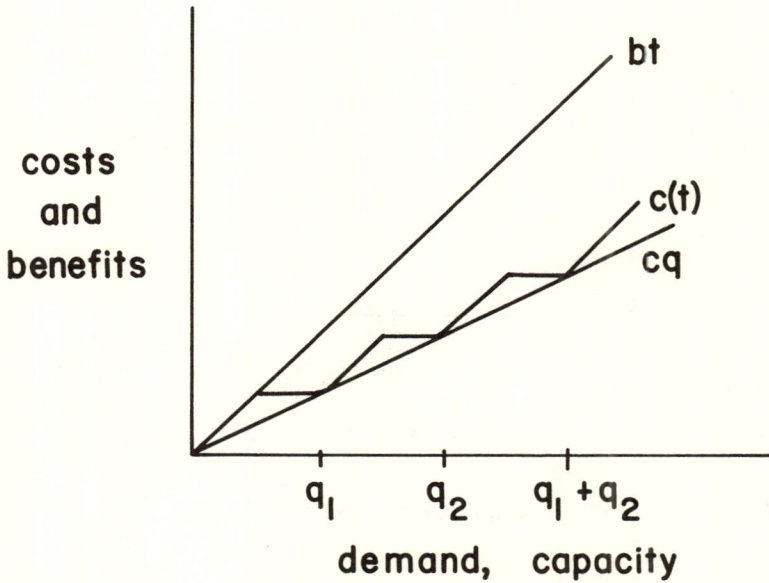

Figure 8-6. Costs and benefits versus demand, capacity. (Line *bt* represents potential revenue.)

where

f_i = fixed cost for plant of capacity i,

f^* = fixed cost of q^*.

Sharkey argues that if multiple plant operation is economic for one firm (i.e., if Eq. [8-12] is satisfied), then there is room in the industry for multiple firms. With a multiple-firm industry structure we can compute the cost to serve any coalition of customers using the framework of Figure 8-5. This is shown as $C(t)$ in Figure 8-6. Using this cost function, $C(t)$, one can define a characteristic function $V(t) = bt - C(t)$ which represents revenues less costs. This function is bounded above by $(b - c)t$, the operating income of the industry. It is shown in Figure 8-7.

We can now investigate the core of the game designed to maximize net surplus $V(t)$. Starting by defining an average

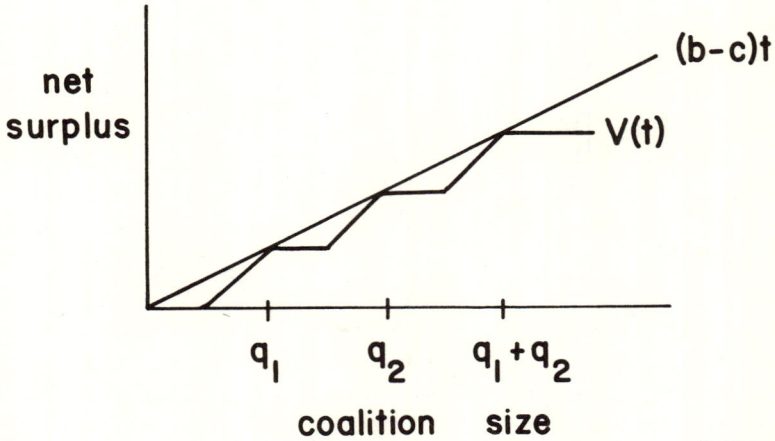

Figure 8-7. Net surplus versus coalition size.

surplus function $V(t)/t$, Sharkey then cites a major result from game theory which provides a characterization of stable or sustainable industry structures.

Theorem

The core of the welfare maximization game is non-empty if and only if

$$V(t)/t > V(s)/s \quad \text{for } \textit{all} \quad s < t \quad .$$

From the definition of the surplus function, the condition of the theorem is only satisfied for declining average cost, i.e.,

$$C(t)/t < C(s)/s \quad \text{for } \textit{all} \quad s < t \quad .$$

Given the flat regions of the cost curve illustrated in Figure 8-6, it is apparent that the two-firm industry is not stable.

This result indicates that the common definition of natural monopoly as depending on declining average cost was actually quite robust. The modern theory has identified a region in the cost structure where natural monopoly exists, but in a fundamentally unstable way. The precise nature of the instability illustrated in this example is fairly representative of conditions in the electric power industry today. The supply/demand balance cannot be maintained in light of fluctuating or uncertain demand and inflexible incremental increases in supply. Declining average costs, on the other hand, always implies a smooth and convex adjustment of supply and demand. There is literally no room in the cost structure of the industry for a small low-cost producer. Therefore the natural monopoly can be maintained against entry by other producers. We are clearly not in such a situation, so we must face the complex problems posed by industry instability.

It is at this point that a theory of regulation becomes necessary. What are we to do about unsustainable natural monopolies? Where does the public interest lie in regulating industries of this type? What should regulators do in these situations? Answering these questions requires a wholly different conceptual framework. We must have both an explicit account of what regulation can offer when markets are unstable and a behavioral theory of regulation in practice. We will sketch these elements briefly. The basic framework we adopt to answer the first question is based on the theory of commodity price stabilization. Electricity is compared to unstable commodity markets. The role of the regulator is analogous to an agricultural stabilization authority. Our behavioral model will be adapted from the University of Chicago school.

8.4 Stabilization Theory of Regulation

The basic analogy underlying this theory is that regulators function like stabilization authorities in agricultural commodities markets. The existence of marketing boards, price support mechanisms or production quotas are all evidence of the pervasive role of government intervention in agricultural commodities markets. This intervention is deemed necessary to help cushion the effects of randomness in both supply and demand. It is felt that both consumers and producers benefit from the reduction of risk that is achieved. We will argue that energy markets also exhibit the supply, price and demand uncertainties characteristic of commodity markets.

Table 8-1

CV of energy prices 1974–80

	Nominal	Real
Unregulated Oil	.53	.32
Fuel Oil and Coal	.38	.18
Piped Gas and Electricity	.25	.08

The regulator can be thought of as a stabilizing agency whose services are used both by producers and consumers.

We will pursue a theory of regulator policy based on the political equilibrium model of Peltzman. In this model the regulators sell their services to various political coalitions, choosing that coalition which maximizes support for a particular policy. In the Peltzman model the regulators' service is a wealth transfer. In our version of this approach, the service will be more precisely characterized as stabilization. This will mean any kind of price or quantity stabilization. These actions will result in welfare changes, but the nature of such changes requires some analysis. The view of regulation as stabilization is also expounded in Owen and Braeutigam (1978).

In the Peltzman model the regulator's decision criterion is somewhat vague. Maximizing support makes some intuitive sense of the political aspect of regulation, but it is not a concept that is readily measured. We will work with a more transparent notion that is directly connected to our specification of the regulator's service. The basic concept is the value of stabilization. We assume that regulators provide stabilization services to consumers or producers in proportion to how much each party values this service.

We will end up paying most of our attention to producers as a way to model the investment strategies available to electric utilities in the current unstable market structure. To take full account of the utilities' dilemma, however, we must also take account of the world market for fuels. It is this market which initiated the disturbances that have made the electricity

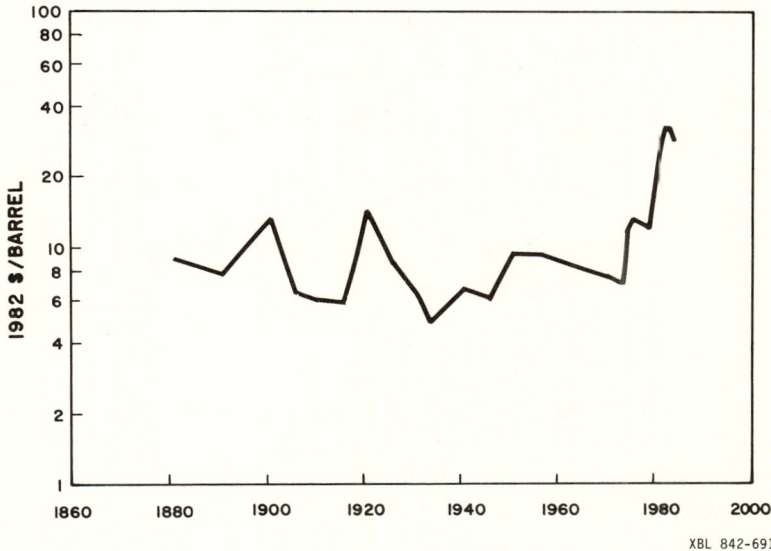

Figure 8-8. Oil prices versus time, 1860–1985.

cost function increase. (We will neglect the cost-increasing effect of regulations that required utilities to internalize environmental costs such as those of nuclear and coal plants in the 1970s, for instance.) With respect to these prices the utility is a consumer, just like any other price-taking buyer. There is no domestic regulatory policy which can permanently stabilize fuel prices. Attempts to achieve this will be shown to have been only wealth transfers.

Let us begin with a brief recap of the price behavior of energy terms subject to differing degrees of regulation during the 1970s. Table 8-1 collects estimates of the coefficient of variation (CV) of energy prices subject to various amounts of regulation during the period from 1974–1980. The CV is a measure of variability or uncertainty; it is the ratio of the standard deviation to the mean of a price series sample. A high CV doesn't necessarily imply a price increase, only a high variation in price. The CV of unregulated oil prices is 32%, approximating that of other widely traded commodities (Newbery and Stiglitz estimate a real price CV of 26% for cotton, 31% for cocoa and 58% for sugar). A graphic representation of the real price variation of oil is given in Figure 8-8.

Table 8-2

Electric utilities mean
return on equity and coefficient of variation

	Mean Real ROE	Real CV
1970–73	5.7%	0.16
1974–81	2.5%	0.76

Table 8-1 shows that as the degree of regulation increases, the CV of energy prices decreases. This data illustrates the proposition that consumers received price stabilization benefits from regulation during the 1970s, the value of which we will estimate below. For now, however, it is important to contrast this data with the changes in utility shareholder income during the same period. Table 8-2 gives estimates of the mean and CV of the real return on equity for utility shareholders before and after the first oil price shock. Not only did the oil price shock increase energy costs directly, it also drove up interest rates, which increased utilities' construction finance burden.

Table 8-2 illustrates that shareholder returns went from a high mean, low variability level before 1974 to a low mean, high risk level after that period. These data together with Table 8-1 suggests that utility regulation during the 1970s transferred energy price risk from consumers to producers. Investors in electric utility shares typically experienced little risk in the period between 1945 and 1974. This stability reflected the sustainable natural monopoly conditions of the time as well as the unique conditions that made natural resources unusually cheap and accessible. The economic turbulence of the 1970's was inescapable, however, and regulatory policy effectively placed the burden of this on the producer.

To understand why this occurred and what a prognosis might be, we need to consider the value of stabilization. For this purpose we rely on an expression for the consumer value of stabilization, or benefit, B, derived by Newbery and Stiglitz, which says that price stabilization reduces consumer income risk in proportion to (1) income variability, (2) price variability, (3) the correlation of price and income, and (4) the consumer's taste for risk. Formally this can be written as

$$B = -r \, \sigma_p \, \sigma_I \, R \quad , \tag{8-13}$$

where

σ_p = CV of real consumer prices,
σ_I = CV of real income,
r = correlation coefficient of price and income,
R = coefficient of relative risk aversion.

The benefit B is expressed as a fraction of stabilized expenditure on the commodity in question. The CV of prices and incomes are the quantities estimated in part in Tables 8-1 and 8-2, and each one affects the value of stabilization. The more uncertain one's income or the demands placed on it by consumer prices, the more important energy price stability would be, because one would face a greater risk of privation if energy prices were to rise. The correlation coefficient indicates how much price stabilization will affect income. If income increases with prices (positive correlation), the value of stabilization will be negative, since potential income gains will be lost. The only interesting case occurs when income goes down as price goes up (negative correlation), the only case with which we will concern ourselves. The least intuitive term in Eq. (8-13) is R, relative risk aversion.

Relative risk aversion is an elasticity of marginal utility. It is defined with respect to a utility function U and an income (or wealth) variable Y as follows:

$$\frac{-Y \dfrac{d^2 U}{dY^2}}{\dfrac{dU}{dY}} \quad . \tag{8-14}$$

The form of this definition is constrained by technical features of utility functions (see Arrow, 1970). The basic idea is that preferences with respect to risk change with income. The second derivative of the utility function captures the rate of change of marginal utility. This must be normalized to $\dfrac{dU}{dY}$ because utility functions are only defined up to a linear transformation. To make this ratio dimensionless we multiply by Y. Since $\dfrac{d^2U}{dY^2}$ is less than 0 when the consumer is adverse to risk, and $\dfrac{dU}{dY}$ is greater than 0 (income is always desirable), a negative sign is added by convention to make R greater than 0.

On theoretical grounds Arrow argues that R is approximately 1, illustrating this with the case of a logarithmic utility function $U(Y)$ equal to log Y, for which R equals 1. Other cases are more complex. The most interesting issues are empirical. What behavior illustrates risk aversion? How do risk preferences change with the level of wealth or income? The evidence reviewed by Newbery and Stiglitz indicates that for low-income farmers, risk aversion increased as income declines. With the prospect of starvation increasing, farmers are less willing to take chances. A practical upper bound in such situations appears to be a risk aversion R of 2. An R of 0 on the other hand, signifies risk neutrality

Let us now apply the framework of Eq. (8-13) to the history of and prospects for regulatory policy in the electric utility sector. The data collected in Tables 8-1 and 8-2 are necessary, but not sufficient for this exercise. In particular, we need estimates of σ_I for consumers and r for both consumers and utility shareholders, and will rely upon estimates made by Kahn (1982). It is immediately apparent that the notion of a homogeneous average consumer group is irrelevant, and that σ_I and r will vary substantially across income groups; r, for example, is a function of budget share, which varies with income. We will focus on low-income consumers. These are likely to place the greatest value on stabilization. We collect parameter estimates and the corresponding benefit estimates in Table 8-3, where benefits are expressed as a fraction of the stabilized fraction of expenditure of electricity. We consider utility shareholders to be a uniform group, all of whom exhi-

Table 8-3

Consumer value of income risk stabilization

	Low Income Consumer		Utility Shareholder	
	Base Case	Case 2	Base Case	Case 2
σ_p	.08	.3	.3	.3
σ_I	.30	.30	.76	.16
ρ	−0.8	−0.8	−0.7	−0.7
R	2	2	1	1
B	.038	.144	.160	.034

bit the same σ_I. We provide a basic estimate for each group based on 1981 conditions, plus a variation which represents the likely 1974 situation.

The base case in Table 8-3 expresses concretely the risk transfer imposed by regulation in the 1970s. Because the consumer price variation is small, there is little additional benefit even to the low-income consumer of additional stabilization. If prices to consumers had not been stabilized, and had reflected the world market (σ_p = 0.3), then consumers would have derived substantial value from stabilization. The imposition of crude oil price controls during this period can be understood as a political reaction to the instability in this market (Kalt, 1981). At the time of the first oil price shock, regulators undoubtedly perceived the utility's ability to bear risk as greater than that of consumers. If we use the pre-1974 value of σ_I in Eq. (8-13), the stabilization value B to the average utility shareholder falls by almost a factor of 5. Similarly, for the regulator contemplating the consumer's position in 1975, if costs were completely passed through, there would be a greater stabilization value for consumers than shareholders (Table 8-3, case 2 vs. base case). Thus the principle that regulation stabilizes on behalf of the party who receives the greatest benefit would account for past regulatory decisions. However, the base case results for the situation in the 1980s suggest that the pendulum must swing back in favor of producers. Given this hypothesis, it is useful to ask what particular form of stabilization is in the producer's interest. To understand the issues, we need a model of the producer benefit from stabilization.

Newbery and Stiglitz derive a stabilization value expression for producers which complements Eq. (8-13), but is considerably more complex. The general procedure is to find a monetary sum that the producer would be willing to pay to reduce income risk to some specified level. The calculation equates expected utility in the unstabilized case with the expected utility of stabilized income, minus the stabilization monetary equivalent B. The relevant income variable is total revenues, i.e., price times quantity. Solving the algebraic equation yields the following expression

$$\frac{B}{Y} = \frac{\Delta Y}{Y} + \frac{R}{2} \Delta(\sigma_I^2) \quad , \tag{8-14}$$

where

Y = expected total revenue in the unstabilized case,

ΔY = $Y_s - Y$ where Y_s = expected total revenue after stabilization,

$\Delta(\sigma_I^2)$ = difference in CV^2 of total revenue after and before stabilization,

R = coefficient of relative risk aversion, as defined before.

The first term in Eq. (8-14) is called a transfer benefit, since any change in average total revenue for producers is matched by an equal opposite change for consumers. The second term is the efficiency or risk benefit. It measures the welfare increase of reducing producer risk.

Equation (8-14) can be quantified in particular cases by making some assumptions about the shape of the underlying distributions. The most tractable case involves using the log normal distribution for output and total revenue (income). The essential properties of the log normal distribution are shown in Figure 8-9. Note that variables with such distribu-

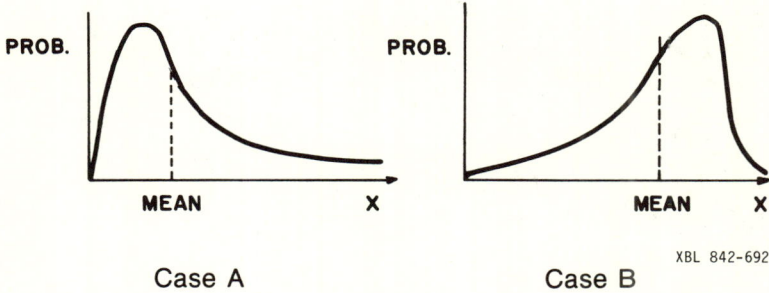

Case A   Case B

XBL 842-692

Figure 8-9. Log-normal density function.

tions always take positive values. Case A shows the usual positive skewness (where the mean is substantially above the median), a shape used frequently for income distribution. Output of individual utilities has also been shown to exhibit a positive skewness (Kahn, 1979). Case B represents the price distribution, illustrating the tendency toward high prices (i.e., mean below the median). Positively skewed output Q implies negatively skewed prices, P, in this case because of price elasticity, i.e.,

$Q = p^{-e}$, for elasticity e (assumed positive by convention) .

If Q has a positive log normal distribution as in Case A, then $p = Q^{-1/e}$ will reflect a distribution in the shape of Case B.

Using these assumptions, Newbery and Stiglitz derive the following expression for the case of complete stabilization with respect to B_T, the transfer benefit

$$B_T = \frac{\Delta Y}{Y} = \frac{(e - 1)\sigma_p^2}{2} , \qquad (8\text{-}15)$$

where σ_p and Y are defined as in Eqs. 8-13 and 8-14. Inspection of Eq. (8-15) shows that for elasticity e less than 1, B_T is less than 0. This means that if demand is not very elastic, stabilizing prices benefits consumers, since stabilization will prevent customers from paying at high prices frequently for approximately the same quantity. Conversely, where elasticity is high, producers benefit from reducing the frequency of

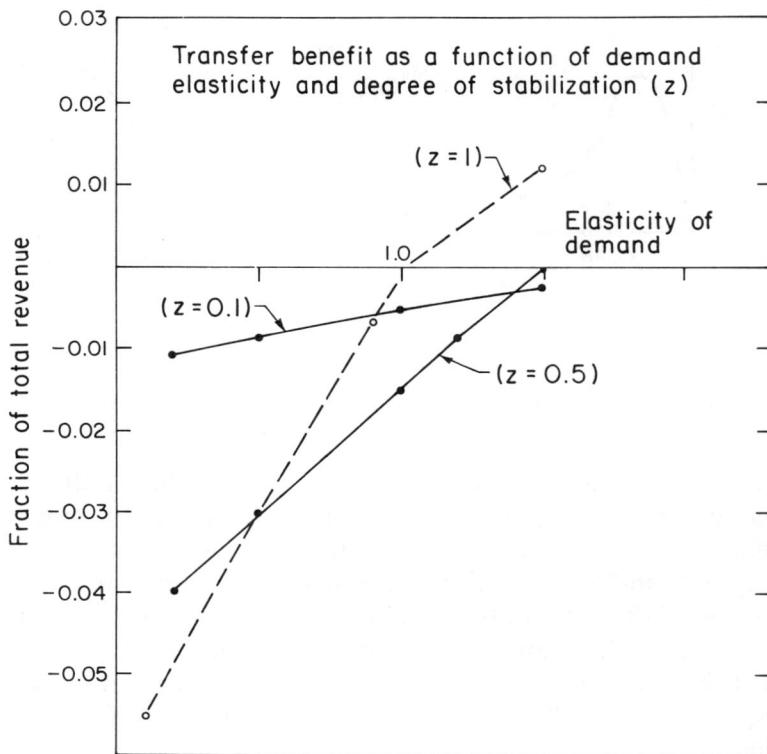

XBL8211— 1337

Figure 8-10. Transfer benefit as a function of demand elasticity and degree of stabilization.

very high prices since high prices cut sales so much that total revenues drop.

Equation (8-15) has a natural generalization to the case of partial instead of complete stabilization. Let us define Z as a measure of the degree of stabilization, with Z = 0 corresponding to none and Z = 1 representing perfect stability. Suppose that partial stabilization reduces the CV of prices to a fraction (1-Z) of its original value. Then Eq. (8-15) can be written

$$B_T = \frac{Z[e - (2 - Z)]\sigma_p^2}{2} . \qquad (8\text{-}16)$$

The effect of this generalization is to change the point at

which B_T changes sign. Figure 8-10 illustrates the effect of the parameter Z on B_T. The basic trend shown here is for partial stabilization to decrease the absolute magnitude of B_T, but to increase the value of price elasticity at which B_T is greater than 0.

Figure 8-10 is useful for analysis of the transfer benefits associated with utility conservation programs. Generally speaking, producers lose in these transfers unless the market elasticity is high (*e* greater than 1) and stabilization is substantial (Z approximately 1). There may be submarkets of utility service in which these conditions obtain. One example might be residential electric space heating. Utilities estimate long-run elasticities of 1 or more in this sector. Promotional rates for this market can be construed as stabilization policies which prevent transfer losses or imply transfer gains.

This case is one in which high elasticity is given, and rate incentives provide stabilization. Additional conservation programs have the effect of increasing the elasticity although they rarely increase it above 1. The only cases where elasticities above 1 are observed are electric space heating and industrial applications. Weatherization financing or appliance rebates essentially accelerate the consumer response to price. As cost-effectiveness studies indicate, the benefit to producers depends upon general rate-making policy (the avoided cost minus lost revenue criterion, for example). In general, the regulator chooses a stabilization policy first through rate levels and tariff design. Conservation programs do not affect these decisions directly. Instead conservation just increases elasticity within a given stabilization framework.

The parameter Z discussed above is typically chosen by the regulator with effects which can be seen in Figure 8-10. Table 8-1 indicates that the value chosen during the 1970s was high, between 0.6 and 0.8 — which we find, for instance,

as $1 - \left[\dfrac{0.08}{0.32}\right] = 0.75$. Assuming a price elasticity $e = 0.5$,

$Z = 0.7$ and $\sigma_p = .32$, then $B_T = -0.028$; i.e., the transfer loss is about 2.8% of revenue. Conservation programs can reduce this loss (by increasing e), but to a lesser extent than policies which destabilize prices in general. This can be shown by

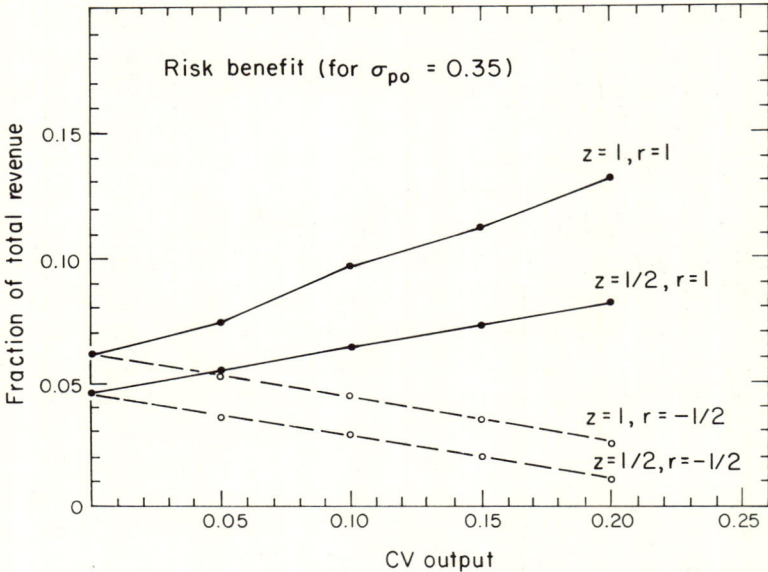

Figure 8-11. Fraction of total revenue versus risk benefit. (σ_{po} = coefficient of variation for the unstabilized price.)

examining the partial derivatives of B_T with respect to Z and e. These are shown in Eqs. (8-17) and (8-18), i.e.,

$$\frac{\partial B_T}{\partial e} = Z \frac{\sigma_p^2}{2} \quad , \qquad (8\text{-}17)$$

and

$$\frac{\partial B_T}{\partial Z} = \left(\frac{e}{2} - 1 + Z \right) \sigma_p^2 \quad . \qquad (8\text{-}18)$$

The absolute magnitude of $\dfrac{\partial B_T}{\partial Z}$ is greater than $\dfrac{\partial B_T}{\partial e}$ as long as Z is greater than $2 - e$, and what's more, Z is an easier parameter to adjust in absolute terms than e is. These results indicate that with respect to transfers, utility conservation programs compete with deregulation or destabilization of prices.

This competition can be made more explicit by considering the producer's investment strategies and choices. These choices are best analyzed by considering the risk benefit term in Eq. (8-14). Producers typically retain the risk benefit. It is, after all, a form of stabilization designed to encourage investment. The producer will know the price or quantity that should be stabilized to reduce investment risk in a particular circumstance. Thus for "business-as-usual" regulated utility production, the inclusion of CWIP in rate base is an appropriate stabilization scheme. We will investigate the value of stabilization (not its form) for various utility production strategies. To do this systematically we need an analogue to Eq.(8-16) for the risk benefit, B_R. Newbery and Stiglitz derive such an expression for the case of log-normally distributed supply and demand uncertainty. Their expression for the risk benefit in this case is

$$B_R = \frac{RZ}{2} \left[(2 - z)\, \sigma_{po}^2 + 2r\sigma\, \sigma_{po}^2 \right] \qquad (8\text{-}19)$$

where

σ = CV of output,
σ_{po} = CV of unstabilized price,
r = correlation coefficient of log P on log Q,
R = relative risk aversion,
and
Z = degree of stabilization.

It is useful to illustrate the sensitivity of Eq. (8-19) to parameter values. Figure 8-11 is helpful in this regard. It shows that the sign of the parameter r is the most significant contributor to variation in the magnitude of B_R. This parameter is similar to the price elasticity of the market. When it is negative, then the market itself is stabilizing income to some degree because fluctuations in price or quantity are offset by the elasticity adjustment. If price goes up, quantity goes down; therefore the product (i.e., income) stays relatively stable. The mechanism operates similarly when price goes down. When r is greater than 0, income fluctuations are not dampened by the market, but are exaggerated and in this case the value of stabilization is great. The value of r is rarely positive for consumers and rarely negative for producers.

To analyze producer preferences, we examine B_R for different producer roles where different parameter values are relevant. It is clear, for example, that utility conservation programs must have r less than 0, since they are elasticity-enhancing. To model supply side production strategies, we distinguish a "business-as-usual" role from the role of unregulated producer. The latter can be thought of as a Qualifying Facility under PURPA, or an unregulated utility subsidiary in this role, and there is evidence that utilities are interested in this possibility. Examining the unregulated producer role will also allow us to quantify the competition between deregulation and utility conservation programs which our analysis of the transfer benefit revealed.

Table 8-4 summarizes the parameter values we will use in Eq. (8-19). These are crude estimates and imply the need for sensitivity analysis. Nonetheless the values are plausible, if not precise. Let us begin with the parameter r (equal to the correlation coefficient of log p on log Q) We have already argued that r is less than 0 for utility conservation programs. The absolute magnitude should approximate the price elasticity. We test $r = -1.0$ and $r = -0.6$. For unregulated production we expect $r = 1.0$. The regulated producer should have r greater than 0 also. Kahn has estimated a value of $r = 0.8$; we test that and $r = 1.0$.

The CV of output should be measured at the plant level for all alternatives. For central station power plants (the regulated producer), one can estimate the CV of plant capacity factor. A utility consultant's statistical study of this variable for new coal plants identified 60% as the mean, with a high of 80% and a low of 38% (Perl, 1981). Assuming this range covers two standard deviations implies CV = 0.15. We adopt this as our base case. If the high and low span only 80% of the probability, then CV = 0.25. The CV of output for unregulated production is harder to estimate. Some technologies like wind or hydro-generation could have CV = 0.30. Cogeneration, on the other hand, might be 0.02. For simplicity we assume CV of output is similar for both supply roles, regulated and unregulated.

The output of utility conservation programs must be measured in the aggregate because it is the aggregate

Table 8-4

**CV price and output for various producers
and conservation programs**

	CV Price	CV Output	r = correlation (log p, log q)
Regulated Producer	CV Coal = 1.8	Base = .15	0.8 – 1.0
Unregulated Producer	CV marginal price = .35	Same as regulated producer	1.0
Utility Conservation Programs	CV marginal price = .35	Less than regulated producer	−.6 – 1.0

supply/demand framework in which their value must be assessed. It has been argued that these programs should be more predictable than supply project output. There are, however, many unsettled measurement problems associated with utility conservation programs. Even if they were resolved, there is very little evidence on the CV of output. We will assume that the CV in this case is less than for supply roles, and test for sensitivity.

The CV of unstabilized prices should be the marginal cost to the utility in all cases. For conservation and unregulated production, the CV of oil prices is a good proxy. Statistical studies of nuclear power plant capital costs also reveal a real price CV in excess of 30% (Komanoff, 1981). The case of a coal plant (regulated production) is somewhat different. The unstabilized price can be thought of as the fuel itself, or in the case in which the coal plant displaces oil, it is the net of oil and coal price instability. In either case the numerical value is about the same.

Table 8-5 summarizes the stabilization risk/benefit results. It is clear from this that unregulated production is the most favored role. The stabilization value is greatest here under any of the listed assumptions about the CV of output. This is

Table 8-5

**Risk benefit for generic production
roles and degree of stabilization**

		$z = 1$		$z = 0.5$	
		$r = 1.0$	$r = 0.8$	$r = 1.0$	$r = 0.8$
Regulated Producer	$\sigma = .10$	.034	.030	.021	.019
	$\sigma = .15$	.043	.038	.026	.023
	$\sigma = .25$	.061	.052	.035	.030
Unregulated Producer	$\sigma = .10$	.096		.064	
	$\sigma = .15$	.113		.064	
	$\sigma = .25$	.149		.090	
		$r = -1.0$	$r = -0.6$	$r = -1.0$	$r = -0.6$
Utility Conservation Producer	$\sigma = .05$	.044	.051	.037	.045
	$\sigma = .10$	.025	.040	.029	.036
	$\sigma = .20$	-.009	.019	.011	.025

a plausible result because this case represents removing an
"excess profit tax" ceiling that is associated with conventional
regulation.

The competition between utility conservation programs and
traditional production depends on parameter values. If the
CV of conservation output is small enough, then it is the
favored alternative. On the other hand, if this parameter is
large, then conservation is not only less attractive, it may
even be harmful. An unpredictable conservation program
may increase the supply-demand imbalance, thereby increasing producer income risk.

This suggests that the modularity or incremental nature of
conservation program output may turn out to be its most
important feature. The key question at this stage is to what
degree the output can be controlled.

8.5 From Theory to Institutional Reality

It now appears that no simple dividing line exists between deregulation and business-as-usual for the electric utilities. It is clear that more competition exists in the market for electricity generation, and that conservation will be a powerful force in the long run. These forces tend to destabilize the utility. The two basic questions facing the industry are: What should management do about this? and What is a socially desirable regulatory policy?

Regulatory stabilization for independent power production has been shown to be very valuable. This suggests that QFs in the long run may find a permanent place as producers. Utilities have only two choices in this area: they can fight or they can join. One way to fight QFs is with conservation. If the utilities can manage demand reduction properly, they can reduce the value of QF production, and hence its market share. This is a risky strategy, however, since too much conservation can induce an unprofitable excess-capacity situation. The alternative is to join the QF industry by becoming unregulated producers themselves. This option has been authorized in New York, has been pursued quite vigorously within the PURPA limitations by utilities such as Southern California Edison and Virginia Power and is under discussion in industry and government circles (Newmark and Cooper, 1984). If it becomes extremely popular, this strategy would probably involve a change in PURPA, but that is no major barrier if a policy consensus exists. It is the policy issues, however, which are most indeterminate. We have characterized the electricity market as uncertain and unstable. This makes it harder to discern a clear direction of evolution. Moreover, it suggests that conditions may vary regionally depending on variations in the supply and demand balance. The job of regulation is harder now that shareholder and consumer interests are more in conflict than they were when costs were declining. From the consumer perspective, for example, large scale conservation might be the least-cost alternative. It is unlikely that shareholders and management would willingly shrink the market with such a strategy. This is particularly true where the utility's large customers are leaving the system to become QFs.

The policy outcome will be determined largely by local economic and political conditions. It is not clear what the stable or sustainable configuration of electricity supply and demand will be, or indeed, if there is just one such outcome. To explore the possibilities in detail it is necessary to enumerate and analyze the prospects for particular institutional changes. This is the subject of Chapter 9.

Chapter **9**

The Evolution of the Industry Structure

9.1 Introduction

The electric utility industry faces a number of long-term problems for which its current structure may be poorly adapted. The competing strategies outlined in Chapter 8 are not compatible with one another, and do not represent an equilibrium in any sense. In light of current competitive pressure, "business-as-usual" regulation may no longer be feasible. Independent power production plainly has an important role to play in the evolution of the industry, but it is uncertain whether this role will be one of a fully deregulated generation segment with no residual role for regulated production. Even the promise of increased consumption efficiency is not an unambiguous social good, because it will result in smaller markets for power, thereby increasing the pressure to shift transition costs onto the utility's captive customers. In the process of finding the boundary of appropriate regulatory action, certain stakeholder interests are certain to suffer.

In this chapter we will consider how the institutions of the industry may adapt to this new environment of competition and strategic conflict. We will begin in Section 9.2 to review the problems faced by existing institutions. In this review we examine the current structure of firms, the productivity trends in the industry, and the responsiveness to competition that has been demonstrated to date. The problems facing the electric utilities have analogies in other industries. In Section 9.3 we explore the parallels in the telecommunications and natural gas industries. Each example offers similarities and differences which give some perspective on the nature of the problems and the likely evolution. Finally in Section 9.4 we examine the two conflicting forces which will shape the evolution of the industry. On the one hand, modern power systems require physical coordination and control of a sophisticated technological character. Many different means are available to achieve coordination, but at some level a centralizing institution must play a major role in this process. Conversely, the forces of competition are fundamentally decentralizing in nature. Independent production and increased end-use efficiency introduce a multitude of decision-makers into the power system who are not under the central control of planners or regulators. This force is also irreversible. We examine how different institutional arrangements offer to mix and blend the need for coordination with increasing decentralization.

9.2 Industry Problems

In this section we examine the structure of firms in the electric utility industry and how well adapted that structure is to current conditions. Among the problems facing the utility industry is a relative stagnation in its fundamental productivity. We examine the evidence for this both at the technological and organizational levels. Productivity stagnation limits the ability of firms to respond to competitive pressures. We review the evidence available to date on the ability of regulated utilities to respond to competition.

For all the turmoil in the electric utility industry during the last two decades, it is remarkable how little the structure of the industry has changed since its last great re-organization in the 1930s. At that time the financial pyramids erected by speculators and other practitioners of the holding company strategy were dismembered and rationalized under the authority of the Securities and Exchange Commission. Since then there have been a few experiments in market aggregation. Several regional power pools have evolved, principally in the Northeast, to achieve scale economies in generation and power system operation. The oldest and largest of these is the Pennsylvania-New Jersey-Maryland Interconnection (PJM). Other large coordinated regional entities are the New York

Power Pool (NYPP) and the New England Power Pool (NEPOOL). In all three of these organizations there is a coordination of investment as well as operations. Among the publicly owned utilities there have been joint-action power agencies formed, such as the Massachusetts Municipal Wholesale Electric Cooperative (MMWEC) and the Washington Public Power Supply System (WPPSS). These organizations were created to finance or participate in large nuclear power projects.

To a large degree it has been the unmanageable consequences of nuclear power projects that have brought about a perception of crisis in the utility industry. The first significant indication of a crisis was the accident at General Public Utilities' (GPU) Three Mile Island plant in 1979. The large clean-up costs associated with this event and the perception of operational mis-management raised the specter of the first utility bankruptcy since the 1930s, although when regulators in New Jersey and Pennsylvania contemplated the dismemberment or re-organization of GPU under the Bankruptcy Act they concluded that there was little to be gained.

By the mid-1980s the utility industry itself began to recognize that nuclear power was a financial liability. They even started asking regulators for higher rates of return to compensate investors for the risks of such investments (SCE, 1986). Regulators began to refuse to allow all costs incurred by utilities for the construction of these plants to be allowed into the rate base. Bankruptcy again emerged as a possibility for companies that had abandoned nuclear investments or whose projects had experienced "unbearable" cost overruns.

Whatever special problems may be associated with nuclear plants, the fundamental situation had become one in which incremental investment in new facilities was too large for the size of the firms involved. Gilbert (1987) has assembled some interesting data on the relationship between industry investments and firm size. This is reproduced in Table 9-1. These data, although anecdotal in nature, tend to show that private industry in general does not support investments in excess of 10% of assets. While the table shows exceptions, they are either in industries troubled with excess capacity and cut-throat competition (iron and steel) or where contracting is on

Electric Utility Planning and Regulation

Table 9-1

Statistics on industry investments and firm sizes

Industry	Project[1]	Proj Size[1] (millions) ($ 1982)	Assets[2] (millions) ($ 1982)	Size/Assets (percent)
Petroleum Refining	complex refinery	1,000–2,000	20,000	5–10
Iron & Steel Steel	steel complex	200–1,000	3,500	5–30
Motor Vehicles	new model	500–3,000	22,100	5–10
Defense	misc.	500–1,000	3,000	15–35
Electric Power	large coal or nuclear plant	3,000–5,000	11,200	25–45

[1] Project and project size are the largest projects that major firms in the industry would be likely to undertake.

[2] Asset size is approximately the size of the fourth largest firm in the industry, except for motor vehicles where, due to industry concentration, it is the second largest firm.

an almost nationalized, "cost-plus" basis (defense). There are two possible implications of this data for the electric utilities. One interpretation is that the firms are too small and ought to grow larger through market aggregation, such as the formation of joint ventures, coordinated regional pools, or, in the most permanent case, mergers. Alternatively, the technology is too large and ought to be modularized through engineering innovation. Neither interpretation necessarily precludes the other.

Mergers have been widespread in American industry as a response to competitive pressure. The relatively small size of many utility companies reflects a Balkanization of administration that represents conditions of a less mobile, more localized economy than that which exists today — there have been relatively few changes of ownership, control and franchise territory in the utility industry since the 1930s. The most recent change in this situation was the merger of Toledo Edison with Cleveland Illuminating Electric Company in 1985, which was facilitated by joint investment in a large nuclear facility and geographical contiguity. Since the two companies had so much in common, the process of unification was orderly and economical. The principal economy realized in the short-run was the reduction in redundant staff. In the longer run, operational economies will also be realized. An additional motivation for the consolidation was the economic burden of nuclear construction on the smaller company (Toledo Edison) and its accompanying financial distress.

There are substantial limits on the potential for mergers. In all industries entrenched management resists takeovers to protect their jobs. In unregulated firms the shareholder interest diverges from management's interest if the value of shares can be increased through acquisition of the firm. This force is much less potent in regulated firms because of the upper bound on profits exerted by regulation. The mechanism is indirect in this case. If a merger were achieved by purchase of shares at a premium above-market value (which is often the case in takeovers), the regulators might interpret this to mean that the cost of capital had declined (since the firm's profits, divided by the market value of its shares, would then be lower). The regulators might decide, therefore, that rates should be correspondingly lowered. Similarly, operational economies can also be expected to induce rate reductions. Therefore shareholders might not capture the benefits of consolidation.

Regulators also pose another barrier to any merger considered between utilities in different states. The merged single firm would incur transaction costs from having to deal with two different state commissions; there is no economy of scale in this situation because each commission will act independently of the other. The Cleveland Electric/ Toledo Edison merger achieved a scale economy in regulation because both firms were under the purview of the same regulator. For this reason future mergers might well be limited to utilities in the same state. While this constraint could limit the potential for consolidation, it does not eliminate it. Indeed, commissioners in New York and Iowa, for example, have invited consideration of mergers of utilities within their respective states. Depending on the economies to be achieved, interstate mergers may also occur. Some have been recently proposed.

If the burden of incremental investment in generating capacity is too large for utility firms, another alternative lies in the down-scaling of generation units to reduce investment risk. PURPA has already instituted pressures in this direction. The issue raised by this approach is one of productivity and economies of scale. It is widely believed that generating capacity costs are lower for larger unit sizes. Statistical studies show that this is generally true for coal-fired units, even when some correction is made for the poorer availability of larger units (Joskow, 1987). On the other hand, classic trends of technological innovation in electricity generation, which focused on raising productivity through scale economies, had played themselves out by the 1970s. Instead, innovation in smaller-scale technologies, which offer the ancillary benefit of reducing investment risks, had proceeded apace. These technologies include fluidized bed boilers, fuel cells, integrated coal-gasification and combined cycle units among others. However, none of these smaller-scale technologies has been demonstrated to be sufficiently competitive to eliminate the size-of-investment issue.

Productivity stagnation is not limited to the equipment vendor. There is reason to believe that labor costs are higher in a regulated environment than in one where competitive pressures are strong. The most persuasive evidence comes from the deregulation of the transportation industries in the late 1970s and early 1980s. An index of average compensation in the trucking industry showed declines of 14–24% from 1977 to 1982 (Moore, 1986). In the airline industry, competitive pressures led to productivity gains from changes in work rules, the institution of two-tier wage structures and in some cases the granting of equity positions to labor (Bailey, 1986). Studies of this issue in the energy industries are more limited. Russo and Teece (1986) found that competition did have a negative effect on wage rates in the natural gas industry, but the magnitude was relatively small. In the electric utility industry there has been a wave of staff reductions among companies that are experiencing competition due to high costs.

As competition from private supply, bypass, and conservation increases, electric utilities will have to respond by increasing labor and managerial productivity. To some degree this may occur through a declining burden of regulatory costs. It is often argued that the administrative requirements of rate hearings and other compliance requirements of the regulatory process are a large source of inefficiency. Crew and Kleindorfer (1985) construct a simple model to argue that the transaction costs of a rate case in excess of 0.5% of utility revenues are likely to reduce total welfare for customers and utilities. This is an upper bound on the costs of regulation that can be justified using their model. In other cases the justifiable expense may only be one-quarter or one-eighth as much. At such levels it is clear that the costs of conducting a rate case may well exceed the benefits to shareholders in the case of a rate increase, and to ratepayers in the event of rate decrease.

If transactions costs such as these were eliminated, it would be unlikely that utilities could save enough to recover the cost advantage necessary to compete with potential bypass or competitive supply. In all likelihood the nature of regulated markets will undergo structural change, and the organization of firms serving those markets would undergo transformation. This process has been occurring in other regulated industries. It will be useful to examine the experience in two of those industries briefly to shed light on the possible evolution of the electric utilities.

9.3 Structural Change in Telecommunications and Natural Gas

Deregulation, a widespread social and economic phenomenon that has affected many American industries in the last decade, has numerous causes. Some of the pressure to reduce government control over economic activity comes from technological change; some is due to international economic competition and some stems from political and ideological currents. Much of this experience is relevant to the forces at work in the electric utility industry. In this section we draw upon the experience of the natural gas and telecommunications industries to illustrate the nature of the changes affecting electric utilities, and to develop a sense of the possible evolution of the industry structure. Natural gas and telecommunications show different aspects of deregulation and structural change. Each will highlight different aspects of the dilemma facing the electric utilities. We will begin with natural gas, where the price instabilities of the 1970s and 1980s parallel the experience in electricity. The theme in telecommunications is the breakup of vertical integration.

9.3.1 Natural Gas

The natural gas industry is substantially less integrated than the electric utilities industry. Although originally gas was distributed locally by firms which manufactured it from coal or oil, when long-distance pipelines became popular, integration declined considerably. The industry's modern form dates from the pipeline era, which began in the 1920s and had several periods of intense construction up through the 1950s. The pipeline companies were the major developers of the gas industry, but they had relatively little corporate connection either to the local distribution companies or the gas suppliers. By "relatively little," we do not mean none. Some pipeline companies had major holdings in the distribution sector (Columbia Gas is a prominent example). Some pipelines also had significant stakes in gas supply (El Paso is the largest of these). In no case, however, did end-to-end integration create the kind of monopoly power that is characteristic of electric utility companies.

The dominant form of regulation in the gas industry occurs at the federal level. Not only are pipeline rates regulated under the federal government's authority over interstate commerce, but so also are the prices of gas at the well-head. It was well-head price regulation which has been largely blamed for the gas shortages experienced during the 1970s (Braeutigam and Hubbard, 1986). To alleviate and manage these problems, Congress enacted major reforms in the pricing of natural gas through the Natural Gas Policy Act of 1978 (NGPA). Among other things the NGPA deregulated the price of new high-cost sources of supply, created a schedule for the removal of price ceilings on other categories of gas, and provided a set of pricing rules for pipelines that required the averaging of prices for high-cost supplies with low-cost supplies.

Developments in the late 1970s and early 1980s created a boom-and-bust phenomenon in gas prices that was a much more exaggerated version of the demand, pricing and supply problems experienced by the electric utilities. NGPA created the incentive for pipeline companies to acquire high-cost resources such as liquefied natural gas (LNG) and "deep gas" (from wells below 15,000 feet). Due to perceived shortages, the price for these supplies was bid up to very high levels. At its 1982 peak, prices for deep gas were in the range of $9–10 per million Btu. This corresponds to crude oil prices in excess of $60 per barrel, a level not seen on the crude oil spot market even at its highest point. Because of the mandated average-cost pricing under NGPA, customers did not see these costs. The average well-head price in that year was around $2.50 per million Btu.

Pipelines also undertook very large "take-or-pay" obligations to suppliers during this period. Having suffered politically for the gas curtailments which occurred before NGPA, pipelines attempted to secure supplies without regard to price. The cost of these commitments soon became clear when world oil prices began first to stagnate and then to decline. Because large industrial and electric utility boilers have dual-fuel capability, there is a significant potential for substitution between oil and gas. Thus the market-clearing price of gas can never diverge very far from that of oil; and oil prices are set on world markets. Declining world oil prices therefore created a marketing and pricing squeeze on the pipelines.

Demand for gas fell in the 1980s due to price competition from oil and an unexpectedly severe recession. Declining demand created the beginnings of a "death spiral" dynamic as pipelines had to raise rates to recover the fixed costs associated with high-cost supplies and take-or-pay obligations. Various mechanisms appeared to allocate the losses associated with what came to be called the gas industry's "contracts problem." Some of the losses were imposed on suppliers, as the pipelines exercised every possible technicality that would allow them to break their contracts. Shareholders bore other losses as pipeline profitability declined. There were mergers and acquisitions — El Paso Natural Gas was acquired by Burlington Northern, a railroad conglomerate, after abandoning an uneconomic LNG terminal in addition to suffering reduced sales and take-or-pay contract problems. CSX, another major railroad, acquired Texas Gas Transmission. Internorth merged with Houston Natural Gas, a major distribution company.

In addition to consolidations and acquisitions, the pipelines also began to evolve toward service differentiation. The most substantial change was the expansion of transportation or "contract carriage" services. This involves the transport of gas by the pipeline from seller to user without the pipeline itself ever taking the ownership or acquisition risk. The growth of demand for transportation services depends upon the emergence of spot markets for gas. With the supply excess that developed in the 1980s, gas producers became more willing to sell on a spot rather than a long-term contract basis because they didn't want to lock in low prices with a contract. In some cases, transportation of spot gas to end-users can reduce the financial problems of pipelines; in other cases it can make things worse by increasing take-or-pay contract difficulties (Saunders, 1986).

Structural change in the gas industry has been more rapid than parallel developments in electricity. The reversals in the relationship of marginal to average cost were larger in the gas industry, and appear to have had greater financial consequences. In large part these differences are due to the smaller degree of integration in gas and the smaller role played by capital-intensive supply projects. Because pipeline companies are less integrated than electric utilities, the inflexible supply commitments which the pipelines made in the 1970s turned out to be even larger, relative to their assets, than large-scale generation projects were for the power companies. The relative safety of distribution plant assets provided something of a cushion for over-committed electric utilities. State regulators have also proved reluctant to force electric utilities into bankruptcy or re-organization as the result of economic losses. Federally regulated pipelines, on the other hand, had no local political constituency to shield them from the consequences of unrecoverable costs. At the same time corporate mergers appear to be less politically constrained in the gas industry, so consolidation is a more natural solution for economic distress.

Both the electricity and gas utilities have suffered from the boom-and-bust energy cycle due to similar problems. Inflexible supply commitments were made in a period of rising costs, and risks of insufficient demand at the resulting high prices were underestimated. In both cases economic shocks from outside the industry induced the instability and loss that it suffered. Technological factors were more important in the electric industry than in gas, where the price of supply technologies such as LNG, although high, was not underestimated as it was for nuclear power. For both electricity and gas, the effect was negative, i.e., productivity due to new technology went down instead of up. As we will see shortly, increasing productivity from technological innovation is a driving factor in the re-organization of the telecommunications industry. On the other hand, LNG, coal gasification, and nuclear power now appear to be marginal economic propositions, if not outright losers.

Finally it is interesting to contrast the role of contracts with the role of capital investment as an influence on the mechanisms available to allocate economic losses. In electric utilities the losses associated with uneconomic supply projects have not yet resulted in the extensive re-organization of firms that has occurred in the pipeline industry. Perhaps there will be additional bankruptcies, more forced mergers and public takeovers of financially troubled electric utilities. Alternatively, it may turn out that customers end up bearing more of these costs than in the gas industry. This follows from the greater degree of integration in electricity. Even without new generation projects, electric utilities need to raise capital for investment in transmission and distribution facilities. Imposing losses from uneconomic generation projects on shareholders will raise the cost of capital for the remaining utility operations. Thus it appears that customers end up paying for some of these losses indirectly even if they manage to avoid their direct consequences through disallowances of imprudent expenditures from rate base.

In the case of pipeline contracts the losses have been either absorbed primarily by the pipeline itself or the gas suppliers. The distribution companies have been relatively shielded. To the degree that pipelines are damaged by absorbing these losses, they become takeover candidates. In electricity the greater barriers to acquisition, which are largely political, limit the ability of the financial system to allocate losses to producers, and provide potential gains for acquiring companies. Other forms of corporate re-organization are possible in electricity. One unsuccessful effort was the proposed leveraged buyout of Public Service of Indiana in the wake of its $2.4 billion write-off due to the abandonment of the Marble Hill nuclear project. At some point, regulators who want to reduce the burden of economic losses on consumers may have to accept the merger and acquisition alternative.

In the telecommunications industry sunk costs are also as large a factor as in electricity, and integration has been historically very great. Thus re-organization analogies between the two industries are instructive.

9.3.2 Telecommunications

From its origin the telecommunications industry has been strongly integrated. Protected by patents on the original Bell inventions, the company that was to become American Telephone and Telegraph (AT&T) formed a system that linked equipment manufacture, local operating companies, and a national long-distance network. This structure was in place by 1885. A period of competition began with the expiration of the Bell patents in 1894. Most of the independent exchanges which arose at this time served rural areas that had been neglected by the AT&T system. Many also competed directly with Bell operating companies. There were also attempts to form a competing national network.

AT&T used a variety of methods to meet this competition (Evans, 1983). Subscription prices were reduced in competitive local markets. More significantly, AT&T was able to capitalize on the strongly growing demand for long distance service. Independent companies required interconnection with the Bell system to provide long-distance service for their customers. AT&T was able to use interconnection agreements in a number of strategically competitive ways. Bell typically imposed an unfavorable division of revenue with independent companies. Selective agreement to interconnect was used to break up combinations among the independent companies that tried to form competing systems to provide long-distance service. Finally, AT&T began to acquire the competing firms and merge them with the Bell operating companies. By 1910 the tide had turned against the independent companies, and their market share declined from its peak of nearly 50%.

This early competitive period in the telecommunications industry was dominated by the extension of service, where unserved markets created opportunity for entry. In contrast, the more recent emergence of competition is driven by technical innovation in customer-premises equipment and long-distance transmission. The same competitive techniques, however, were used by AT&T. Control over interconnection standards and prices was one of the principal weapons that the Bell system has tried to use in the decades after World War II to limit the role of technologies not developed and marketed within their corporate domain. Under the current regulatory system these attempts have had limited success.

In a series of unrelated rulings the Federal Communications Commission (FCC) gradually allowed increasing entry by unregulated firms into the customer premises equipment market. Similar developments occurred in the area of long-distance transmission. The most famous of these cases involved the entry of MCI as a competing vendor of long-distance services. In parallel with these FCC decisions, the Justice Department filed an antitrust suit against AT&T in

1974 seeking divestiture of Western Electric, AT&T's manufacturing subsidiary. After lengthy litigation and negotiation, a new divestiture arrangement was accepted by all parties. AT&T agreed to spin off the regional operating companies that provided local phone service. These would remain regulated. The rest of AT&T would be unregulated and free to compete in any market. The new AT&T retained the long-distance business, Bell Laboratories, Western Electric and the terminal equipment business. This arrangement freed AT&T from the 1956 Consent Decree in which it had been restricted from from entering certain computer and data processing businesses in order to retain its regulated monopoly in telephone equipment.

The divestiture was implemented in 1984. It did not eliminate the problems associated with defining the boundary between regulation and competition, but it did shift the boundary problem. One major area of contention is the determination of local network access charges (Brock, 1986). Under the integrated system long distance rates produced revenues that subsidized the costs of local service. With divestiture, if access charges were designed to recover the same amount of revenue, then prices would be so high that bypass investment by large customers would become economic. Regulatory policy has attempted to undo the past history of cross-subsidization, without imposing price shocks on the class of small inelastic users.

This past subsidy problem has also appeared in the electric utility industry. As the possibility of competition becomes more real, it is imperative that rates reflect costs. In states such as California, where industrial utility rates have been used to subsidize residential rates, a strong incentive is created for industrial customers to bypass the utility. If the subsidies are not undone, bypass may end up harming small users more than cost-based rates. This will happen as recovery of the utility's fixed costs is shifted from the rates of the elastic consumers to the rates of the inelastic ones. In telecommunications the problem is less difficult because of the underlying productivity of technological change. Over time the costs in all segments, regulated and unregulated, are decreasing due to innovation. Thus the rate increases to inelastic customers can be limited by productivity gains. There is substantially less likelihood of that happening in electricity.

It is possible that lagging productivity in electricity may be a product of regulation rather than an inherent technical phenomenon. This possibility makes most sense in the generation segment. It raises the question of whether some form of deregulation might have beneficial effects on consumer costs. A large fraction of the competitive activity to date in electricity generation has increased productivity. This is due to the realization of cogeneration opportunities that were not exploited by utilities in their regulated business. Yet not all cogeneration activity represents efficiency gains. There are bypass and PURPA projects that are not economic, having been induced by artificial pricing, although these probably represent a minor share of the competitive activity. The more interesting long-run question is whether profit opportunities in electricity generation will induce other technical innovations. At some point the new opportunities for cogeneration will be exhausted and productivity gains will depend on new technology.

Deregulation of electricity generation will require that divestiture issues which have arisen in telecommunications also be faced by electric utilities and their regulators, including the critical question of defining the boundary between regulated and competitive activities. The boundary issues involve both corporate structure and the pricing of transactions which go across the boundary. AT&T ultimately had to re-define its corporate mission and separate the regulated and unregulated activities in different corporations without any common control or ownership. Even so it remains difficult to draw the boundary of regulation very precisely. Long distance rates are still regulated by the FCC. There is a continuing legal struggle about what activities are appropriate for the regional operating companies. Many of the same issues involved in the Justice Department suit against AT&T are re-emerging in that context, as the regional companies seek to enter the equipment-vendor markets.

While the boundary definition problems in telecommunications regulation stem largely from the broad range of opportunities for technological innovation, in electricity these potential benefits are less substantial. Further, the much more fragmented electric utility regulatory structure mixes state and federal authority in a way which is difficult to coordinate. These differences in innovation and regulatory structure will make the process of re-defining the boundaries of regulation much more difficult in electricity than in telecommunications. Innovation at the federal level may be blocked at the state level and vice versa. The large number of firms relative to the size of the market will make transactions costs more burdensome. In the next section we examine the possibilities for drawing these boundaries in the interest of expanding the constructive role of market forces in electricity.

9.4 Coordination and Decentralization in Electricity Markets

Efforts to re-structure the organization of firms in the electric utility industry must contend with the conflicting forces of centralization and decentralization. A host of technical and economic forces create pressure for some form of central organization in the production and marketing of electric power. The technical factors center primarily on the real-time nature of the supply/demand matching process. These include the need for centralized commitment and dispatch at the generation level, and the requirement that one entity have responsibility for the integrity of the bulk-power transmission network. The economic factors favoring centralization are the natural monopoly characteristics of low-voltage distribution and the benefits of integrated planning and operation. The forces of decentralization stem principally from competition. The efficiency gains of competitive supply markets require the decentralization of decision-making.

The decision on how much regulation is appropriate involves trade-offs between the efficiency gains expected to result from competition on one hand, and the increased transaction costs on the other. The same trade-off was observed in airline deregulation, where the costs of increased hassle and reduced flexibility are balanced against lower prices that make it possible for many more people to fly. In telecommunications, more consumer attention is required to the increasingly complex choices of equipment and long-distance carrier, and the benefits have accrued primarily to heavy users of long-distance. We see here the distributional aspects of the trade-off: in the case of airlines, the benefits are greatest to those who have now become financially able to fly; in telecommunications, the benefits are distributed primarily to large business users.

In this section we examine the institutional arrangements that can facilitate the resolution of these conflicting forces. On the coordination side, the institutional choices include formal power pooling, holding-company organization of firms, and joint ventures. On the decentralization side, wholesale spot markets and futures markets can facilitate the effective diversification of authority and responsibility. Negative effects of decentralization include the pirating or poaching of franchise territories, and supply-switching games by customers seeking pecuniary advantage from regulatory differences in prices and service terms.

9.4.1 Coordinating Institutions

The coordination of investment and operations of the power system for a region has traditionally been achieved at the level of the firm. To realize scale economies beyond the firm, utilities have formed power pools. There are varying degrees of centralization a pool may impose upon members. The closest operational coordination comes from centralized dispatch. In this case all electric resources in the region are controlled from a single center. The large eastern pools, PJM, NEPOOL and the New York Pool, operate in this manner. A somewhat looser form of coordination is the "brokerage" arrangement. In this case member utilities retain control over their own resources, but trade economy-energy generated in units already committed (as defined in Sec. 5.3) among themselves through a centralized exchange. One purpose of the exchange is to set transaction prices. Centralization presumably also increases the number of transactions by making traders aware of the possibility for exchange. Utilities in Florida and Texas use brokerage forms of coordination. Without a centralized exchange utilities must rely on pair-wise negotiations to achieve a transaction. This requires more communications and therefore tends to limit trade. Despite these problems there is still a good deal of non-brokered trade.

Power pool transactions are usually priced on a "split-savings" formula. This is calculated by comparing the marginal costs of buyer and seller and charging a price that lies half-way between them. This procedure is meant to represent an equitable division of the gains from trade. (It has been argued that this pricing rule is not as efficient as a marginal cost rule would be [Bloom, 1984]). The continued use of split-savings arrangements has permitted utilities to negotiate better deals on the side than they would obtain through the pool. Another opportunity for strategizing involves the actual "split-savings" calculation. The computation depends upon a characterization of what the costs would have been to the purchasing party, a calculation subject to some arbitrariness.

The coordination of investment within a power pool is usually based on a capacity allocation formula. The pool as a whole determines the aggregate need for capacity, based on the aggregation of demand forecasts supplied independently by members. Reserve requirements beyond load growth are estimated on a pool-wide basis. Once a total capacity requirement has been estimated over the forecast period, it is allocated to members. The allocation formula typically takes account of the demand characteristics of each member, and perhaps also the characteristics of its supply contributions.

For investment coordination to work successfully, there need to be substantial areas of agreement among members. Demand forecasts must have credibility, and not be perceived to be part of a gaming strategy such as that of deliberately underestimating future demand, which would allow one utility to be a "free-rider" to some extent on the investments of others. The type of capacity additions made by one member will affect reserve requirements, and therefore the capacity requirement of other members. These indirect effects impose costs on companies who do not participate in particular projects. Therefore the type of capacity added by one member must in some sense be acceptable to all others.

The evolution of power pools with independently owned generation could follow several paths. Pool membership could remain restricted to utilities with retail customers. These utilities would purchase power from independent producers (i.e., the current PURPA system, modified to remove restrictions on ownership and technology). The capacity planning and allocation procedures would remain unchanged. The purchases made by utilities from independent producers may or may not be traded in short- or long-term transactions with other pool members. Another alternative is that the pool itself might enter into long- or short-term purchase contracts with independent producers. The auction mechanism, described in Chapter 7, is one way in which long-term contracts could retain a competitive quality. This alternative is beyond the PURPA framework because the pool is not a utility, and does not, strictly speaking, have any obligation to purchase. It is nonetheless an attractive alternative because it would allow for scale economies that might not otherwise be achieved.

A third alternative is that pools could serve only operational functions and not capacity planning functions. In this case there would only be short-term pool transactions. With independent unregulated production, however, the split-savings price formula would no longer make sense. It is not the independent producer's costs which are relevant, but the spot value of power which would determine what price such a producer would receive. Independent producers might seek to sell some output under long-term contract and some on the spot market. If the spot market price were not profitable, they would curtail production.

Although some kind of operational coordination is necessary for power systems, there is more uncertainty about the need for planning coordination. In the extreme, it would be possible to de-couple production and distribution of power completely. Existing utilities would undergo a divestiture of assets, and market transactions would govern how distribution companies met the needs of their customers. We discuss the institutions needed to make decentralization effective in the next section. If we assume for the moment that coordination of planning is still desirable, then it is important to think of ways that this can be achieved without vertical integration.

Two forms of industrial structure allow for some planning

coordination. First, the utility may reorganize itself into a holding company. The bulk power assets can be spun off into an unregulated subsidiary and the regulated distribution assets would form another subsidiary. Many utilities are currently moving in this direction. The holding company framework allows for administrative coordination and smoother information flow between the "supply" and "demand" sides of the market. In parallel to the holding company structure, firms in either the production or distribution business can engage in joint ventures to achieve some planning coordination. Projects which may be "too big" for one company can be achieved with a single-purpose agreement to co-operate. The joint venture form makes sense when the opportunities for coordination are sporadic and inherently limited. If these opportunities were continual, merger or integration is more reasonable.

It is inevitable that increasing the role of market forces in electricity will reduce integration and increase certain kinds of economic risk. For the benefits of competition to be realized it will be necessary to create institutions that distribute the increased risk efficiently and equitably distribute the benefits of lower costs. In the next section we address the formation of such institutions.

9.4.2 Decentralization

For a decentralized power market to work effectively in the long run, institutions with potential market power must not abuse that power. Toward that end, it may be necessary in the name of decentralization to separate distribution companies from bulk power suppliers, and to encourage mergers among those distribution companies. A distribution company which is too small to negotiate with suppliers effectively is not likely to benefit from a competitive bulk power market. Thus individual municipalities or agricultural co-operatives might have to merge operations to cope with the competition among purchasers for the cheapest power supplies. The whole system of public power may not be easily compatible with unregulated bulk power markets. Even if we neglect the public ownership issue, small private distribution systems will not fare well without some aggregation.

A second arena where market power may interfere with market efficiency is in transmission. Bulk power transmission facilities have capacity limits that can be used strategically in competitive situations. Currently this power is used by utilities who refuse to "wheel," or transmit, electricity from a private seller to a buyer. Competitive markets require that buyers and sellers have equal access to each other. To achieve this it may be necessary to impose common-carrier status on transmission systems. An operating power pool could more easily achieve equal access because of the centralization of control in a region. Implementing decentralized, open-access transmission may be more difficult technically, and more difficult to monitor politically. For this reason it may be necessary to require the formation of regional pools.

Drawing the boundary between regulated and unregulated activity will be one of the major problems of introducing market forces in electricity. (In this way the industry will come to resemble telecommunications, where boundary definition problems are constantly recurring.) One example of the boundary problem in electricity lies in the construction of special-purpose transmission lines by private producers. It is often necessary to construct transmission facilities for new generation projects. These usually link the generators to the existing "backbone" transmission network. In a system of private independent generation, new projects will have to incur these costs. Once they are built, however, these lines become part of the regional system and affect the opportunity costs of future projects. Some system will have to be developed that accommodates the rights of original developers with the economies potentially available to new entrants. Private developers might be required to sell off transmission capacity at regulated prices as a way of preventing the duplication of facilities or the limitation of access. Since there may be costs and benefits to the network that are not reflected in costs to private developers, it is not clear that a system of private incremental investment will lead to a least-cost regional transmission grid.

An alternative approach is to make all bulk power transmission part of a regulated entity with an obligation to serve new generation projects. Such an entity would then charge new projects for the cost of extending service. It might be able to plan system development more coherently and efficiently than a mixed regulated and unregulated arrangement. Given scale economies in transmission, however, it would be difficult to devise capacity and pricing rules without any knowledge of future needs. There is no simple way to choose between alternative ways of organizing bulk power transmission in a decentralized framework. A period of some experimentation supervised by federal regulators would no doubt be required.

Another major question involving the definition of regulatory boundaries is the characterization of the franchise concept, which under traditional regulation has been essentially defined by geography. Any customer in a particular service area is served by the utility that has the franchise for that particular region. In an unregulated and more competitive market however, customers may want to "shop around" for power. Due to local differences in costs, it may be advantageous for large customers to take service first from one distribution company and then from another when conditions change. If this is allowed, it may induce problems for the distribution companies as customers jump in and out of one service area or another. A similar problem involves bypass customers who may want to resume regular utility service as bypass costs change.

One approach proposed by Joskow (1987b) is to divide customers into a "core" and a "competitive" segment, much the way that natural gas service is evolving. The "core" market would be price-regulated with a corresponding utility obligation to serve. In the "competitive" segment, there would be no obligation to serve and no price regulation. Customers would have to choose their segment and there would be no free passage between the two. Only customers in the competitive segment would have the option to bypass. If a customer wanted to change the terms of service, there would have to be a system of entry or exit fees to compensate the utility for its costs, such as those historically incurred to meet its obligation to serve. Implementing such a division of customers would pose many difficulties. Determining the prices charged for services between segments would be controversial, as would the determination of entry and exit fees. Problems of this kind are inescapable, however, as regulated and unregulated activity gets separated in the marketplace.

Decentralization places a considerable burden on the negotiation of contracts between producers and consumers. The capital-intensive nature of electricity generation requires long-term price assurances of some kind to secure financing. This means that some negotiation of the sharing of economic risk between buyer and seller must take place. One way of reducing the amount of risk-shifting that will be the subject of these negotiations is to introduce futures and options markets in electricity. Creating markets of this kind will allow speculators to shoulder some of the economic risk that would otherwise have to be borne by either producers or consumers.

An economic setting in which there would be a futures market in electricity would be substantially different from that in which industry exists today and the industry itself would have to change accordingly. The number of producers would be larger and the volatility of prices might be greater. In effect, electricity would have to be treated as more of a commodity than it is today. This means that all the transaction-specific features of individual power contracts would be standardized and abstracted into something that could be easily traded. The emergence of a futures market would signify the effective decentralization of the power market as well as facilitate its operation. It is probable that a whole new generation of communication and control technology would be required to achieve a fully decentralized system. Of course, it is not clear whether the industry will ever evolve in this direction. From our current perspective, the future promises a tension between the forces of decentralization and competition, on the one hand, and centralization and regulation on the other.

Whether social institutions will be capable of the adaptation required for the transition to a decentralized power industry is problematic. Innovation brings risks and the potential for failure. Electricity is so fundamental to modern society that a certain conservatism may be expected. Nonetheless, the forces of change are potent. The traditional firm will undergo considerable transformation. New organizations and businesses will emerge. Managing this process in an efficient and equitable fashion will be a major challenge for the rest of the twentieth century.

Bibliography

Chapter 1

The history of the U.S. electric utility industry has been described from several perspectives. Hughes (1983) adopts an international perspective on the formative period 1880–1930. Modern case histories of environmental problems are ably assembled by Roberts and Bluhm (1981). Gandara (1977) and Vennard (1979) characterize the modern planning process from different points of view. Useful historical perspective is found in the standard biography of Insull by MacDonald (1962). The viewpoint of suppliers can be found in Hammond (1941). Individual corporate histories such as Coleman (1952) and Wainwright (1961) are valuable. The role of government policy is surveyed by the Twentieth Century Fund (1947). Jarrell (1978) provides an interesting analysis of the origins of U.S electric utility regulation. Additional overviews include Chapman (1983), Gormley (1983), Roe (1984) and Praul, *et al.* (1982).

Arnold, T. 1935. *The Folklore of Capitalism.* Yale University Press.

Chapman, D. 1983. *Energy Resources and Energy Corporations.* Cornell University Press.

Chapman, D., T. Mount, *et al.* 1975. "Power Generation: Conservation, Health and Fuel Supply." U.S. Federal Power Commission National Power Survey.

Coleman, C. 1952. *PG&E of California.*

Environmental Defense Fund. 1981. *A New Alternative to Completing Nine Mile Point 2 Nuclear Station: Economic and Technical Analysis.* Berkeley, CA.

Gandara, A. 1977. "Electric Utility Decisionmaking and the Nuclear Option." Rand Corporation Report No. R-2148-NSF.

Gormley, W. 1983. *The Politics of Public Utility Regulation.* University of Pittsburgh Press.

Hammond, J.W. 1941. *Men and Volts: The Story of General Electric.* J.P. Lippincott.

Hughes, T.P. 1983. *Networks of Power: Electrification in Western Society, 1880–1930.* Johns Hopkins University Press.

Jarrell, G.A. 1978. "The Demand for State Regulation of the Electric Utility Industry." *Journal of Law and Economics.* Vol. 21, 269–295.

Joskow, P. 1987. "Productivity Growth and Technical Change in the Generation of Electricity." Energy Journal. Vol. 8, 17–38.

MacDonald, F. 1962. *Insull.* University of Chicago Press.

Praul, C., W. Marcus, and R. Weisenmiller. 1982. "Delivering Energy Services." *Annual Review of Energy.* Vol. 7, 371–415.

Roberts, M. and J. Bluhm. 1981. *The Choices of Power*. Harvard University Press.
Roe, D. 1985. *Dynamos and Virgins*. Random House.
_____. 1984. "Look at the Economics, Not the Politics." *New York Times*. January 15.
Twentieth Century Fund. 1947. *Electric Power and Government Power*.
Sioshansi, F. 1984. "Integrated Resource Planning with Emphasis on the Integration of New Technologies." ORSA/TIMS Meeting.
Vennard, E. 1979. *The Management of the Electric Power Business*. McGraw-Hill.
Wainright, N. 1961. *History of the Philadelphia Electric Company 1881–1961*.

Chapter 2

There are many standard references on project evaluation from an engineering economics perspective. Modern examples include Bussey (1979). Application of this perspective to electric power is developed most completely by Jeynes (1968) and embodied in handbooks such as EPRI (1978). Lucid brief accounts with interesting examples are given in Gulbrand and Leung (1975) and Leung and Durning (1978). Among the controversial aspects of these methods are the supposed capital bias discussed by Averch and Johnson (1962) and controversies over the correct discount rate to be used. Corey (1982) gives a useful discussion of theory and practice on this other issue. Modern texts on corporate finance such as Brealey and Myers (1981) emphasize different procedures than the classical methods used by utility planners. Selected financial data on electric utilities can be found in Moody's (1987), NERA (1981) and Brigham and Shome (1982).

Averch, H. and L. Johnson. 1962. "Behavior of the Firm Under Regulatory Constraint." *American Economic Review*. 1053–1069.
Brealey, R. and S. Myers. 1981. *Principles of Corporate Finance*. McGraw-Hill.
Brigham, W. and D. Shome. 1982. "Equity Risk Premiums in the 1980s Earnings Regulation Under Inflation." Institute for the Study of Regulation.
Bussey, L. 1979. *Economic Evaluation of Industrial Projects*. Prentice-Hall.
Corey, G. 1982. "Plant Investment Decision Making in the Electric Power Industry, Discounting for Time and Risk in Energy Policy." Johns Hopkins University Press.
Electric Power Research Institute. 1978. "Technical Assessment Guide." EPRI PS-866-SR.
Gulbrand, K. and P. Leung. 1975. "Power System Economics: A Sensitivity Analysis of Annual Fixed Charges." *ASME Journal of Engineering for Power*. Vol. 97, 465–472.

W.B. Hickman, "Statistical Measures of Corporate Bond. Financing Since 1900." Princeton Univ. Press. 1960.

Jeynes, P. 1968. "Profitability and Economic Choice." Iowa State University Press.

Leung, P. and R. Durning. 1978. "Power System Economics: On Selection of Engineering Alternatives." *ASME Journal of Engineering for Power.* Vol. 100, 333–346.

Linhart, P., J. Liebowitz, and F. Sinden. 1974. "The Choice Between Capitalizing and Expensing Under Rate Regulation." *The Bell Journal of Economics and Management Science.* Vol. 5, 406–419.

Moody's Investor Services. 1987. *Public Utility Manual.*

National Economic Research Associates. 1981. *Selected Financial Data on Electric Utilities.* Aspen Institute.

Chapter 3

Capital cost escalation for power plants has been studied most systematically by Komanoff (1981). It is useful to consider previous expectations embodied in planning committee reports such as FPC (1964) or NEPOOL (1978). Additional data on lead time and cost are found in Mooz (1978) and DOE (1983). Discussions of construction financing cost are found in Pomerantz and Suelflow (1975) for accounting treatment, Comtois (1978) for capital cost implications, and Livingstone and Sherali (1979) for multiple project evaluation. Cost of capital studies that are particularly interesting include Haugen *et al.* (1978) on interest rate risk and Benore (1978) and Peck (1983) on shareholder interest. Reliability and reserve margins are discussed in Sullivan (1977) and Bhavaraju (1982); Garver (1966) calculates this for incremental units. Incremental units are accounted for in project evaluation by Lyons (1979) and Deb and Mulvaney (1982). Capacity expansion models are discussed by EPRI (1978) and Sullivan (1977) for methods, and Platts and Womeldorff (1980) for assumptions. Advanced methods dealing wih unequal attributes are treated by Merrill (1983) and Keeney and Sicherman (1983).

Benore, C. 1978. "Dividend Policy and Common Share Valuation of Electric Utilities." Edison Electric Institute Financial Conference.

Bhavaraju, M. 1982. "Generating System Reliability Evaluation. IEEE Tutorial Course." 82 EHO 195-8 PWR.

Caramanis, M., F. Schweppe, and R. Tabors. 1982. *Electric Generation Expansion Analysis System. Volume 1: Solution Techniques, Computing Methods and Results.* Electric Power Research Institute Report EL-2561.

Comtois, W. 1978. "Power Plant Construction Schedules, Escalation and Interest During Construction." In *Proceedings of the American Power Conference.* Vol. 38, 409–414.

Deb, R. and J. Mulvaney. 1982. "Economic and Engineering Factors Affecting Generator Unit Size." *IEEE Transactions on Power Apparatus and Systems*. Vol. PAS-101, no. 10, 3907–3918.

Dept. of Energy. 1983. *The Future of Electric Power in America: Economic Supply for Economic Growth*. DOE/PE-0045.

Electric Power Research Institute. 1978. *Technical Assessment Guide*. EPRI PS-866-SR.

Energy Information Administration. 1983a. *Delays and Cancellations of Coal-Fired Generating Capacity*. U.S. Dept. of Energy Report DOE/EIA-0406.

————. 1983b. *Nuclear Plant Cancellations: Causes, Costs and Consequences*. U.S. Dept. of Energy Report DOE/EIA-0392.

Federal Power Commission. 1964. *National Power Survey*.

Garver, L. L. 1966. "Effective Load-Carrying Capability of Generating Units." *IEEE Transactions on Power Apparatus and Systems*. Vol. PAS-85, no. 8, 910–919.

Haugen, R., A. Stroyny, and D. Wichern. 1978. "Rate Regulation, Capital Structure and the Sharing of Interest Rate Risk in the Electric Utility Industry." *Journal of Finance*. Vol. 33, no. 3, 707–721.

Hiltzik, M. 1984. "Nuclear Power Plant Threatens Utility's Future." *Los Angeles Times*. March 4.

Kahn, E. 1979. "Project Lead Time and Demand Uncertainty: Implications for the Financial Risk of Electric Utilities." E.F. Hutton Fixed Income Research Conference.

Keeney, R. and A. Sicherman. 1983. "Illustrative Comparison of One Utility's Coal and Nuclear Choices." In *Operations Research*. 50–83.

Komanoff, C. 1981. *Power Plant Cost Escalation*. KEA.

Leung, P. and R. Durning. 1978. "Power System Economics: On Selection of Engineering Alternatives." *ASME Journal of Engineering for Power*. Vol. 100, April, 333–346.

Livingstone, J. and A. Sherali. 1979. "Construction Work in Progress in the Public Utility Rate Base: The Effect of Multiple Projects and Growth." *Financial Management*. Spring, 42–50.

Long Island Lighting Company. 1982. *Annual Report*.

Lyons, J. 1979. "Optimizing Designs of Fossil-Fired Generating Units." *Power Engineering*. February, 50–56.

Merrill, H. 1983. "Cogeneration — A Strategic Evaluation." *IEEE Transactions on Power Apparatus and Systems*. Vol. PAS-102, no. 2, 463–471.

Mooz, W. 1978. *Cost Analysis of Light Water Reactor Power Plants*. RAND Corp. R-2304 DOE.

New England Electric System. 1982. *Annual Report*.

New England Power Planning. 1978. "Summary of Generation Task Force Long Range Study Assumptions." NEPOOL.

Pacific Gas and Electric Company. 1982. *Annual Report*.

Peck, S. 1983. "Electric Utility Capacity Expansion: Its Implications for Customers and Stockholders." *Energy Journal*. Vol.4, Special Electricity Issue, 1–12.

Philadelphia Electric Company. 1982. *Annual Report*.

Platts, J. and P. Womeldorff. 1980. "The Significance of Assumptions Implied in Long Range Electric Utility Planning Studies." *IEEE Transactions on Power Apparatus and Systems*. Vol. PAS-99, no. 3, 1047–1056.

Pomerantz, L. and J. Suelflow. 1975. *Allowance for Funds Used During Construction: Theory and Application*. Institute of Public Utilities, Michigan State University.

Schwartz, B. 1981. "Urban Cogeneration: A Wolf in Sheep's Clothing." *Public Utilities Fortnightly.* Vol. 108, no. 4, 15–19.
Southern California Edison Company. 1982. *Annual Report.*
Sullivan, R. 1977. *Power System Planning.* McGraw-Hill.
U.S. Department of Energy. 1981. *The National Electric Reliability Study: Technical Study Reports.* DOE/EP-0005.
Value Line Investment Survey, 1983. Value Line, Inc.

Chapter 4

The best overall guide to the rate-making process is still Bonbright (1961). The level of detail there is low, however, but more detail can be found in ICF (1981). Another traditional source is NARUC (1973). Discussion of the average and excess demand method of cost allocation is confusing in NARUC; Coyle (1982) presents a simple account of this.

California utilities make a fairly complete marginal cost analysis in their general rate case applications. We use Pacific Gas and Electric Company, Fiske (1982) as an example. The cost basis of demand charges is illustrated in the discussion of stand-by rates for cogeneration in a famous Consolidated Edison case (Arnett, Beach, Monsees, 1980). Lifeline or inverted block rates for residential consumers are discussed by Nichols (1981) citing load studies of Cincinnati Gas and Electric (1979). California experience is summarized in Howard (1983). Detroit Edison experience is described in Falletich (1983) and Welch (1983). Industry methods for estimating revenues from non-linear rate schedules are found in American Gas Association (1960). Modern mathematical treatments are found in Liittschwager (1971) and Kahn and Levy (1982).

American Gas Association. 1960. *Gas Rate Fundamentals.*
Andersen, D. 1981. *Regulatory Politics and Electric Utilities.* Auburn House, Boston.
Arnett, H. 1980. Testimony in New York Public Service Commission Case 27574.
Baldwin, L. 1980. Testimony in California Public Utilities Commission Application Number 60153.
Beach, C. 1980. Testimony in New York Public Service Commission Case 27574.
Bonbright, J. 1961. *Principles of Public Utility Rates.* Columbia University Press.
Cincinnati Gas and Electric Co. 1979a. *Residential Non-Air Conditioning Customer Load Survey, August 1976–July 1977.* Rate and Economic Research Department.
_____. 1979b. *Residential Air Conditioning Customer Load, July 1974–July 1975.* Rate and Economic Research Department.

Cleveland State University. 1980. *Lifeline Electric Rates and Alternative Approaches to the Problems of Low-Income Ratepayers.* U.S. Department of Energy Report DOE/RG/10066-01, 02, 03. Three volumes.

Coyle, E. 1982. "Average and Excess Demand Once Again." *Public Utilities Fortnightly.* Vol. 109, no. 13, 51–52.

Deschamps, C., Z. Yamayee, and M. Chan. 1982. "Analytic Treatment of Hydro Units with Random Energy in Stochastic Production Simulation." In *IEEE Transactions on Power Apparatus and Systems.* Vol. PAS-101, 113–119.

Falletich, E. 1983. Testimony in Michigan Public Service Commission Case No. U-6590-R.

————. 1983b. Supplemental Testimony in Michigan Public Service Commission Case Number U-6590-R.

Fiske, G. 1982. Testimony in California Public Utilities Commission Appl. No. 82-12-48.

Hanks, James J. 1934. "'Ready-Made' Residential Electric Consumer Analysis." *Journal of Land and Public Utility Economics.* Vol. 10, 232–242.

Howard, R. 1982. Testimony in California Public Utilities Commission Appl. No. 82-12-48.

————. 1983. *Residential Rate Design: Transition to Baseline Rates.* Pacific Gas and Electric Co. Rate Dept.

ICF Inc. 1981. *Costs and Rates Workbook.* EPRI Electric Utility Rate Design Study Pub. No. 93A and 93B.

Kahn, E. and Levy, D. 1982. "Preliminary Development of a Forecasting Procedure for Weather Sensitive Sales Frequency Distributions."

Liittschwager, J. 1971. "Mathematical Models for Public Utility Rate Revisions." *Management Science.* Vol. 17, B-339–B-353.

Monsees, J. 1980. Testimony in New York Public Service Commission Case 27574.

National Association of Regulatory Utility Commissioners. (NARUC). 1973. *Electric Utility Cost Allocation Manual.*

————. 1982. *1981 Annual Report on Utility and Carrier Regulation.*

National Oceanographic and Atmospheric Administration. 1982. *Local Climatological Data.* U.S. Government Printing Office.

Nichols, D., J. Stutz, and T. Austin. 1981. *Lifeline Rates in Maryland.* Energy Systems Research Group, Boston, Massachusetts.

Pacific Gas and Electric Company. 1982. MARCOST Outputs, Work Papers for PG&E Exhibit 13 in CPUC Application Number 82-12-48.

Pacific Gas and Electric Company. 1983. Electric Revenues by Tariff Class — Residential. Private communication.

Welch, J. 1983. Testimony in Michigan Public Service Commission Case No. U-6590-R.

Zuck, E.S. 1936. "Consumption Block Curves." *Electrical World.* February 15, 32–34.

————. 1936. "Rate Results Analyzed on a Simplified Basis." *Electrical World.* March 14, 44ff.

Chapter 5

Baleriaux, H. E. Jamoulle, Fr. Lenard de Guertechin. 1967. "Simulation de l'exploitation de'un parc de machines thermiques de production d'électricité couple a des stations de pompage." *Revue E (édition S.R.B.E.).* Vol. V, no. 7, 3–24.

Bloom, J. 1984a. "Generation Cost Curves Including Energy Storage." *IEEE Transactions on Power Apparatus and Systems*. Vol. PAS-103, no. 7, 1725–1731.
_____. 1984b. "Modelling Economic Operation of Power Pools." Paper presented at ORSA/TIMS meeting.
Booth, R. 1972. "Power System Simulation Model Based on Probability Analysis." *IEEE Transactions on Power Apparatus and Systems*. Vol. PAS-91, no. 1, 62–69.
California Public Utilities Commission. 1986. Decision No. 86-07-004.
Caramanis, M., F. Schweppe, and R. Tabors. 1982. *Electric Generation Expansion Analysis System*. Vol. 1, EPRI EL-2561.
Caramanis, M., J. Stremel, W. Fleck, and S. Daniel. 1983. "Probabilistic Production Costing: An Investigation of Alternative Algorithms." *International Journal of Electrical Power and Energy Systems*. Vol. 5, no. 2, 75–86.
Decision Focus Inc. 1982. *Load Management Strategy Testing Model*. EPRI EA-2396.
Environmental Defense Fund Inc. 1986. *ELFIN Overview and Summary of Simulation Methods*.
Gerber, M. 1985. Testimony before the California Public Utilities Commission in Appl. No. 85-04-019.
Jabbour, S. 1986. *The Short-Run Value of Non-Utility Generated Power, IEEE Transactions on Energy Conversion*. Vol. EC-1, no. 1, 11–16.
Kahn, E., C. Pignone, and A. Comnes. 1987. *LMSTM Calibration for Least-Cost Planning*. LBL-2207.
Kahn, E. 1986. "Comparison of ELFIN, GRASS and SAM." Pacific Gas and Electric Company.
_____. 1985a. *Production Cost Modelling of the Pacific Gas and Electric System*. California Energy Commission P500-85-010.
Kahn, E., D. Kirshner, and D. Yardas. 1985b. *Production Cost Modelling of the Southern California Edison System*. California Energy Commission P500-85-011.
Levy, D. and E. Kahn. 1982. "Accuracy of the Edgeworth Approximation for LOLP Calculations in Small Power Systems." *IEEE Transactions on Power Apparatus and Systems*. Vol. PAS-101, no. 4, 986–996.
Lotus Consulting Group. 1986. *UPLAN Reference Manual*. USAM Center.
Mazumdar, M. and Y. Wang. 1985. "On the Application of Esscher's Approximation to Computation of Generating System Reliability and Production Costing Indexes." *IEEE Transactions on Power Apparatus and Systems*. Vol. PAS-104, no. 11, 3029–3036.
Merlin, A. and P. Sandrin. 1983. "A New Method for Unit Commitment at Électricité de France." *IEEE Transactions on Power Apparatus and Systems*. Vol. PAS-102, 1218–1225.
National Economic Research Associates. 1977. *How to Quantify Marginal Costs*. EPRI Electric Utility Rate Design Study #23.
Pacific Gas and Electric Company. 1985a. *The Mixture of Normal Approximation of Equivalent Load Duration Curves*. EPRI EA/EL-4266.
_____. 1985b. Exhibit 3–Long Term Planning, CPUC Appl. No. 85-12-50.
_____. 1986. Compliance Filing in OIR-2, CPUC Appl. No. 82-04-044.
Southern California Edison Company. 1986. *Estimation of Historical Short Run Marginal Production Costs*.
Stremel, J. 1985. *LMSTM Version 2.0 User's Guide Supplement*. Decision Focus Inc.

Stremel, J. and S. Bubb. 1985. "Comparing Direct Simulation and Proba-
     bilistic Production Costing Models." Decision Focus Inc.
Stremel, J. and T. Jenkins. 1981. "Maintenance Scheduling Methods for
     Planning Models." Tennessee Valley Authority.
Weisenmiller, R. and D. Yardas. 1986. Testimony before the California Pub-
     lic Utilities Commission in Appl. No. 86-04-012.
Wu, F. and G. Gross. 1977. "Probabilistic Simulation of Power System
     Operation for Production Cost and Reliability Evaluation." In *IEEE
     International Symposium on Circuits and Systems.*

Chapter 6

Spreadsheet analysis of small power projects is usually found
in the prospectuses associated with particular projects. Published examples include Bos (1982, 1983), Kahn (1982) and
Kahn and Goldman (1987). Levelized price contracts have
been proposed in particular cases (PG&E, 1981). Non-
standard arrangements are discussed generally by Weisenmiller (1983). Cogeneration is discussed by Joskow and Jones
(1983), Hess, *et al.* (1983) and OTA (1983). Project financing
is reviewed by Nevitt (1980), Wynant (1980) and Danziger
and DeVito (1984). Bypass is discussed by the California
Energy Commission (1987), and auctions by Rothkopf, *et al.*
(1987).

American Bar Associations. 1981. *The Need for Power and the Choice of
     Technologies: State Decisions on Electric Power Facilities.* U.S. Dept. of
     Energy Report DOE/EP/10004-1.
Bos, P. 1982. *Financing Alternatives and Incentives for Solar Thermal Central
     Receiver Systems.* Polydyne Inc. DOE/SF/11587-1.
_____. 1983. Testimony before the Subcommittee on Energy Develop-
     ment and Applications, U.S. House of Representatives Committee on
     Science and Technology.
Boston Edison Company. 1986. Request for Proposals in Massachusetts
     Department of Public Utilities Docket No. 84-276.
California Energy Commission. 1987. *The Economic Impacts of Self Genera-
     tion.* P500-87-002.
Cox, A., C. Blumstein, and R. Gilbert. 1987. "Gone With the Wind: The
     Economics of Tax Subsidies for Windpower in California." *Develop-
     ments in Energy Regulation.* Universitywide Energy Research Group,
     University of California.
Danziger, R. and R. DeVito. 1984. "Balancing Risks and Benefits in Cogen-
     eration System Financing." *Creative Financing for Energy Conservation
     and Cogeneration.* Fairmont Press.
Federal Energy Regulatory Commission. 1980. *PURPA EIS.*
Hess, R., J. Turner, W. Krause, and R. Pei. 1983. *Factors Affecting Industry's
     Decision to Cogenerate.* U.S. Dept of Energy Report DE 85006474.
Internal Revenue Code. Sec. 46 (c) (8) (B).

Joskow, P. and D. Jones. 1983. "The Simple Economics of Industrial Cogeneration." *Energy Journal*. Vol. 4, no. 1, 1–22.

Kahn, E. 1982. *Regulatory Boundaries and the Development of Alternative Energy*. California Energy Commission P110-82-004.

Kahn, E. and C. Goldman. 1987. "Impact of Tax Reform on Renewable Energy and Cogeneration Projects." *Energy Economics*.

Merrill, H. 1983. "Cogeneration—A Strategic Evaluation." *IEEE Transactions on Power Apparatus and Systems*. Vol. PAS-102, no. 2, 463–471.

Nevitt, P. 1980. *Project Financing*. Bank of America.

Pacific Gas and Electric Company. 1981. California Public Utilities Commission Application No. 61073.

Rothkopf, M., E. Kahn, T. Teisberg, J. Eto, and J. Nataf. 1987. *Designing PURPA Power Auctions: Theory and Practice*. LBL-23406.

U.S. Congress Office of Technology Assessment. 1983. *Industrial and Commercial Cogeneration*. Report No. OTA-E-192.

Weisenmiller, R. 1983. Testimony before the California Public Utilities Commission in Southern California Edison Application No. 83-03-36.

Western Massachusetts Electric Company. 1986. Request for Proposals in Massachusetts Department of Public Utilities Docket No. 84-276.

Wynant, L. 1980. "Essential Elements of Project Financing." *Harvard Business Review*. May–June, 165–173.

Chapter 7

Cost-benefit methods are discussed by White (1981), Fiske *et al.* (1981), Florida PSC (1982), CPUC and CEC (1983) and Ford (1983). Particular cases are examined by Kahn (1982) for Southern California Edison, GPU (1982), Czahar (1982), Hirst *et al.* (1985), and Baldwin (1982). The conservation supply curve notion is worked out in Meier *et al.* (1983). Variability in long-run price elasticity is estimated by Lawrence and Robinson (1982) and Berkovec *et al.* (1982) using REEPS, CSI (1982). Barkovich (1987) provides an interesting account of the regulatory politics of conservation programs.

Baldwin, L. 1982. "Economic Evaluation of Conservation and Load Management Resources." Testimony in California Public Utilities Commission Appl. No. 82-12-48.

Barkovich, B. 1987. Changing Strategies in Utility Regulation: The Case of Energy Conservation in California. Ph.D. diss.

Berkovec, J., T. Cowing, and D. McFadden. 1982. "An Analysis of the Distributional Impacts of Energy Policy Affecting Residential Energy Demand: The REEPS Model." MIT Energy Laboratory Discussion Paper No. 26.

California Public Utilities Commission. 1981. Decision No. 92653.

California Public Utilities Commission. 1980. *Energy Efficiency and the Utilities: New Directions*.

California Public Utilities Commission and California Energy Commission. 1983. *Standard Practices for Cost-benefit Analysis of Conservation and Load Management Programs*.

Czahar, R. 1982. Workpapers for _Special Economic Projects Initial Report on Southern California Edison Company Power Production Planning, Pricing and Policy_. California Public Utilities Commission.

Cambridge Systematics Inc. 1982. _Residential End-Use Energy Planning System_. Electric Power Research Institute EPRI EA-2512.

Eto, J., J. Koomey, J. McMahon, and E. Kahn. 1987. "Integrated Analysis of Demand-Side Programs." _IEEE Transactions on Power Systems_. (to appear).

Fiske, G., E. Law, and D. Seeto. 1981. "The Economic Analysis of Load Management: The Case of Cycling Residential Air Conditioners." _IEEE Transactions on Power Apparatus and Systems_. Vol. PAS-100 (4725–4732).

Florida Public Service Commission. 1982. Conservation Cost Effectiveness Data Reporting Format. Proposed Rule 25-17.08.

Ford, A. 1983. "Calculating the Cost Effectiveness and Limitations of Electric Conservation Subsidies." Rep. No. LA-UR-83-1339, Los Alamos National Laboratory.

Ford, A. and J. Geinzer. 1986. _The BPA Conservation Policy Analysis Models_. Office of Conservation, Bonneville Power Administration.

General Public Utilities. 1982. Residential Energy Conservation Action Program (RECAP). Corporate Planning Division.

Hirst, E. and R. Goeltz. 1985. "Estimating Energy Savings Due to Conservation Programmes." _Energy Economics_. Vol. 7, no. 1, 20–28.

Kahn, E. 1982. "Uncertainty and the Distribution of Benefits from Utility Conservation Programs." In _What Works: Proceedings of the ACEEE 1982 Santa Cruz Conference_. American Council for an Energy-Efficient Economy.

Kahn, E. 1986. "Proxy Plant Valuation Methods for Demand-Side Utility Programs." _Energy_. 1988 (in press).

Lawrence, A. and M. Robinson. 1984. "Unit Energy Consumption Analysis of the National Interim Energy Consumption Survey." In _Measuring the Impact of Residential Conservation_. Vol. 1, EPRI EA-3606.

Linhart, P., J. Liebowitz, and F. Sinden. 1974. "The Choice Between Capitalizing and Expensing Under Rate Regulation." _Bell Journal of Economics_. Vol. 5, 406–419.

McMahon, J. "The LBL Residential Energy Model: An Improved Policy Analysis Tool." _Energy Systems and Policy_. Vol. 10, no. 1 (1987).

Meier, A., J. Wright, and A. Rosenfeld. 1983. _Supplying Energy Through Greater Efficiency_. University of California Press.

Rosenbloom, B. and J. Eto. 1986. _Utility Benefits from Targeting Demand-Side Management Programs at Specific Distribution Areas_. EPRI EM-4771.

Saut, R. _Least Cost Energy Strategies_. 1979.

Southern California Edison Company. 1981. California Public Utilities Commission Application No. 61138.

Southern California Edison Company. 1981. California Public Utilities Commission Application No. 61066.

White, K. 1981. "The Economics of Conservation." _IEEE Transactions on Power Apparatus and Systems_. Vol. PAS-100, 4546–4552.

Chapter 8

Sharkey (1982) provides a good modern treatment of the theory of natural monopoly. The notion that regulation principally provides stabilization of market forces is worked out most explicitly by Owen and Braeutigam (1978). Trebing (1981) puts this theory in broader perspective, contrasting it particularly with the behavioral theory of Peltzman (1976). The work of Newbery and Stiglitz (1981), the most comprehensive model of stabilization benefits, depends upon the theory of risk-aversion discussed in Arrow (1970). Application of this perspective to electric utilities is worked out in Kahn (1984). Underlying data are found in EEI (1982), U.S. Dept. of Commerce (1981), Komanoff (1981), Perl (1981) and Kahn (1979).

Aitchison, J. and J. Brown, 1957. *The Lognormal Distribution.* Cambridge University Press.

Arrow, K. 1970. "The Theory of Risk Aversion." *Essays in the Theory of Risk-Bearing.* North Holland Publishing Co.

Baumol, W., J. Panzar, and R. Willig. 1982. *Contestable Markets and the Theory of Industry Structure.* Harcourt, Brace and Jovanovich.

Chao, Hung-Po and R. Wilson. 1987. "Priority Service: Pricing, Investment, and Market Organization." *American Economic Review.* Vol. 77, no. 5, 899–916.

Edison Electric Institute. 1982. *Statistical Yearbook of the Electric Utility Industry.*

Kahn, E. 1979. "Project Lead Time and Demand Uncertainty: Implications for the Financial Risk of Electric Utilities." E.F. Hutton. Fixed Income Research Conference.

_____. 1984. "Stabilization Theory, Regulatory Policy and the Investment Preferences of Utility Shareholders." *Energy Systems and Policy.* 8, 3, 237–267.

Kalt, J. 1981. *The Economics and Politics of Oil Price Regulation.* MIT Press.

Komanoff, C. 1981. *Power Plant Cost Escalation.* KEA.

Newbery, D. and J. Stiglitz. 1981. *The Theory of Commodity Price Stabilization.* Oxford University Press.

Newmark, N. and D. Cooper. 1984. "Prospects for Utility Ownership of Cogeneration." *Public Utilities Fortnightly.* Vol. 113, no. 3, 24–27.

Owen, B. and R. Braeutigam. 1978. *The Regulation Game: Strategic Use of the Administrative Process.* Ballinger.

Peltzman, S. 1976. "Towards a More General Theory of Regulation." *Journal of Law and Economics.* Vol. 19, 211–240.

Perl, L. 1981. Testimony in Pennsylvania Public Utility Commission Docket No. I-80100341. Harrisburg, Pennsylvania.

Sharkey, W. 1982. *The Theory of Natural Monopoly.* Cambridge University Press.

_____. 1977. "Efficient Production When Demand is Uncertain." *Journal of Public Economics.* Vol. 8, 369–384.

Trebing, H. 1981. "Equity, Efficiency and the Viability of Public Utility Regulation." *Application of Economic Principles in Public Utility Industries.* W. Sichel and T. Gies, ed. University of Michigan.
U.S. Department of Commerce. 1981. *Statistical Abstract of the United States.*

Chapter 9

Bailey, E. 1986. "Deregulation: Causes and Consequences." *Science.* Vol. 234, 1211–1216.
Bloom, J. 1984. "Modeling Economic Operation of Power Pools." Paper presented at ORSA/TIMS Meeting.
Braeutigam, R. and R. G. Hubbard. 1986. "Natural Gas: The Regulatory Transition." *Regulatory Reform.* L.Weiss and M. Klass, ed. Little, Brown and Company, 137–168.
Brock, G. 1986. "The Regulatory Change in Telecommunications: The Dissolution of AT&T." *Regulatory Reform.* L.Weiss and M.Klass, ed. Little, Brown and Company, 210–233.
Crew, M. and P. Kleindorfer. 1985. "Governance Costs of Rate-of-Return Regulation." *Journal of Institutional and Theoretical Economics.* Vol. 141, 104–123.
Evans, D., ed. 1983. *Breaking Up Bell: Essays on Industrial Organization and Regulation.* North-Holland.
Gilbert, R. 1986. "Issues in Public Utility Regulation." *Developments in Energy Regulation.* Universitywide Energy Research Group, University of California.
Joskow, P. 1987a. "Productivity Growth and Technical Change in the Generation of Electricity." *Energy Journal.* Vol. 8, 17–38.
———. 1987b. "Competition and Deregulation in the Electric Utility Industry." MIT Center for Energy Policy Research.
Joskow, P. and R. Schmalensee. 1983. *Markets for Power.* MIT Press.
Moore, T. 1986. "Rail and Trucking Deregulation." *Regulatory Reform.* L. Weiss and M. Klass, ed. Little, Brown and Company, 14–39.
Russo, M. and D. Teece. 1986. "Natural Gas Distribution in California: Regulation Strategy and Market Structure." *Developments in Energy Regulation.* Universitywide Energy Research Group, University of California.
Saunders, B. 1986. "Pipelines 'Constantly Regroup' to Cope with Changes." *Oil Daily.* October 20.
Southern California Edison Company. 1986. "Cost of Capital Methodology." Testimony in California Public Utilities Commission Application No. 86-12-047.
Tussing, A. and C. Barlow. 1984. *The Natural Gas Industry.* Ballinger.

Index by Subject, Author, and Title